MAR 2 4 '89

BETHEL
MERRIDAY

BETHEL
MERRIDAY
SINCLAIR
LEWIS

"Until the nineteenth century, actors were classed as Rogues & Vagrants. They were outside of respectable society —like Kings—and I am not sure but that this was better for their art and their happiness than to be classed as lecturers, tax-payers, tennis-players, suburban householders, and lovers of dogs." ARTHUR KULOSAS

NEW YORK 1940
DOUBLEDAY, DORAN & COMPANY, INC.

PRINTED AT THE *Country Life Press*, GARDEN CITY, N. Y., U. S. A.

To
CORNELIUS HORACE TRAEGER
Dramatic Critic, Physician
and Friend

NOTICE

No CHARACTER in this novel is the portrait of an actual person, and if there is any resemblance to the name of a real person, it is accidental.

Such notices as this have become increasingly familiar because of an increasing habit among readers of finding themselves portrayed in every novel, and of being annoyed or unduly pleased. It is particularly necessary in this book because in recent years I have been acquainted with six summer theaters and with a touring play. I declare vigorously that the Nutmeg Players of Point Grampion, in my tale, are not drawn from the Stockbridge, Cohasset, Ogunquit, Provincetown, Clinton or Skowhegan companies, and that the tour of a *Romeo and Juliet* company here chronicled is not the history of my *Angela Is Twenty-two*. And Sladesbury is not Hartford or Waterbury, but the county seat of Cloud-Cuckoo-Land.

I hope that this signboard may have some effect. After the appearance of *Arrowsmith* I was informed that at least half my medical characters had been drawn from professors

vii

of whom I had never heard. With *It Can't Happen Here,* adherents of two editors, one in Vermont and one in Connecticut, gave rather convincing proof that each of these gentlemen was the model for Doremus Jessup. But the happy days were with *Elmer Gantry* when, on the same Sunday morning, in the same Western city, each of two clergymen announced from his pulpit that the Reverend Elmer had been drawn solely from him, but that the portrait was crooked.

I shall not explain to self-elected prototypes of my Bethel Merriday or Roscoe Valentine just how I probed their own lives; and if it shall prove that there really are persons so unfortunate as to be named Zed Wintergeist or Mrs Lumley Boyle or Mrs J. Goddard Deacon or Jerome Jordan O'Toole or Tudor Blackwall, I shall merely point out that there is a tradition that fiction characters have to be called *something.*

Of course writers might call them X76–4 or Pi R Square.

But if we did, all the persons with automobile licenses numbered X76–4 and all the coolies named Pi Lung Squong would write to us, which heaven forbid.

SINCLAIR LEWIS

BETHEL
MERRIDAY

1

THAT WAS THE FIRST TIME that anyone ever called her an actress—June 1, 1922, Bethel's sixth birthday. There was no spotlight, no incidental music, and her only audience were her mother and a small dog looking regretfully through the window of a boardinghouse. But she was sensational.

Her mother and she were on their way to the A. & P. Store, and as usual Bethel had with the greatest violence been running in circles. She was slight and small and entirely feminine, but she was the best runner in her neighborhood.

She stopped, then moved with a queer slow hitching. In front of them an old lady was scraping along, sunk forward from her shoulders as though she had given up all hope of ease and love. Her whole life seemed to be in her painfully sliding feet. Bethel tried to re-create that dejected walk, and she went at it so earnestly that the back of her neck ached with the weight of sagging shoulders, and every step was a frightened effort.

Her mother interrupted.

"Good gracious, don't copy folks that way, Bethel. You'll hurt their feelings."

The small, black-eyed child halted, in protest.

"Oh! I'm not copying her. I'm trying to be her. I can be a lot of different people."

"My, aren't we grown-up! I'm afraid that you like to show off, dear—the way you always say your text so loud in Sunday school."

"I love to say texts! 'I will praise thee, O Lord, with my whole heart. I will show forth all thy marvellous works.'"

"It all sounds like maybe you're going to be an actress. I guess that wouldn't be a bad text for an actress."

"Look how the poor old lady's heels are run down," said Bethel, too busy with her career for prophecies of glory.

Bethel was born in 1916, on the day after the Battle of Jutland. Her father, kneeling by the bed, had prayed, *"Dear Lord, please make this baby a child of peace and justice— yes, and happiness, Lord."*

Five months after the six-year-old Bethel gave her imitation of the old lady, the Black Shirts marched bravely into the maws of the movie cameras in Rome; and five months after that, Hitler bounded out of a Munich beer garden. But perhaps it was as important that at this time John Barrymore was playing *Hamlet* and Pauline Lord *Anna Christie* and the Theater Guild producing *Back to Methuselah.* They were so much less stagy.

Herbert Merriday, Bethel's father, was a dealer in furniture, to which, later, he was importantly to add electric refrigerators and radios. They lived in Sladesbury, a city of 127,000, in central Connecticut, a fount of brassware, hardware, arms, precision instruments, clocks. Here is the renowned establishment of Lilydale & Duck, makers of machine guns for killing policemen and revolvers for killing gangsters and the Duck Typewriter for joyfully chronicling both brands of killing.

Sladesbury is Yankee, not Colonial, and it envies and scorns the leisurely grace of Litchfield and Sharon. It proclaims itself constantly as "modern," and is beginning to boast of being "streamlined."

Even for Sladesbury, the Merriday family stood high in modernity. They had been the first family to have a radio installed in their car, and Mrs Merriday, though she was a solid Universalist, was so advanced as to belong to the Birth-Control League.

In May of 1931 Bethel was almost fifteen, and finishing sophomore year in high school. It was suitable to the neighborhood modernity that her brother Benny, now twenty-one, should be working in the Dutton Aeroplane Works, and talking about designs for transatlantic clippers, talking about (though never actually reading) the Bible by Karl Marx, and that the girls she knew should be talking about careers. They wanted homes and babies as much as their mothers had, but none of them expected to be entirely supported by husbands. Most of them were, they asserted, going to be aeroplane hostesses, motion-picture stars or radio artists, though certain of the less studious sort confessed that they would not mind being "hostesses" in the large dance halls.

Bethel could not look upon serving cold consommé at an altitude of a mile, or dancing the rhumba, as having much meaning. She was learning touch typewriting in high school —that was her father's one insistence about her studies— and she could become a secretary, busy and important, receiving the boss's magnificent callers. But privately, ever since her sixth birthday, she had yearned to be an actress.

As she had never seen a play with professional actors, she was shaky as to just what being an actress implied, and certainly she never admitted to her companions so eccentric an ambition. She was one of a whole generation of youngsters under twenty who considered the London of Shakespeare and the Paris of Molière as barbaric and rather comic, who were familiar with radio broadcasts from Madrid and aeroplanes just landed from Alaska and two-million-dollar film dramas and the theory of the atom, but half of whom had never seen a real play or entered an art gallery or heard an orchestra play anything but dance music.

Bethel herself had seen only a high-school farce, in which a football player in a red wig kept kicking a fat boy; a Republican party pageant in Brewster Park, with Lawyer Wilkie as Lincoln, heavily accented as to shawl and beard; and the melodramas about gun-molls and sunken submarines which Alva Prindle and Bethel herself performed on the workbench in the Prindle garage. So altogether futile and babyish seemed the intention of acting that probably she would not have confessed it to her friends Alva Prindle and Charley Hatch, on that evening in May 1931, had the newspapers not been hinting that, for the first time in ten years, Sladesbury was to have a professional stock company all summer long.

And it was one of her queer, secret, sensitized days when she saw everything with intolerable acuteness.

When she awoke, that Saturday in May, the morning was bewitched with fog.

She had, proudly, a room of her own, with a candlewick cover on a spool bed of 1860. Benny, the worshiper of new machinery, laughed at the bed as old-fashioned, but she prized it as somehow connected with Pilgrims who shot wild turkeys with blunderbusses on Thanksgiving Day, and came home to drink hot toddies in the company of gray ladies in poke bonnets.

She also had a shaky white-painted desk of her own, with a bookshelf on which were a complete Shakespeare, an Edgar Wallace novel, a Mary Roberts Rinehart novel, a ragged volume of Keats, a manual of tennis, and No. 1567 in the Haldeman-Julius Little Blue Books, namely, *Making Men Happy with Jams and Jellies*. The wallpaper was canary yellow, with small scarlet birds; the rug was blue. She loved her secure retreat and its friendly brightness.

But this morning of mist was forlorn to her as she crawled

out, in her blue-and-white-striped pajamas, her bobbed hair, which was very black, flickering above her charming shoulders, which were very white. She was afraid, or pretended that she was afraid, to look out of the window—and then looked. The Hatch house, next door, had alarmingly vanished in the fog. The elms were hard pillars, their foliage unseen; the silver birch was chilly as winter.

On such a day, even at her mature age of fourteen years and eleven months, she could again convince herself that she was the foundling child of wicked gypsies.

She knew that all this was quite insane. But there was a good, efficient, earthy Bethel who always guarded the mad Bethel, and who now insisted that being a gypsy was no crazier than her father's love for assaulting golf balls, or her mother's stated belief that anyone born in New Hampshire was handsomer and healthier than any Vermonter.

As Bethel wriggled and rubbed herself under the shower bath—oh yes, the Merridays were as modern as all that—and drew on her bloomers, her rolled stockings, her flowery cotton dress, she was prim and a little stern, that she might not betray her Crazy Ideas.

Things were not right, downstairs.

The house was only ten years old, and the living room was still of suitable modernness, with interior decoration correct by the highest standards of the women's magazines: a large, frameless mirror over the white fireplace, reflecting two marble vases; a glass-topped nickeled coffee table in front of the convertible davenport; on the wall, a travel souvenir in the way of a "Ye Motor Mappe of Ye Quaint Olde Cape Codde," depicting whales and Pilgrims; an enormous combination radio and phonograph, shining like syrup; and no books whatever. But to the revolutionary Bethel, this morning, the room was as oppressive as too hot a bath.

She apologized to herself that her father and her mother and her house were really very nice. But a little smug . . . ?

Then she first really discovered ash trays; then she found

that ash trays can be fascinating but horrible. On the coffee table was a still unemptied tray; a half-sphere of rock crystal, which should have been spotless shining as a handful of upper air, but was smeared now with black ash stains and filled with dead paper matches and cigarette stubs like the twisted dead white arms of babies. The whole thing, she shuddered, was a shell pit, only smaller.

But she seized herself and pushed herself on into the dining room, with a reproving, "You're *imagining* things!"

"Good morning, Beth. That's doing pretty well. Only ten minutes late. You look as if you slept pretty well," said her father.

"Foggy enough for you today?" said Gwendolyn, the hired girl.

"Hya, Toots. Hya, handsome," said her brother.

"Good morning, dear. You look cheerful, this morning," said her mother.

(She didn't feel cheerful, and she was hanged if she'd *be* cheerful, not all day long, she reflected. But if they thought she looked so, she must be doing some good acting.)

She studied her corn flakes, and found that corn flakes are as fantastically improbable as ash trays, once your eyes are open. They certainly didn't look like food. Food was lamb chops and chop suey and corn on the cob and apple pie à la mode; these things were twists of brown paper, with minute bubbles on their speckled surfaces. What a thing to eat!

She did eat them, and enjoyed them very much, but now she was at the fascinated vexation of studying just how they all ate. Her father sturdily opened his lips up and down like a pair of trap doors, showing his teeth. Her mother nibbled like a rabbit, her faded pink lips (she would not use her lipstick till she went to the bridge club this afternoon) trembled a little and hid her teeth. And Brother Ben twisted his mouth sidewise, with the right corner of it scornfully elevated.

She tried to imitate them all.

"What are you daydreaming about, dear?" said her father.

"Eat your nice hot muffins, Beth," said her mother.

"I hope you'll know me the next time you see me," said her brother.

"What makes it foggy today?" said Bethel.

"The fog," said Ben.

For two hours, that schoolless Saturday morning, she worked in her father's store, polishing tables and radio cabinets. Her hands were swift, and she liked seeing the sleek grain of the wood emerge from dullness. But as this was, she luxuriously sighed, one of her poetic days, she would spend all afternoon in Brewster Park. It had a grove of thick Japanese walnuts with a tiny stream, and there, on a small pad of the best linen correspondence paper, she would write a poem about the Grecian city hall. . . . She was much given to writing poetry, except that she never had been able to write more than a dozen lines of it.

But into the store bounced her friend Alva Prindle, to demand that she come to the North Side Tennis Club that afternoon.

Alva Prindle was a big, beautiful, bouncing blonde. She was born that way; she was spiritually like that; she would have been a big, beautiful, bouncing blonde even if she had been as dark and delicately made as Bethel. It was Alva whom the high-school girls had nominated as a future Queen of Hollywood.

Bethel did play tennis that afternoon, and she played well enough, and she hated it. She felt that there must be something complicated and wrong in herself, for while just that morning she had been able to see herself as Lady Macbeth, satisfyingly murderous and flamboyant before an audience of two thousand, this afternoon, showing off her rapid, accurate, nervous little serve before an audience of not more than a dozen musical young gentlemen aged sixteen, she was terrified; she was embarrassed every time Alva answered the gallery's "Good work, beautiful," with a merry: "Go climb a tree." (Alva varied it by retorting, "Go lay an egg" or "Go jump in the lake.")

The North Side Tennis Club was founded by the medium-successful retail merchants, the minor doctors and lawyers and insurance agents and real-estate sellers of Sladesbury, to give their children something of the social glory of the private *en-tout-cas* courts of the bank vice-presidents and the factory owners. Its clubhouse was a one-room shack with a counter at which were sold Coca-Cola, orangeade, cigarettes, chewing gum and stale sweet crackers, but this counter was to Bethel what Twenty-One and El Morocco and the Stork Club and the like New York exhibits of elegance and celebrity were someday to seem.

Alva dragged her in there after the match. The young men lounged on high stools, drinking soda from bottles through straws, and singing "She Didn't Say Yes, She Didn't Say No."

The sanctities of Prohibition had more than two years to run, and the young people still considered it a social duty to drink raw gin. The oldest of their group—Morris Bass, the handsome, the fast-driving, the generous, the loudly lecherous, eighteen and the sole scion of a catsup factory— was urging on them cheer from a gin bottle with a counterfeited Gordon label. Alva had a shot of it in her root beer and began to giggle.

Not till now had anyone like Morris Bass ever given heed to Bethel, but this afternoon (she was flattered, so baronial was he in his pink-and-apricot sweater, his white-linen plus fours, his oiled chestnut hair) he dragged her by the arm to a bench outside the club shack, poured half a glass of gin into her sarsaparilla, and with heavily breathing satisfaction pushed his heavy arm about her waist. . . . In her life, she had tasted gin perhaps twice; certainly no gallant had embraced her publicly. The Modern Merridays did not hold with drunkenness and public slobbering.

"Please!" she begged.

"What's a matter? Don't you like hootch?"

"Oh yes, I think I do, but I've been playing tennis so hard——"

"Go on! Bottoms up!"

A stir of pride and rebellion ran through her profound shyness. She set the drink on the ground and drew his arm from about her.

"Little Puritan, eh? Haw, haw, haw!"

"No! I'm not! Of course I'm not!"

It must be admitted that to Bethel, like most children in most Sladesburys in the 1930s, it was worse to be prudish than to be loose. She was sorry that she didn't like to have Morris's thick red hand pawing her white linen blouse.

"No! Of course I'm not a Puritan!"

"Then what's a matter? First time I ever got a good eyeful of you, this afternoon. You played pretty good tennis. And you got nice legs. I guess you won't ever get thick ankles, and that's a girl's best point, believe you me. So what's eating you? Not afraid of a little necking, are you?"

He kissed her, greasily.

She was up and away from him, all in one compact movement. "I just don't like uncooked beefsteak!"

She ran like a leopard.

As she reached home, her only conclusion was that "necking" in itself seemed interesting but that, unfortunately, something in her would always make her sick of the Morris Basses and all persons who drank out of bottles and exploded in laughter. Were actors ever like Morris? she wondered. Would it keep her from being an actress?

"There won't be any people like that in *my* theater, when I'm running a show!" she snapped; and it is curious, not to be explained, that she should have said that, because never in her life had she heard of an actor-manager, of an actress-producer.

She knew nothing beyond the names of Sarah Bernhardt

and Duse and Mrs Fiske and Ethel Barrymore; nothing
of the young Helen Hayes, except as a movie actress, nor of
the young Katharine Cornell, who just then was appearing
in *The Barretts of Wimpole Street*. Like a child born to be
a painter, she got her ideas from the wind, the earth; and
this moment she, who couldn't possibly have known about
anything of the kind, saw herself in a star's dressing room,
halting her making-up to look at a bill for new props, and
then, ever so gently and sympathetically, giving a drunken
leading man his two weeks' notice.

After such eminence, it was with a good deal of quiet
dignity that she went into the kitchen to help Gwendolyn,
the youthful cook, wash the vegetables for dinner. (For
fifteen years now the Modern Merridays had had evening
dinner at seven instead of evening supper at six.)

"Have a nice time playing tennis?" bubbled Gwendolyn,
who was the lady-love of a prominent bus driver.

"Oh—yes—pretty nice . . ."

(Silver lace and a tiara—the queen enthroned, center-
stage. Dirt-crusted bars and the hateful teeth of grinning
guards—the queen waiting for the guillotine.)

"Still foggy near the river, Beth?"

"I don't—no, I don't guess it was quite so foggy."

(A young farmwife who has hidden her murderer-
husband in the attic, and who faces expressionless the
searching sheriffs.)

"What're you so quiet about? Guess you must be in
love."

"I am not!" And Bethel shuddered. Love did not, to her,
seem a mystery to be funny about.

With dignity and a degree of hunger for all the whipped
cream of culture, she paraded royally into the living room
and put an aria from *Carmen* on the phonograph. She did
not hear it through. She was so suddenly and bewilderingly
sleepy that she dashed up to her little room and till dinner-
time slept like a kitten.

The star is sleeping, as only stars can sleep.

With the blonde goddess, Alva Prindle, and Charley Hatch, the sturdy, soothing, rather stupid boy next door who was Bethel's trustiest friend, she went to the Connecticut Palace Motion Picture Theater that evening, and breathlessly viewed *The Heart of an Understudy*.

There was, it seems, a woman star, beautiful but wicked, and jealously devoted to ruining the fine young leading man by scandal-hinting and cruel looks instead of by the simpler and much more effective weapon of upstaging him. This lady fiend had an understudy, a poor foundling girl, who had learned her histrionic craft in a Seventh Day Adventist Home for Orphans. The understudy hadn't a friend in the company except the kind young leading man, who carried her bags on overnight jumps.

So the wicked star also persecuted the understudy, till the glorious night when the star fell ill (with a particularly sudden onset of author's-disease) and the understudy went on, and played so radiantly, so competently, that the critics and a lot of reporters—who just happened to be in the theater on that ninety-third night of the New York run— wrote reports which were given two-column heads in all the dailies "Miss Dolly Daintree Greatest Theatrical Find of Years: Unknown Girl Thrills Thousands at the Pantaloon Theater."

The star seemed distinctly annoyed by this until, dying, she discovered that the unknown female genius was her own daughter, by some marriage that she had forgotten, and handed her over to the arms of the hero, along with a sizable estate—presumably so that they wouldn't have to go on acting.

It was a gorgeous movie, with shots of the Twentieth Century train, supper with the producer at the Waldorf, and gilt cupids on the star's pink bed. There was even a tricky shot in which a minor movie actor acted as though he were a trained actor acting.

When the screen had darkened, Bethel did not merely hope—she joyously knew that she was going to be an actress.

She confessed it to Alva and Charley Hatch at their after-theater supper at the Rex Pharmacy & Luncheonette.

The Rex, a drugstore which was less of a drugstore than a bookstore, less of a bookstore than a cigar store, less of a cigar store than a restaurant, was characteristic of a somewhat confused purpose in American institutions, whereby the government has been a producer of plays and motion pictures, movie producers are owners of racing stables, churches are gymnasiums and dance halls, telegraph offices are agencies for flowers and tickets, authors are radio comedians, aviators are authors, and the noblest purpose of newspapers is to publish photographs of bathing girls.

The actual drug department at the Rex consisted of a short counter laden with perfume bottles and of a small dark man who looked angry; but along one whole side were magnificent booths with ebonite tables shining like black glass. Here, cozily, the three children, world-weary connoisseurs of radio programs and ventilation systems for motorcars, supped on a jumbo malted milk, a maple pecan sundae and a frosted coffee.

"That was a wonderful movie. That dress the star had on at the dance must of cost a thousand dollars," said Alva.

"Yuh, pretty good. That was swell where she bawled out the young fellow in an aeroplane and *he* said he'd chuck her overboard if she didn't shut her trap," said Charley.

"I'm going to be an actress," said Bethel.

Alva gurgled noisily with a straw. "Look who's here! You don't think you're serious?"

"Yes, I am!"

"Honest, Beth, you aren't so bad, in a mousy kind of way —you got nice big eyes and a kind of, oh, ivory skin, but if you tackled Hollywood, the producers would laugh themselves sick. Now I *am* going in the movies. Maybe I'm dumb —I can't do Cicero like you can—but I got the build."

Alva made rather indelicate motions, denoting curves.

"I'm not going to Hollywood. I'm going to be a stage actress. And be able to *act,* like that understudy."

"Honest, Beth, you slay me!"

"I am! I'm going to study voice in college——"

"You better study mascara! Beth, there ain't any stage actresses any more! All that old-fashioned junk has gone out. Plays!"

"You've never seen one."

"I read about 'em in *Movie and Mike Weekly*. What's a stage play got? Couple scenes, maybe three, and six—eight actors, where in the movies, lookit what they show you—a castle on the Riveera and a submarine torpedo room and the Paris fashions and a Chinese geisha girl and everything; and in a show you wouldn't get but sixty dollars a week, but in the movies I'll get a thousand! Hot dog! I'm going to have a sable coat!"

More sympathetic, Charley offered, "No, you don't want to be an actress, Beth. They all lead immoral lives. And you wouldn't like it on the stage. You'd be scared. You're kind of shy. You better be a nurse."

"I will not! I'm going to act."

"Maybe you could organize an amateur show in the hospital."

"I'm not going to be an amateur. I'm not going to play at playing. No! *It isn't good enough!*"

2

ONCE UPON A TIME Sladesbury, with its population of more than a hundred thousand, had known a dozen touring companies a year: Sothern and Marlowe, Maude Adams in *Peter Pan,* Arnold Daly in *Candida;* and had supported a permanent stock company, presenting fifty plays, from *As You Like It* to *Charley's Aunt,* in fifty weeks of the year.

Now in 1931 not one professional play had been presented in Sladesbury for more than five years. The block of old-fashioned spacious buildings which had contained the Twitchell Theater—opened by Edwin Booth—the Latin Academy, and the Armory of the Honourable Company of Foot had been replaced by a gold-and-scarlet filling station, a Serv-Ur-Self food market, and a Bar-B-Q Lunch which lent refinement to hamburger sandwiches by cooking them with electricity.

The former stock-company theater, the Crystal, had long been a motion-picture establishment. But by Bethel's fifteenth birthday, June 1, 1931, it was certain that the Crystal would gamble again with living actors. The Sladesbury that manufacturered aeroplane motors was going to become as modern as Athens in 500 B.C. The *Daily Advocate* announced that the "Caryl McDermid Stock Company of Broadway Actors" would take over the Crystal, on June 15th, and play through the summer.

For Bethel, heaven had come to Charter Oak Avenue.

She cut out the daily notices and pictures of the company. She pondered over the photographs of McDermid, the actor-manager, with his handsome square face, his lively eyes, his thick hair low on his forehead, his wide mouth. Proudly, as though he belonged to her—was she not the greatest local patroness of the drama?—Bethel noted that sometimes he looked like a factory executive, sometimes like a soldier-explorer, once, in rags, like a poet vagabond; proudly she learned that he had been a star in the silent motion pictures and had toured with Otis Skinner and Frank Craven.

She had always considered it shameless to be seen loitering on Charter Oak Avenue, whistled at by the interested knots of young loafers who at this period were called "drug-store cowboys," but now she went out of her way to stop in front of the Crystal and study the pictures of the cast: McDermid bejeweled in *Richelieu* and terrifying as the Emperor Jones; Miss Maggie Sample comic as Mrs Wiggs; and the pale glory of Irma Wheat as St Joan.

Dearest to Bethel of all these pictured gods was Elsie Krall, a fragile girl who seemed, for all the stiffness of her Shakespearean ruff and brocade, not much older than herself. If she had one friend like Elsie, she would attack Broadway in another year, and a year after that she would be a famous actress!

When the large red-and-black show bills were plastered about town, and the names of Mr McDermid and Miss Wheat stared at her, she felt as though it were her own name that was thus startlingly discovered.

The first play of the McDermid season was *The Silver Cord*, by Sidney Howard, of whom Bethel had never heard

—as she had never heard of Pinero or Somerset Maugham or Clyde Fitch. The press notes said that the play was "a story of mother love fighting for itself." Bethel pictured the mother as a pioneer in a log cabin, doing exciting things with an axe.

She wanted so feverishly to go to the opening night that she did not let herself go till Wednesday. But it was a youthful self-discipline in her (the kind that might some-day take her through all-night rehearsals), rather than a Connecticut Puritanism whereby anything she wanted to do was wicked. By no discipline, however, could she keep away longer than Wednesday.

It was a part of the era and the country that it did not occur to her parents, since it was known that she had no taste for glossy young drunks, to prohibit her going out by herself in the evening, provided she was back by eleven-thirty. And even in these depression days, when the family were putting off buying a new car and Mr Merriday was worrying about having to cut the staff in his store, it was sacred to them that Bethel should have "her own income" —two dollars a week, theoretically her salary for working in the store on Saturdays.

She could get no one to go with her to the theater.

She knew that her father and mother and brother would no more go to a play than to a chess tournament, and that neither Charley Hatch nor Alva Prindle would pay a dollar to hear six actors, when for half of that they could see six hundred. Bethel felt as lone and venturous as a young-lady Christian martyr in a den of Roman lions. She longed to wear her party dress of yellow taffeta, but even as a Christian martyr she could not endure the comments of her brother, and it was in the humility of skirt and sweater that she went off to her first play.

"Give you a lift?" yelled Charley, as she passed the Hatch cottage.

"No! I—I got to meet a friend," said Bethel.

The crowd that was wavering into the Crystal Theater

was none too large, but Bethel was a little frightened by it. She felt herself the only greenhorn and hoped that she would not betray herself. By the most acute figuring she had arrived at the theater exactly five minutes before the announced curtain time, so she was a quarter of an hour early. She was in awe of the veteran-looking doorman, who snatched her ticket and irreverently tore it, of the young gentleman who was demanding hats to check, of the supercilious girl ushers.

She climbed, panting, to the balcony, and came out under a noble ceiling with frescoes of pink goddesses sitting on gilt clouds and leering. She was shamed by having to crawl past the rigid knees of four early-comers, and wanted to apologize to them, and was afraid to. But when she had sunk down on the stony leatherette seat in the front row of the balcony, she felt secure, she felt at home.

She looked beatifically at the curtain, which appropriately depicted the Bay of Naples. The orchestra members, handsomest and most artistic of men, crawled from under the stage and scratched themselves a little and whispered and looked up—not at her, Bethel hoped—and then relented and sat down to play a Wienerwalz.

Bethel's soul skipped with ecstasy. She read every word in the slim program, even the advertisement of The Mount Vernon Funeral Home, Where Sympathy Is Our Watchword, Phone Night or Day. She noted that Elsie Krall, the girl actress whose picture she had loved, was playing a character called Hester. She primly folded the program, then bent over the rail and prayed for a larger house. But the place was only half filled when her heart turned over as the orchestra shivered and stopped. The house lights were dimmed, and for the first time during the fifteen years that she had waited for it, Bethel knew the magic pause, the endless second of anticipation, with just a fringe of light at the bottom of the curtain, before it went up.

She had never been so happy.

Instantly she was disappointed. Here was no battling mother in a frontier cabin, no fetching young man in buckskins, but a girl of today reading Sunday newspapers of today in a room that might have been in any of the old "mansions" on Bucks Hill, Sladesbury. But she saw that the girl on the couch was Elsie Krall, and that the pictures had not revealed Elsie's surprising copper hair, or the eggshell texture of her skin, pale above cheeks scarlet with make-up. She seemed frightened; and Bethel loved her for it; felt herself up there on the stage, reassuring Elsie.

But Bethel's affections, so bewilderingly fickle this evening, instantly shifted to Caryl McDermid, as the star himself opened the double doors and smiled his way on stage. He was Apollo in single-breasted heather mixture. He couldn't be more than twenty-eight, decided Bethel. Of course that was thirteen years older than herself, but if she grew fast and caught up with him, maybe she could someday know him and win his heart.

He was speaking, in a voice hearty and electric: "Isn't Mother at home?"

She loved the lily-swaying Irma Wheat, as Christina; and with a hate warmer than love, she hated Maggie Sample, the stage mother; a handsome, authoritative, menacing Juno of fifty. And all the while she forgot that she was at a play. This was life, and she was in it.

She hadn't known that there were plays in which the characters talked like real people, and in which you could live and struggle and forget yourself.

The story was of a mother who, to hold her sons, was willing to break up their marriages and reduce them to babyhood. Bethel particularly loved the brave Hester—Elsie Krall—fiancée of the younger son; she bounced in her seat with hope that Hester would leave the young pup.

In the intermissions, she did not go out, and she glanced rather snippily at people so unimaginative that they could chatter and walk about. And all the time she knew, beyond argument, that she was going to be an actress.

CRYSTAL THEATER
Charter Oak Avenue, Sladesbury

Week of June 15, 1931

CARYL McDERMID PRESENTS

THE McDERMID STOCK COMPANY

in

"The Silver Cord"

a drama by
Sidney Howard

Cast
(In order of appearance)

Hester............................	*Miss Elsie Krall*
David..........	*Mr. Caryl McDermid*
The Maid	*Miss Jane Yule*
Christina...	*Miss Irma Wheat*
Robert...	*Mr. Matt Pudgett*
Mrs. Phelps..	*Miss Maggie Sample*

Scenes

The action of the play takes place in a prosperous New England suburb. The first act, in Mrs. Phelps' living room, Sunday afternoon. The second in the living room, that evening; then in David's bedroom. The third, the living room, the morning after.

Miss Sample's and Miss Wheat's gowns by Isidore Oleson & Son's, Putnam Square. Stockings by Narcissa Brown, Inc. Scenery built by Murphy Construction Company, New York. Cocktail glasses by Woolworth.

After the "Theater"

FUN, FROLIC, and "FRIED DOGS"

at

D I N T Y ' S   D I N E T T E

**"Where all of
Sladesbury's Bohemia
Hangs Out"**

She came out of the theater as drunk as a bacchante; a pitiable and happy sight. She wavered home under the summer elms, and felt that she was shouting poetry, though she was not thinking at all about moonlight and roses or swords and barricades, but repeating over and over, rather queerly, "Sterility—that's your professional mother's stock in trade." As she came up to the Merriday porch, where Charley Hatch and her brother Ben were dangling their legs and discussing gliders and Colonel Lindbergh, she stopped, staring at them, swaying.

"What's the matter with you, Toots? You stay up too late. Gwan, get to bed," said her brother.

"All right."

"Did you like the show?" demanded Charley.

"Yes—I guess so—all right."

"I knew you wouldn't like it!" crowed Ben.

"I did so! I thought it was the most wonderful thing I ever saw."

"Rats!"

"I did!"

She wanted to cry, but she mastered it and crept up to her room, her refuge.

She paced, unable to stop and undress. She found herself re-enacting the play and, curiously, it was not her own Elsie Krall whom she mimicked, but the mother. Sitting on the edge of the bed, crouched, obviously broken, yet with a hint that she enjoyed showing off her woes, her elbows on her knees and her hands dangling absurdly, she muttered, " 'I'm not asking you to be sorry. It's———' How did it go, now? 'It's Robin I'm thinking of. And now that I'm old and sick . . . dying———' "

Her memory ran out, but she could not sleep. She was acting a thousand plays; she was an Arabian woman watching her son die of hunger; she was a Russian princess and then she was a Russian commissar accusing the princess; she was a "bathing cutie," very tough; and she was a ghost-pale abbess. She clawed her complete Shakespeare down from the shelf and read a dozen speeches from *The Merchant of Venice* aloud, sitting primly in a straight chair by the window, where the net curtains whispered in the night.

Portia's speech, of course; but more eagerly, Jessica and Lorenzo.

She was on the avenue in Belmont; the trunks of the great trees—lime trees, was that right?—were whitewashed, and visible in the silvered darkness.

"The moon shines bright: in such a night as this,
When the sweet wind did gently kiss the trees
And they did make no noise, in such a night
Troilus methinks mounted the Troyan walls,
And sigh'd his soul toward the Grecian tents
Where Cressid lay that night."

Thus Lorenzo, round and manly. She laid the book down on the edge of her small bureau, on the starched white cover embroidered with violets; she held out unsteady hands; she leaped up (not in the least knowing that she was doing so) and in the mirror watched her face grow soft, her lips imploring. She hastily sat down and read on. She was Jessica:

"In such a night
Did young Lorenzo swear he loved her well,
Stealing her soul with many vows of faith
And ne'er a true one."

The audience was hushed. She had been so wistfully gay; so tender yet so appealing. Then the applause, like a breaker!

By the window again, she was reading:

". . . Antonio hath a ship of rich lading wrecked on the narrow seas; the Goodwins, I think they call the place; a very dangerous flat and fatal, where the carcasses of many a tall ship lie buried . . ."

Thus Salarino, on a street in Venice. She saw the street perfectly; it ran by a canal, under archways. (She laid her head on her arm on the window sill.) She herself—yes, she was Salarino; masked and cloaked, hand on rapier hilt, slipping off to a rendezvous. A gondola, in the canal below, was revealed in the light from a lamp far up in a harsh wall, and Salarino saw—Bethel saw—a girl in white satin, flower-crowned, in the arms of a man young but bearded and angry-eyed . . .

She started out of her dream and it was dawn. She was painfully stiff, but she was in ecstasy. Then she shook her head vigorously, rubbed her shoulders, and snorted, "Don't be so silly, Bethel! Go to bed!"

3

HowevER MUCH SHE TRIED to conceal her emotion when she told him about having seen *The Silver Cord*, Charley Hatch saw that it was going to be difficult to "cure her of this crazy notion that she was going to try and be an actress."

Charley was a friendly boy, rather like a kind old milk-wagon horse. His hobby was collecting stamps. "You learn a lot about geography and foreign places and so on from stamps," he stated. He wanted to be a farmer; but to his father, who himself had come from a farm, this would have been a shocking retrogression from his urban position as superintendent of a bus line; so Charley was planning to become an osteopath. He had soft tow hair on a large, thick skull, and he whistled constantly.

"Lookit, Beth," he implored, as they sat on a branch of a maple, twenty feet up in the air. "Of course a girl wouldn't know about all such things———"

"I bet I would!"

"—but you got no idea what you'd be up against if you

23

tried to go and get to be an actress and went looking for a job on Broadway. It's full of pitfalls."

"Pitfalls?"

"Pitfalls."

"What kind of pitfalls?"

"Awful pitfalls! Managers and all like that, that betray young girls."

"How do they betray them?"

"You wouldn't understand."

"What do they do to 'em?"

"Beth! What language! It ain't ladylike. Golly! You're already showing what awful influence the stage has got on you. You don't want to be immoral and bohemian, do you?"

With the utmost sweetness, like an indignant wren, Bethel explained, "How do I know? I don't know what you have to do to be immoral, but of course if I have to, to be a great actress, why then I have to. Don't you see?"

"This is awful! I never heard anything like it! You don't know what you're talking about!"

"I do so know what I'm talking about!"

"You do not know what you're talking about."

"Oh, shut up!"

"Shut up yourself, telling me to shut up!"

"Oh, Charley, I'm sorry if I was rude."

"Oh, that's okay. But I don't think you had ought to be immoral, just the same."

"Well, maybe I won't have to. And honestly I like loganberry juice much better than beer. Gee!"

Upon Bethel's solicitation, Alva Prindle did go to *The Silver Cord* Wednesday matinée. And she hated it. Bethel met her at the Rex Pharmacy for her report.

"It was so talky!" Alva complained into her cherry sundae. "Maybe some folks might like it, but what I say is, it don't hold your attention, like a movie."

"Twice as much!"

"It did not! There wasn't anything happening. Not even a penthouse or a machine gun. All talk!"

"Alva, you just wait till I get to be an actress———"

"So you're still going to be an actress!"

"I certainly am. And I'm going to talk on the stage—oh, about everything—about patriotism, and love———"

"Why, Beth-el Mer-ri-day!"

"—and why a person feels religious———"

"It would be awfully improper to talk about religion, right up there on the stage. They never do, in the movies. People hate it."

"But I will—honestly I will. And I'm going to get up a dramatic society in high school next year."

"That 'd be kind of fun."

"It 'll be kind of hard work, too, let me tell you! There's not going to be any fooling around when I get up a play!"

"Oh, there isn't, eh! You think you know so much! I bet you don't even know what a stage door is!"

"I do so!"

"How do you know?" scoffed Alva.

"I read about it."

"That's a heck of a way to learn about things—to read about them! But I bet you didn't dare go to the stage door at the Crystal."

"*You* didn't?"

"I certainly did!"

"Alva! And you saw the actors, close?"

"I certainly did. And I got old McDermid's autograph, and Elsie's and Irma's."

"Oh, you didn't bother them for their *autographs!*"

"I certainly did! What would you talk to actors for, except to get their autographs?"

"Tell me, Alva—oh, tell me! Is Mr McDermid as handsome as he is on the stage?"

"Him? Old Mac? No! He's maybe forty-five, and he wears a wig."

"Oh no! Oh, darling! It couldn't be! Oh, not forty-five!

Almost as old as my father! And a wig! But I don't care. I think Mr McDermid is just—uh—adorable."

"You do, eh?" Alva had regained all her Hollywood superiority. "Well, let me tell you, baby, Mac's married to that red-headed little dumbbell, Elsie Krall. You better stay off."

"Oh no! How do you know he is?"

"The stage doorman told me. And Mac treats Elsie terrible, the poor kid."

"Do you know what I think?" said Bethel.

"What?"

"I think you're a liar. You're like that mother in the play. Good-by!"

This from the meek Bethel who, year by year, had let Alva snatch her lollipop, her scooter, her beaux.

She waited till no Wednesday, the second week of the McDermid company's season, when they played *Dulcy* with Elsie Krall as the ingénue Angela. She had to know about Alva's strictures on her favorite gods. She was there on Monday evening, not embarrassed now, and when her last agitated laugh was finished, she marched down the alley to the stage door, rather wishing that Alva could see how professionally she went about it.

The stage entrance was at the back of the theater, on a rotting balcony overhanging Swan Creek, now a sewerlike trickle between muddy banks but once, when Sladesbury was a country town, a handsome stream. She was annoyed by the crowd of three girls with autograph albums, but she wrapped herself in an imaginary cloak—black lined with crimson—and waited, mysterious under an arch in Venice.

The magic beings were coming out of fairyland, and Bethel knew that she was right about them.

Caryl McDermid—yes, he must be forty-five or more— quite an old man—but that certainly was no wig, that lovely mane thick as horsehair, and he smiled so easily, took in the autograph hunters with his gaily curved lips, his innocent eyes. Elsie was on his arm, clinging, adoring. And there were Irma Wheat, whose smiling made her more beautiful than on the stage, and the terrible Maggie Sample, the overwhelming character woman, who was a pillar of ice.

Bethel tried to resist, but as these four walked through the alley, down Charter Oak Avenue, with its red neon lights over bowling alleys and cafés, she followed them, glad that they really were so beautiful . . . even if she did notice that Mr McDermid's elbows were shiny, and Elsie's heels worn down. To what glamorous party were they going? Would they meet professors and newspapermen from great Hartford? Was Mrs Beaseley Payne's sixteen-cylinder Cadillac waiting to whisk them to splendors at her pine Gothic castle on Bucks Hill?

Her idols were turning into Boze's Beanery . . . they were casually sitting down at a long marble-topped table . . . they were ordering hamburgers and flapjacks and coffee . . . and Bethel heard Elsie addressing Mc-Dermid: "Oh, darling, I think I'm stinking in *Dulcy*. I wish to God I could act," and heard Maggie Sample's snappish, "So do I—wish you could!"

Bethel was sitting at the other end of that Beanery table, too scared to move, her voice breaking as she ordered, "P-please, a chocolate éclair and a g-glass of m-milk."

There was an elegance about Caryl McDermid that was hard to define. His suit, of soft blue flannel, was glassy at the seams; he wore a commonplace soft white shirt and solid blue tie; but there was an unwrinkled firmness and smoothness about his cheeks and chin; and the lapel of his coat curved as though he had magnificent shoulders. His smile was consuming; it took in everybody, as though he loved them yet realized all their absurdities.

Elsie Krall, his wife—the child must have been thirty years younger than he—was frail copper and ivory; the statuette of a stilled dancer; but her eyes were not alive like McDermid's. They rested always on him, gratefully; and imploringly on the bitter Miss Maggie Sample.

They were real gods, as Bethel had known they must be.

She was not shocked by the undivinity of their chatter. Probably she really had the professional stage virus in her system.

"Maggie," said McDermid, "I wish you wouldn't wave your arms so, when you make your cross in your scene with Forbes, in two."

"Elsie, listen darling, don't yell so when you say to me, 'It was just the most romantic thing that ever happened in the world.' Can't you underplay it a little? *Dulcy* is a comedy, you know!"

"Say, did you see that Ramona Snyder has been cast for the name part in *Stop It, Rosika?* They go into rehearsal in August," said Irma Wheat.

"And is she lousy! I bet they don't pay her a hundred and fifty, and no run-of-the-play contract," said Maggie Sample.

"Don't mention money. I don't know what we got a box office for," said McDermid.

It was the catsup bottle that introduced Bethel to them, though this did not surprise her, since she loved the romantic catsup label with its legend: "Made only of fresh ripe tomatoes, onion, salt, and rare and imported spices from the Orient."

"Please pass us the catsup," said McDermid to her.

"Oh—yes." It was a convulsive effort, but Bethel got out, "I—I loved the play tonight."

"Oh, did you, honest? Was I terrible? I just can't seem to do these swell society girls," wailed Elsie Krall.

For all her loyalty, Bethel had confusedly felt that Elsie really had been fairly "terrible" on the stage; awkward and bouncing. But she lied like a gentleman. Then—oh, she *had* to know; it was her whole life—Bethel blurted:

"How can you get to be an actress?"

Elsie stared. She looked as though she were asking the

same question herself. McDermid smiled. Irma Wheat said, "God only knows! But what do you want to go on the stage for, anyway?"

Maggie Sample was like Lady Macbeth in one of her moments of exasperation with her husband, as she protested to Bethel, "Do you want to starve? I've been on the stage thirty years, and here I am in this flop of a stock company in the sticks——"

McDermid smiled. "Hey, hey!" was all he said.

"——and next fall I'll be lucky if I get a job as a kosher ham sandwich in a Number Two Company of *Abie's Irish Rose*. When you grow up, child," and she smiled at Bethel, "you try to squirm into prison, or get a nice job hustling hash, or even get married, or anything to avoid going on the stage."

"You know you'd rather act than eat, Maggie," said McDermid.

"That's only because I never get a chance to eat."

"Now don't discourage this young lady. She has wide-awake eyes. Maybe she's felt the call to the stage.

"Shabby and crouched and shockingly fed,
Whistling, he sits on his unmade bed
In the airless bedroom down the hall,
And smiles because he had heard the call
(At Equity minimum!) back to the stage—
Rusty beggar or golden page—
Claudius, Hamlet, or Player King—
The glory that flutters wing on wing——"

"Oh, you and your Lambs Club poetry!" Miss Wheat scolded at McDermid, as she arose, with the sardonic Maggie Sample. "You're going to be telling this poor, deluded kid that it's better to climb up on the steam pipes in a dressing room in order to keep your feet out of the water when the toilet has busted, and to sit up all night learning seventy-five sides, at sixty bucks a week, closing on Saturday, than it is to work in a grocery store. Me, that 've got it on Gloria Swanson from ankles to consonants, playing in a dump behind a factory in Connecticut. You can keep it. Caryl, darling, if you weren't my boss, and if I didn't love you distractedly, I'd tip you off that you're as screwy as a Russian director."

"No. He's not bright enough," said Miss Sample.

Exeunt, Irma and Maggie.

"It isn't true, what she said. It is fun to be on the stage, isn't it?" Bethel begged of Elsie.

"Yes, I guess it is. I don't know yet. I been acting such a little time." Elsie looked troubled. "I was waiting on table in Teneriffe Junction, in Iowa, when Mr McDermid came along and married me. He's been so sweet—yes, you have, too, Caryl—but I guess he gets kind of impatient—oh, I don't blame you, darling. It's so kind of hard for me to understand why a lot of the characters act like they do. Take like last week; why did Hester—— Did you see me in *Silver Cord* then?"

"Oh *yes!*"

"Oh, I'm glad. But I don't guess I was very good. But why did Hester fall for a softie like Robin? Honest, it's so kind of hard, all this acting. But I love the travel. I collect things—from department stores. We only been married a year, and I got an Austrian peasant costume from Marshall Field's and a pair of python shoes from Halle's, in Cleveland, and a brazeer from Sicily, all hand-embroidered, in Columbus, and all kinds of things. But I do get scared—all those hellhounds in the audience coughing!"

McDermid said hastily, "Elsie is about as new to it as you are, my dear, but you'll both make good. And—— How do you get a chance to act? Well, first you get all the training you can. *Training!* Act wherever you can—even if it's in the barn. And then get God to pass you some good luck. That's all I know. And it's worth it. Even if you aren't much good—and me, I guess I'm probably just the run-of-the-mill ham—even so, when you've been creating a human being, and living in him, then the rest of the world outside the theater, with all its fussing about houses and motorcars and taxes, seems pretty shabby. Acting—it's a heightening of life. I guess we're all stage-struck, us old troupers, no matter how we kick."

"And do you think maybe I could do it?"

McDermid studied Bethel, rubbed his nose, droned, "Maybe so—maybe so. Let's see. Get up and walk to the door and back." When she returned, his appraisal was warmer. "You're pretty graceful, and you have some spirit in you, and a rather warm voice, for such a thin kid, and you watch things—you see how things are done—I was watching you watch us. Yes, I think you probably can act!"

It was her accolade.

As they went out, Elsie whispered to her, "Come see me in my dressing room."

"Oh, I'd be pleased!"

"And we can play with my doll. I got such a funny doll —so long-legged and so sweet. I've never told a soul but you that I still play with it—not even Mac—Mr Mc-Dermid. I don't know anybody in Sladesbury—they all seem so grown-up and busy here. Will you come see me?"

"Oh, I'd love to!"

"Come next week then."

"Yes!"

Bethel was intoxicated with the friendship of this, her first real actress. But she never saw Elsie's dressing room. The McDermid stock company closed, that Saturday night, and she did not meet Caryl McDermid again till years afterward, when he told her of Elsie Krall's dying of pneumonia in a hospital in Hollywood, looking bewildered and a little frightened, and clasping to the end a long-legged armless doll.

4

You know Gale Amory—she's such a grand girl, you'd never expect to find her in a hen college. Well, she was to play the husband's part in *Doll's House,* you know, Ibsen, it was the senior-class play, and she came to rehearsal all made up like a man, I mean, double-breasted blue suit of her brother's, and she's so feminine, everybody laughed their head off. So, of course, they all began to cut up and laugh and kid their lines, and the girl who played Dr Rank, she ran out and came back with a burnt-cork mustache, and of course, I mean that simply convulsed them, and she said in a deep voice, I mean, it was a serious line from the play, but she burlesqued it and she said, 'At the next masquerade, I shall be invisible,' and everybody simply howled! And then Gale goes out and puts on a mustache, too!

"Why even Miss Bickling—Professor Bickling, who teaches Drama, Poetry, and the Novel and that coaches the plays—of course I mean she's deadly serious about art and culture and she's so fat and respectable and eyeglassy, but she got to laughing as hard as anybody, and it was terribly hard to go on with the rehearsal, but then it was such fun

and after all, wasn't that the real reason for doing the play
—to have fun, the last few weeks of those long four years
of college?

"In fact the only person that beefed about it was Bethel
Merriday; she was playing Nora, so probably she felt like
a star or a prima donna or something. Beth is a sweet
girl, even if she does get so daydreamy, and she's not a
grind, and she certainly does share her candy and introduce
her dates around. But for some reason or other, she takes
plays so doggone seriously. And she turned on Gale and
she had a regular fit of temperament and she screamed,
'Will you take off that fool mustache and quit trying to play
Room Service? You haven't got the slightest idea yet
whether, as the husband, you're supposed to be a stupid,
decent bookkeeper, or a sadistic stuffed shirt, or what, and
here dress rehearsal is only a week away!'

"Well! You did have to admire Bethel, mostly so quiet,
like a sparrow, standing up to that big Gale Amory, but
still——

"Poor Miss Bickling looked so uncomfortable. Of course
she was supposed to be coaching the play, but all she ever
said to any of the actors was, 'I don't know—maybe if it
feels awkward to stand there so long, you better move
around a little, and make some gestures—that's it: try to
think up some gestures that will look interesting,' or 'Maybe
you better speak a little louder.' So when Bethel butted in
like this, Miss Bickling was embarrassed as the dickens. She
was kind of fond of Bethel, because she always read poetry
aloud so lovely, but of course she couldn't stand a tantrum
like this, and she said, 'Bethel dear, I know you're very interested in drama, but after all, this is college, and we want
to act like ladies and not like paid actresses, don't we!'

" 'No, I don't,' Bethel said.

"Imagine!"

It was seven years—or seven excited moments—since
Bethel had talked to the Caryl McDermids. The time was

May 19, 1938; twelve days before she would become twenty-two, three and a half weeks before she would graduate from Point Royal College for Women, in Connecticut. Tonight she would be starring in *A Doll's House,* but this afternoon, at the panicky, hastily called extra rehearsal, it did not look as though there would be any senior-class play whatever.

The dress rehearsal, last night, had lasted till two A.M., and it had been scandalous. Miss Gale Amory, as Torvald Helmer, did not know her part, and whenever the prompt girl—a terrified and outlawed freshman, crouched on a chair, almost hanging her head inside the window in the right wall—was able to find her place in the script and to throw the line to Miss Amory in an edgy whisper, Miss Amory screamed, *"Please!* I can't *hear* you." Nils Krogstad did know her, or his, part, but she wasn't sure whether she was a comic villain who ought to close one eye and tap her nose, or a Russian victim of fate who talked deep down and inaudibly. She tried it both ways.

The amateur stagehands had dropped one of the flats for the rear wall and torn a gash, and not till the dress rehearsal had anyone discovered that the music of the third-act tarantella, conveyed by an aged phonograph, could not be heard in the second row.

Bethel was better than that. She did know her part, and she could be heard, and she had some notion that Nora was an amiable little housewife who had never been trained by responsibility. Whether she shouted too loud and wrung her hands too much is a matter of opinion, but just now the appalled Professor Miss Bickling looked on Bethel as a combination of Nazimova and Max Reinhardt, and it may be that our Bethel, just for the day, felt that way herself.

This afternoon, five hours before the performance, they were, with glue and frenzy, repairing the irreparable. Six people were cuing Miss Amory all at once. Miss Bickling was urging Krogstad to take it easy, and Bethel was begging Krogstad to take it hard.

The rest of the time, Bethel was standing absent-eyed in corners, muttering "Noyesterdayitwasparticularlynoticeableyouseepausehesuffersfromadreadfulillness." The college engineer—a male, and no artist—was patching the ripped canvas of the flat, and one of the girl musicians was practising a Spanish dance on a hastily imported piano, so placed behind scenes that no one could reach the dressing rooms without banging her legs on the keyboard. The pianist, though she would not be seen by the audience at all, already had such stage fright that her music sounded like terrified teeth.

In the midst of this merriment Miss Bickling received a message, beamed, and called Bethel aside, with "What are your plans for the summer, Beth?"

"I guess I'll just stay home."

"But you still want to try and go on the stage, in the fall?"

"Yes. Anyway, I'll tackle all the managers on Broadway. They might give me a chance as walk-on."

"What's a walk-on?"

"It's where you walk—*on.*"

"I see. Well, of course I think being a librarian or getting married or going to Switzerland is more educated than being an actress, but still—— You'd like to act in one of the summer theaters, wouldn't you?"

"Oh yes, but I wouldn't have a chance."

"You know, I tell all my girls that I look after their careers just as much as I do their conjunctions, and I've used all my 'pull,' as you girls call it, and tonight, right in the audience, will be two ve-ry celebrated proprietors of summer theaters in southern Connecticut—Mr Roscoe Valentine and Mr Jerome Jordan O'Toole."

"Oh dear!" said Bethel.

At dinner in Bemis Hall, before the play, it was dismaying to Bethel that none of the girls were nervous and taut like herself; six hundred hearty young women, gulping chicken hash, clattering their forks, yawning, shrieking about biology and the boys, and making up their lips; carefree and pink and scornful. How could she make them believe in Nora tonight?

She ate her pudding (cornstarch pudding with canned raspberries) as slowly as possible, to put off the terrifying hour of going to Assembly Hall, their temporary theater. She tried to smile cordially while the girl beside her related with vulgar cheerfulness her experiences with a canoe, a portable radio and a C.C.N.Y. man. They were precisely such experiences as the girl's mother had had with a canoe, a banjo and a Princeton man, and to Bethel they seemed antiquated compared with the woes of the Nora who had first slammed her door sixty years ago.

She wanted to escape from these chatterers, but as she slipped out of Bemis Hall, a LaSalle drove up, and in it were her father and mother and brother and Charley Hatch.

"We thought we'd drive down and surprise you and see you act!" cried each of the four, in turn—so smiling, so sweet, so devastating.

"Oh, that's dandy! I'll see you right after the show. Come backstage!" she chirruped, while she was quaking that it was going to be bad enough to forget her lines and make herself ridiculous before the jeering students and two summer-theater managers, without giving herself away to her trusting family.

She cried for a good two minutes in her dressing room, which until one hour ago had been the consultation room of the Professor of Pedagogy and Vocational Psychology; she rolled her head on her dressing table, which had been the professor's desk, covered with graphs about the relationship of coffee drinking at lunch to the three-P.M. sale of (a) automobile tires, (b) Dopey Dolls, (c) advertising-column-inches in trade journals. She did not belong with graphs or anything else that was new and brisk and important in A.D. 1938.

She was pale enough always; now she felt herself funereal; and as she shakily started to make up, she plastered her cheeks with a vermilion base and felt better and braver about it. She knew nothing about make-up, but then, neither did the college theatrical dictator, Miss Bickling, who would have felt it rather low to let Ophelia associate with blue lining salve. The one thing Bethel was convinced of was that you always use heavy grease paint and always extend your eyebrows with burnt cork (which you don't). She was proud of slapping her face with powder and getting the powder all over a huge apron she had borrowed from the Bemis Hall kitchen.

While she made up, she stared now and then, like a solemn child, at the portrait of Professor Maria Martin Mitz being vocationally psychological in cap and gown.

When Bethel was done, she looked like an extravagantly painted doll, with very red cheeks, very long black brows, and a very white little nose absurd in the middle of the sunset. Later tonight, on the stage, the effect would not be improved by lighting that was a ferocious illumination by spots, with no gelatins to soften the glare. But nobody minded. The college dramatic enthusiasts—if they were going to have make-up, they wanted it made *up,* and no nonsense.

To Bethel and the other members of the cast, Professor Miss Bickling was of the greatest help. She came in every two minutes and patted their shoulders and cooed, "I know you're going to be just wonderful, dear, and be sure now and don't forget your lines." This was a mild form of what was known in Point Royal College as a "pep talk," and it had, on writhing amateur actresses, the effect of so irritating them that they were sure now and did forget their lines.

Despite this balk, Bethel was much clearer than at dress rehearsal as to how she saw Nora's shrill little character. She had asked Miss Bickling about it all, and the benevolent professor, who kept culture as she would have kept a tearoom, had purred, "You mean you want to break down the character? Oh, leave all that psychological fussing to the

left-wing theater. It hasn't anything to do with Art. Just
be careful to say the lines as the author wrote them—only,
you must say them beautifully, of course—lines like 'Never
to see the children again—oh, that black icy water'—and
then you can't go wrong."

But, in rebellion, Bethel had tried to think out by herself
what Nora really was; what she herself was, as Nora;
and having heard the whole cast and Miss Bickling agree
that Nora was a very nice young married woman who suffered from an unimaginative husband, Bethel was agitated
to find that she considered Nora a fool, in expecting a
banker husband to regard forgery as just a little joke between friends, and none too kindhearted a fool, in boasting
of her domestic security to the desolate Christina.

If this was true, fretted Bethel, wouldn't it be much
more explosive if, in the last act, Nora were more aware of
her own childishness than of her husband's stuffiness?

"I'll do her that way!" exulted Bethel. "It'll be tremendous."

But she had the grace to jeer, "Of course there is the
little matter of your being such an amateur that the audience
won't know whether you see Nora as a gun-moll or an
abbess!"

The cast took turns, feeling ever so professional, in
peeping out through a hole in the curtain at the audience,
which was brutally cheerful in not having to remember
lines: cynical fellow students in bright sweaters, officially
cheerful professors, timid parents. Bethel could not find her
own family, and felt abandoned, and she could not make
out any two men who might be the fate-laden summer-
theater directors, Messrs Valentine and O'Toole. . . . Oh,
what of it, what of it, what *of* it! They'd laugh at her feeble
Nora anyway, and she'd have to go home . . . maybe
marry Charley Hatch . . . no, she wouldn't . . . oh, why
not?

She stood outside the double-door entrance, ready to go

on at the beginning of the play. She was a small, resigned figure in a bobtailed Victorian jacket, a small bustle, a skinny fur and a prim little hat. For a moment, in panic, certain to be jeered by the audience out there, the fiendish demanding Audience, the AUDIENCE, she had been certain that she couldn't remember a single line. Now she was too numb to care. If the curtain would just go up, so she could get it over! Did the student orchestra have to go on showing off all evening? She hated the sour and trailing air of *"Weis' du wie gut."* She concentrated on the wheat-colored canvas and the flimsy crossbar of the backstage side of the double doors. She wondered in what previous play they had been used; what the stenciled DL7 on the canvas meant.

Then she was jarred almost into screaming by Miss Bickling's loving and altogether devastating pat on her shoulder. Then silence from in front—no music, no rustle of audience. Something gone wrong? Then the stage manager's confident voice, "Curtain's going up, Beth," and instantly, propelled by a power not her own, Bethel-Nora was scampering on the stage and saying cheerfully, her voice as steady as her hands were jittery, "Hide the Christmas tree carefully, Ellen."

She was Nora; she was an actress; she was born.

5

Bethel PLAYED the first two acts in a still and competent
fury. Gale Amory, her stage husband, was the creator of
the fury, and the cause was not Gale's incompetence, but her
extreme competence in faking.

Perceiving that she would never be able to remember
her lines, the bonny Gale decided to treat it as a joke and
to share the joke with the audience. So whenever she stopped
to listen to the prompter, she smiled at her friends down
there like a toothbrush advertisement—if Gale wasn't strong
in intellect, she was extraordinary in whiteness of teeth—
and her pals wriggled with affectionate entertainment and
muttered that this was the first time that Ibsen had ever
been amusing.

For the first time, when Gale burlesqued her line "My
little bird must never do that again" and got almost as good
a laugh as if she had kicked a baby or fallen on her nose,
Bethel had enough wholesome ham in her to be tempted to
join in the fun, but she angrily rejected it, and fought
through, making herself as much the kindly, half-baked, tor-
tured Nora as she could. She was too busy keeping up pace

to notice whether she herself was good or not, while she was on the stage, but in her dressing room between acts she had time to decide that she hadn't been too bad.

She had felt authority. But not till her great last scene of breaking with her husband did she feel inspired.

Then (she believed) a great new spirit filled her, and she was Nora, she was all Noras, all women who are bewildered by the brutal and incomprehensible whims of stranger-husbands. As though she were hammering nails she pounded at Torvald—at a Gale Amory now a little embarrassed and much less sportive—"I believe that before all else I am a human being, just as much as you are—or at least that I should try to become one." She raised her voice, raised her arms; a priestess before the altar; the priestess of the new cult of the awakening women. "Henceforth I can't be satisfied with what most people say, and what is in books. I must think things out for myself, and try to get clear about them."

The applause came crashing; and at the end, when she slammed the door, she felt that she was not closing a door but opening one on life . . . first nights on Broadway, velvet-hung first nights in London, famous authors with scripts, and a terrace in Bucks County, Pennsylvania, where she would sit being gaily learned with Lunt and Fontanne and Noel Coward and Helen Hayes and Katharine Cornell and Orson Welles.

She scampered to her dressing room—a complete success, after eight curtain calls.

It was the first dressing-room reception she had ever held. It was a whirlpool of beaming eyes, handshakes, voices saying that she was "wonderful," that she "had a great future if she should ever care to accept a position on the stage," that "she had been much the best thing in the play —much!" She wasn't deflated even by the fact that from next door, from Gale Amory's dressing room—which to-morrow would again be the Domestic Science and Dietetics

Seminar—she could hear "You were much the best thing in the play, Gale—you were wonderful—you were so *human!*"

Bethel felt that she was acting an actress in the dressing room rather competently—the pleased modesty, the clinging smile. In the midst of people she could make out her family, and see Charley Hatch looking at her as wistfully as a lost lone dog, Miss Bickling coming down from her synthetic ivory tower to say firmly, "You did splendidly, and I was very angry with Gale for clowning, and I'm going in and tell her so," and a whole puppy-rollick of classmates, mocking, "You certainly showed up the husbands, Beth!"

Miss Bickling cleared them all out. Mr O'Toole of the Dory Playhouse was waiting; Mr O'Toole had to get back to New York that night.

So, in glory, Bethel met her first producer.

Mr Jerome Jordan O'Toole, at forty-five, had directed seven Broadway plays—two of them surprisingly successful —and for twenty years before that had acted chauffeurs, tramps, detectives and such other examples of what playwrights, peering out of their clubs, regard as the Common People. He was Yankee-Irish, from Bangor. He was tall and dry and sunken-cheeked; hard and exact and honest. In summer he was managing director of the Dory Playhouse, at Hardscrabble Beach, Connecticut, which was classed as one of the dozen summer theaters that were competent and professional.

Bethel, heart fluttering, didn't know whether to sit still, as a confident actress, doing something or other with cold cream and Kleenex, or to stand humbly in the presence of power, and before she had time to figure out the interpretation of her role, Jerry O'Toole was in the doorway, like Abraham Lincoln in tennis costume, and she had popped to her feet and stood blushing.

Miss Bickling crowed, "This is our lovely little heroine, Miss Merriday."

O'Toole shook Bethel's hand with a croaking "The performance was very interesting" that was more completely a nothing than anything Bethel had ever heard.

"Was I as bad as that?" she begged.

"No. You weren't bad. Of course the others were all of them excellent—splendid."

"Oh-uh!" of bliss from Miss Bickling, and a diminutive "Oh" of chagrin from Bethel.

"They weren't trying to act at all, and they did that very well. They managed to turn Ibsen into a farce, and I guess that requires a college education—I never had one. But you, my dear——" He held Bethel's hand in his long wide brown hand, which felt comforting. "You were trying to act, so I'll compliment you by applying professional standards, and by them, you were pretty bad. You showed that someday you may be able to act, if you ever get any training. But you were pretty bad! You overplayed everything. You made Nora sound like a kitchen mechanic scrapping with the iceman. But you were alive."

"But——" She did not know that she was copying his hitching style. "Then I guess there's no chance for me to get into your summer theater this season?"

He gave what seemed to her a curious answer: "Not till you've been lucky enough to fail a few times. Then come see me, my dear. Good luck!"

He was gone; a broad-shouldered, gaunt man who moved easily.

Miss Bickling had scarce got through protesting to Bethel that she was disappointed, that Mr O'Toole had proved to be nothing but a Broadway Commercialist and a Heartless Algonquin Wit, when they were interrupted by the pleasant exuberance of Mr Roscoe Valentine, who always carried his own private sun.

Mr Jerome O'Toole's summer stock company, the Dory Playhouse, and the Nutmeg Players, conducted by Mr Roscoe Valentine at Point Grampion, Connecticut, were both on the shore between New Haven and New London, twenty miles apart, and the feeling between them was that of caviare for butterscotch sundae. Roscoe Valentine, aged fifty, was a man composed, except for his brains and his indignant red eyes, entirely of powder puffs. In winter he was a Bostonian and a scholar, editor of a magazine of the arts called *The Spiral,* and director of The Spiral Theater, where Back Bay met the backwoods in one-act glorifications of a proletariat that they actually hated and misunderstood.

Bethel had never seen a man like this: so squashy, so giggling, so spiteful, yet so calmly understanding of everything a woman thought before she finished thinking it. His hand felt like a cold wet piece of oiled silk, as he held hers and bubbled:

"Splendid, my dear! You gave an entirely new conception of the role of Nora."

"Do you hear that?" said Miss Bickling.

"Oh, thank you!" said Bethel.

"Yes—oh, indeed yes," said Mr Valentine.

"Mr Jerome O'Toole told Bethel that she overacted," said Miss Bickling.

"Jerry O'Toole must have been reading a book again. It always takes him that way. One time, he was quite a good stage manager. He knows all about carpentry, but don't you think, my dears, it's just on the too-too side when he talks about the social drama? No, my poppet, don't you worry. You did Nora with real éclat. So beautifully fallible."

Bethel didn't know what it was all about. She never would be adept at doing word tricks. She looked at Valentine like a shivering kitten, and Miss Bickling carried on for her.

"That's so kind of you. I'm sure Bethel and I appreciate it a lot." (Bethel wasn't at all sure.) "Now she feels that she has a calling to the stage, and after tonight I'm sure she has, and we're wondering if you could make a place for her in your summer theater?"

"Why, I think perhaps I could."

"Oh, how gorgeous!" said Miss Bickling.

"Oh!" said Bethel.

Valentine sat down facing the back of a wooden chair. And that was the first time, outside of the movies, that Bethel had ever seen this posture, and she noted and put away the fact that it made his fat knees prominent and very silly.

He spoke youthfully:

"Now as we're just three girls together, let's let our hair down and be frank. You know there's no box office at all in the summer theaters. Even a roundneck like O'Toole can't make it pay—in fact, if you want to know, I make more than he does! But even so—— And for the apprentices, such as you'll be, Miss Merriday, I have simply splendid teachers, with practical lessons in voice and eurythmics, and the chance to appear in my plays with famous actors. So I'm compelled to charge each student actor two hundred and seventy-five dollars for the ten-week season, and fifteen dollars a week for room and board—really below cost. Do you think you could dig up all that fabulous wealth—four hundred and twenty-five dollars?"

And to Bethel it *was* fabulous wealth. "I don't know. I'll try to. I'll try so hard."

"When can you find out?"

"My family are waiting outside. I'll see them now."

The senior Merridays and Charley looked small and rustic in the stretches of the Assembly Hall stage, gazing distrustfully at a red-headed co-ed in shorts who was moving scenery. Bethel flew up to them, her dress three-quarters buttoned, her hair uncombed.

"What is it—what *is* it, dear?" urged her mother.

"Anything gone wrong?" her brother demanded, rather gladly, as though he were going to have a chance to hit someone and restore his own superiority in this over-feminine maze.

"Oh no, it's just—— Daddy, I can be in a summer theater this summer, with real actors, and then be ready for a job on the stage this fall, in New York, if you can let me have four hundred and twenty-five dollars for the lessons. But honestly, I'll pay it all back, as soon as I get a job——"

Her father fretted, "Well, finances are pretty tight, just now, and I had hoped you'd begin bringing in a little before long. And I guess I don't understand girls now. When I was young, girls were glad to stay home and marry some nice fellow, but now seems like they all want to go off some place and be actresses or fly to Australia. No, I don't understand it but—— Yes. We'll fix it somehow. My girl's going to have her chance!"

"I don't *need* a new Chevvy this year," said her brother.

For years, Bethel was to be at a disadvantage when young actresses explained that they had the most interesting excuses for every lapse, because their parents and brothers had been so unimaginative, unsympathetic and generally so American.

As she went to bed, she exulted that she was a real employed actress now; that in just a month she would be at the Point Grampion school. But there was something irascible lurking behind the bland joy, and she dared to drag it out:

"I *did* overdo Nora. It wasn't good enough. I wasn't good enough!"

6

ALL THOSE TWO DAYS at home, June fifteenth and sixteenth, 1938, before she went off to the summer theater at
Grampion, she earnestly enacted the role of a girl saying
good-by to childhood and to every loved spot that her
infancy knew: the cement garage, the pergola on which
the Concord grapevines were always rather dry, the basement playroom with the tracks of the electric railroad which
she had inherited from Ben.

She also devoted herself to sound self-examination—she
tried to.

She felt, and quite guiltily, that she ought to be devoting
herself to worrying about the dispossessed Jews in Ger-
many and Poland, the share croppers in Oklahoma; and,
if not doing anything about them—for obviously she never
would do anything about them—at least showing herself a
right-thinking liberal by hourly agonizing, "Oh, isn't there
something I *can* do?" But she had to admit that what she
wanted was much simpler: she just wanted to act.

She felt guilty because none of her life had been con-

spicuously devoted to "doing things for other people." That
was Professor Miss Bickling's war cry and nursery ditty:
"The greatest joy and privilege in life is doing things for
other people." But Bethel found that she coveted dancing
lessons, fencing lessons, French lessons, piano and voice
and make-up, for herself.

"Well then, I guess I'm just that kind of a selfish pig,"
she lamented.

She was equally dissatisfied with her examination of the
status, to date, of the Heart of Bethel Merriday. She
wasn't quite sure that she had one.

Certainly, if the test was, as she often read, lying awake
longing for the smiles and caresses of some particular
young man, she had no heart, as yet. She liked the laughter
of the young men and their hard handshakes, but she
wanted to jeer when she heard Alva Prindle or Gale Amory
yearn that some curly-headed, pipe-flourishing young male
was "just wonderful."

Alva had given up her claim to Hollywood. Already a
little stringy at twenty-three, she was devoted to the hope
that one A. Alexander Brown, a fat insurance agent with
the optimism characteristic of all insurance agents, would
marry her and provide a mink coat and a set of etched
cocktail glasses. Not toward Alva, not toward her father and
mother and brother, did Bethel feel guilty, but toward that
shaggy house dog, Charley Hatch, who had been compelled
by family deficits to give up his dreams of osteopathy for a
job in the sales department of the Flamolio Percolator
Corporation.

"You don't think maybe you'd rather marry Charley, he'll
be making thirty-five dollars a week pretty soon, instead of
going off and taking such an awful chance on the stage, do
you?" her father had said.

"No!" said Bethel.

"Well," said her father.

On her last night in Sladesbury, Charley came calling, and
they sat on the porch.

Americans making love have always sat on porches, except for those who were too poor or too rich. In the house was electricity; Mr Merriday was reading about the tear-gas bombing of strikers in the aeroplane industry, and Ben drawing television diagrams; but Bethel and Charley sat on a porch in New England and, despite all announcements that the whole world has changed since 1920, no one could have told them from their grandparents.

"Look, Bet, while we got the chance to be alone together——"

"You must drive down to Grampion this summer. I'll bet it 'll be awfully cool on the shore."

"I sure will, but look——"

"I hope there won't be a lot of mosquitoes."

"I guess there won't be, but——"

"Isn't it funny how you can be awfully earnest and excited about something like acting, and then some silly little thing like mosquitoes will throw you right off!"

"Bet! I want to talk seriously——"

"Please don't."

"You know how doggone fond I am of you."

"Yes, I think I do, but—— Oh, Charley, don't make me feel guilty. Maybe I'm the bloodless kind of girl that can't ever devote herself to any man. But I've got to go on. Honestly, please believe me, I do envy the girls that can settle down to a nice little home, but for me—prob'ly I'm crazy—it doesn't seem good enough."

"You'll never find folks that you can depend on like you can on your home folks. In the world outside, they'll use you and then throw you away like a worn glove."

She studied Charley. His soft hair was babyish and pathetic, yet his large, solid head seemed fatherly and protective. Was she a fool to leave this eternal kindness?

She sprang up. She cried "No, no, no, no!" and fled into the house.

None of them could drive her down to Grampion that day—Friday, June 17—and she went by train, which was, for one of the Modern Merridays, like traveling by oxcart.

She was overwhelmed into complete guilt by Charley's farewell present: a make-up box.

It was the most beautiful, most elaborate make-up box, with every cosmetic she had ever heard of: two kinds of rouge, evening and daytime lipstick, skin freshener, powder, mascara, nail polish in two shades, "Dawn Delight" and "Faint Memory," "nourishing cream" and the humble cold cream.

She cried over it. Not for three weeks did she discover that the only things that were of the smallest use to her were the cold cream and the empty tin box.

7

GRAMPION CENTER was a picture-book village. Red-fronted chain stores and crimson gasoline pumps had enterprisingly tried to improve its quiet quality out of existence, but Grampion was all gambrel roofs and elm trees and white steeples and white cottages with small-paned windows, and the quickening smell of salt marshes.

It was Bethel's new-found-land, and she was another pioneer of the American tradition.

The only conveyance at the station was a sedan, at least ten years old. The driver, a young man with a yellow sweater and a blue denim shirt, thrilled her by clucking (and not laughing at her, either), "You one of the actresses, miss? Jump in. You'll have a good time this summer."

They drove through marshes, gray-green and still, crossed a tidal creek, and came to a mile-long bay, with sun-clipped waves. Twoscore sailboats were at anchor. On one of them, three handsome burnt youngsters, in white ducks, white jerseys and white boating hats, were getting up sail, and they waved at her hopefully. Then the sedan skirted a

private estate with bayberry hedges and came abruptly into
the Nutmeg Theater grounds, which occupied a quarter of
the square-shaped Point Grampion and had Long Island
Sound to south and westward.

Born in the hill-circled city, going to a college on the
Housatonic River, Bethel little knew the sea. She looked
across the Sound some ten or twelve miles to the blurred
shore of Long Island, near Greenport. Fishing schooners
were slanting northward, the lofty sail of a yacht leaned
perilously, and through the middle distance slipped a
freighter from foreign lands. The flickering stretch of the
Sound was to her bluer and more fluid and ever-changing
than the blue sky above her own hills. She felt superstitiously
glad. The Sound was a tributary of open ocean, and she
was a tributary of the great theater. Actresses, she assured
herself, if God is good to them, come down at last to the
sea and to a ship which will bear them to the lights and
cheering in far-off lands.

The grounds had a sand beach on one side, which promised
bathing, and rocks on the other, for loafing in the sun. The
flat top of the low bluff was a whole village in itself: the
actual theater building, which had been a church; a one-
room building as office; the house of the old-time pastor-
farmer, where splendidly lived the director, Mr Valentine,
and most of the seven permanent members of the stock
company—all professional actors—and such lordly "guest
stars" as might adorn the casts from week to week; a shop
for painting and carpentry; the School of the Theater—
the old pastor's barn, with a small stage and rows of doubtful chairs inserted; and at last, on the sea edge, with tennis
courts beside it, Bethel's new home, the dormitory and
dining quarters for the apprentices. She was too excited to
be critical; otherwise she might have noticed that the dormitory was shakily knocked together of second-hand boards
and painted with pigment guaranteed to peel immediately.
The windows were narrow and low, their mosquito netting

of cotton. But to Bethel it was the Temple of the Muses, all
cool marble and bright gold.

"Good luck, miss! Hope you drag the crowds in!" said the
driver.

"Oh, thank you. It's wonderful to be here," she crowed,
and her friend drove off, leaving her alone in the Temple.

Uncomfortably alone.

She ventured into the hallway, which was also the
living room, of the apprentices' dormitory. With a scratched
upright piano, a long, bare table, a cushionless window seat
and a litter of third-hand chairs, rockers and wicker and
canvas deck chairs, the room was a charity home. But
Bethel was pleased. She was a worker in the theater and
an insider, not one of the luxurious "carriage trade" who
came in limousines and demanded upholstered seats but were
never (she innocently believed) welcomed in the holy places
backstage.

The room was still; there was no one on the uncarpeted
stairs; the only stir was from an outboard motor on the
Sound.

"Oo-hoo!" she cried, timidly.

Through a door at the back resentfully emerged a lean
man, in overalls, with a stained white mustache.

"What d' you want? You one of the students?"

"Yes, I think so."

"You *think* so? Don't y' know? My name is Johnny Meddock. I run this place."

"You *do!*"

"Yes, I do! I'm the caretaker. And janitor. I'm responsible
for keeping the floors clean and the windows washed and
chasing the small boys off. Folks also think I'm a Quaint
Local Character. I let 'em think so. It's worth money to me.
I even let 'em think I used to be a fisherman here, when
this place was a decent churchyard and a fish wharf and not
no theayter, with a lot of you young women chasing around
and flirting and not enough clothes to dress a pussycat in. I

never was. I hate fish. I used to be a janitor in the State Capitol, in Hartford. Well, what d' you want?"

"I suppose I ought to see Mr Roscoe Valentine, first. Do you know if he's anywheres around?"

"He's in the office—that one-hen coop by the front of the theater. Yes, I guess you might 's well see Roscoe, as Andy Deacon ain't come yet."

"Andy Deacon?" It was the first time that Bethel had ever heard even the name.

"Yuh, he's the real boss here. Andrew Deacon. He makes out he's just one of the actors, but it's him puts up most of the money for Roscoe to blow in. He went to college and everything. Long about twenty-eight, Andy is. Acts on the stage regular—God knows why, rich fellow like him—his dad was J. Goddard Deacon; run the big gun factory up in Worcester. Nice-spoken fellow, Andy is, too—like a Hartford man. But you better see Roscoe. So long."

Johnny Meddock vanished. He who often remarked that he "hated theayters and hated their guts" was the most theatrical object in the place. He was Punch and Judy and Policeman and Devil all in one.

Bethel, having decided that he was either very hateful or lovable, went searching for the high priest, Roscoe Valentine.

Mr Valentine, in sandals, lilac trousers, a dark blue shirt, a voluminous white tie and English eyeglasses, was at his desk in his small cabinlike office, simultaneously writing an advertisement for *The Petrified Forest* which, on June 27, would open the season, dictating a letter to an agent in New York complaining because he had not received another script, scratching his left calf with his right foot and planning a lecture on "Relaxation, the Secret of Acting." He looked up at Bethel blankly.

"Yes? What do you want?"

"I just came to say I'm here, Mr Valentine."

"I'm so bright that I might have deduced you were here, but I still don't know why you are here or who you are."

He looked for applause from his secretary, a sensible, agreeable-looking young woman, and didn't get it. He was irritated, and demanded, "Are you one of the apprentices?"

"Why yes, don't you remember? I'm Bethel Merriday. Point Royal College?"

"Oh yes. Nora in *Doll's House*. You overacted it atrociously."

"That's what Mr O'Toole said."

"Oh, he did, eh? But even Mr Jerry O'Toole can sometimes be right. Well, you go and report to Cynthia Aleshire, my scene designer. She'll put you to work. And begin to learn right now, my pigeon, that if you're serious about your stage career, you've got to do everything you can around here—learn everything about the theater—everything."

"Oh, yes sir."

"Very well then. Marian, skip out and show this baby the shop, and hustle back here."

The girl secretary, outside, patted the dismayed Bethel amiably. "Don't worry about him. His bite is worse than his bark. But he does know something about acting and producing. . . . I hope he does! . . . My name is Marian Croy."

Miss Croy was twenty-six or -seven, and placid.

"You're his secretary?"

"No. I'm an apprentice, like yourself. I've been teaching school for six years, out in Nebraska—I organized a town dramatic club. I've saved up enough money to take one year off, for a shot at this place and then Broadway. God knows why I want to act! I always say it's because I like to read Maeterlinck aloud (I hope *you* don't think he's too sentimental, too!), but maybe it's to try and escape from the prairie winters. If I don't make a go of it, I'll go back and marry Oscar Heyden—he's a nice man, but he looks just the way his name sounds. . . . Am I babbling, Bethel?"

She loved this kind woman, as Marian went on:

"I am, but you know, I'm just as lonely and scared here as you are. But busy! Roscoe found out I knew shorthand, so he put me to work. That's how you learn to act here—doing everything that Roscoe would have to pay to have done —scrubbing floors or addressing envelopes to theater subscribers or driving up town to buy cigarettes. I do hope you don't know pedicuring, or Roscoe 'll probably have you doing his sweet, pink, plump toes. Good luck, dear. Miss Cynthia Aleshire, scenery boss—Miss Bethel Merriday, freshman."

Cynthia was a trim, tall, Greek-coin lady of thirty-five. Bethel did not believe that she would ever know Cynthia, but she instantly felt herself one with the apprentices, sprawled inside the work shed and in front of it, repainting last year's scenery a flat gray. They were a joyful crew: two girls in shorts and jerseys; three young men in overalls, or sweaters and gray flannels.

There was the plump, jolly, hither-eyed Toni Titmus, who had just finished freshman year in the University of Wisconsin but who at the moment thought that she preferred playing English duchesses to playing basketball.

An almost anonymous, fresh-faced girl named Anita Hill.

Pete Chew, a round, stupid, wistful, rich young man who had taken to the drama only after having been dropped by Amherst, Rollins College and the Schenectady Flying School.

Walter Rolf, slim, competent, decent, twenty-three or four and a track runner. It was Walter Rolf's misfortune that, however much you tried to avoid the word "clean" in describing him, you were sure, in the end, to pigeonhole him as a Clean Young American. He looked like a Princeton Man, and by a coincidence he was a Princeton Man, with a dash of Oxford.

Last of the crew, incredible as a student actor, was Harry Mihick.

Like Marian Croy, Harry had come to the theater late; unlike her, he was that most portentous of bores, the yearner who knows that he is much more artistic than he is. Harry was forty, and at home, in Hannibal, Missouri, he was a

bookkeeper. He was also an actor, in the Y.M.C.A. Drama
Guild; a poet, in the *Southwestern Christian Advocate;* and
a dramatist, in nothing perceptible. The gang had concluded that Harry had come to Grampion to find someone
who would listen to his play plots. He would stop swimming to discuss his psyche, and he wrote poetry to all the
girl students. It was pretty good poetry, too—by Richard
Lovelace.

Of these apprentices, Bethel guessed that only Toni
Titmus and Walter Rolf had talent. But that made two
more young actors than she had ever worked with before,
and she was content, though later she was to calculate that
her estimate may have been too high, by two.

They all knew so very much about the theater. As they
painted and glued and hammered, and constructed the lunch
counter for *The Petrified Forest,* they gave final verdicts:

"Claire Luce and Wally Ford were both of 'em too doggone *sophisticated* in *Mice and Men.* I wouldn't of played
Claire's role that way at all. I'd of made her more awkward. You know. Small-town."

"I didn't think Cedric Hardwicke was so hot. He made
the canon so darn heartless. I felt he was showing off, all the
while. Too much technic. Now if I'd had that role, I'd of
shown how deeply he felt everything underneath. Of course
Sir Cedric is nothing but an Englishman. How could he play
an Irishman? Of course, I'm not Irish, either, but still . . ."

"I don't know how the Lunts could waste their time on
foolishness like *Amphytrion.* I like a play that's got some
social significance. Maybe if I'd been running their schedule,
I'd of stood for *The Sea Gull,* but these *French* plays——
Whatever you may think about the Russians, you certainly
got to admit they got *art!*"

The practically senile Harry Mihick (aged forty) had
greeted her, "Well, Miss Merriday, I hope you're going

to take advantage of this intimately associating with artists and having a chance to brush up on ideals this summer." Nobody laughed much, either.

Listening to their wisdom, peeping in awe at Toni Titmus as she perkily revealed that she had once been introduced to Jo Mielziner, the scene designer, at Sardi's, Bethel felt that she was again a freshman.

How many more times would she find that she had graduated only into new freshmanhood? Freshman as a baby, freshman in her first year in grammar school, freshman in high school, freshman in college, freshman in a summer theater, freshman on the professional stage—perhaps freshman in marriage and freshman as a star—would it end only with death and her awakening to freshmanhood in heaven?

But she was rescued from humility when she discovered that these airy habituées of the Nutmeg Playhouse, these blasé upper-classmen, had been here only twenty-four hours longer than herself. By the end of an hour's painting she was becoming one of them and was saying some pretty profound things about gag lines. She had discovered that if she endured their idiocies without laughing, they would stand for hers.

The sea wind ran across the rough wild grass, touching her hair; and she was really painting a stencil on real scenery; and she was in a world where she could talk about the theater from eight A.M. to two A.M.

"I—I—I think I'm going to like it!" she burst out to the beautiful Walter Rolf.

"Sure," he said convincingly.

It was more than good enough.

8

Bᴇᴛʜᴇʟ'ѕ ᴅᴏʀᴍɪᴛᴏʀʏ ʀᴏᴏᴍ, a double room which she was
to share with Iris Pentire of the stock company, was as utili-
tarian as a boxcar. It had two cots, two straight chairs, two
tilted bureaus, with blisters in the paint, and a row of hooks.
But to Bethel, washing up for dinner on her first evening in
Grampion, it was enchantment, for on the wall was a last
season's poster:

THE NUTMEG PLAYERS
Present
Mɪѕѕ Eᴛʜᴇʟ Bᴀʀʀʏᴍᴏʀᴇ
in
THE CONSTANT WIFE

This was no bedroom but the anteroom to glory! Here
her friend Iris Pentire and she would be queens of the stage,
along with Ethel Barrymore.

Cynthia Aleshire, the scene designer, said that Iris, who
would arrive tomorrow, was a phenomenon: slim, lovely,
only twenty, but already a professional actress and one of
the seven Equity-member professionals of the Nutmeg
permanent stock company at Grampion. Iris had, reported

Cynthia, been a chorus girl, a photographer's model, played stock in Baltimore, and toured in a minor part in *Teacher Mustn't Slap*. In fact, at only twenty, Iris had as much grilling stage experience as, a generation before, she would have had at the age of six. But as the youngest of the professional stock company, at minimum salary, Iris was to live not in the Bostonian luxury of The House but with the submarginal citizens of the dormitory.

Bethel was going to love Iris even if she hated her.

She stripped off her sweater and slacks, sang in the shower, and in the pride of blue skirt and clean white sweater she ran down to dinner.

There were sixteen student-apprentices at Grampion. They were unpaid, and classed as amateurs, but each of them was permitted by Equity to appear in three plays during the summer. Higher in the hierarchy were the permanent stock company, with Mr Andrew Deacon and Miss Mahala Vale as leads, and other visiting professional actors and "guest stars" who appeared in one or two out of the schedule of ten plays presented during the summer of 1938.

Tonight eleven out of the sixteen apprentices had come, and were being dramatic over veal loaf, cottage-fried potatoes, coleslaw, stuffed peppers, and huckleberry pie about a table which was made of two retired barn doors resting on sawhorses.

Pete Chew, the rich and roundly young, of whom it was already obvious that his best role in the theater world would be donating scholarships to the hat-check girls in night clubs, had wondrously changed from overalls (by Abercrombie, Fitch) to checked gray trousers, black and white shoes, and a sweater from the Isle of Uist. (But why Uist?) He had been buzzing about Toni Titmus at the workshop; now, as Bethel ventured into the dining room, Pete looked brightly at her, approached her with a festive waddle, seized her arm and cheered, "Uncle Pete'll sit beside you, pretty-pretty, and save you from the sharks."

"So the poor little rich boy is going to tell another prospect how unappreciated he is," said Marian Croy, the teacher-secretary-apprentice.

"Let him alone. Maybe he'll put money into a show for us someday!" screamed Toni.

"I don't think it's nice of you to mock a fellow traveler on the gypsy trail of the arts," said Harry Mihick.

Bethel listened doubtfully. But Cynthia Aleshire was talking about things called "functionalism" and "formalism" in stage settings, and how you can play *Macbeth* all up and down and under a staircase.

The sea, filling the windows, was softening into apricot over toward the horizon; and now Bethel met Fletcher Hewitt . . . quite the nicest man, she decided, whom she had ever seen.

Fletcher Hewitt, though he could not have been over thirty, was the traditional Yankee; Uncle Sam without his whiskers; tall, thin, rusty-haired, speaking with calc'lation. His father had been a Rhode Island carpenter, his mother an ambitious New Jersey school teacher, caught in matrimony on an innocent summer vacation. At eighteen, with his widowed mother, Fletcher had gone direct to Broadway. He was a good stage manager. He had nursed twoscore plays in New York and on the road. In the Nutmeg Players it was his job not only to watch entrances and off-stage noises and curtains and all the other housekeeping and kitchenwork of the arts, but to carry on direction when Mr Valentine was sick after one of his nauseas of temperament, and to keep Cynthia from making the scenery so functional that it wouldn't function.

Fletcher's pale blue eyes were serene as summer.

Looking at the Higher Thinkers—Marian Croy, Cynthia Aleshire, Fletcher Hewitt, Walter Rolf—Bethel was certain that she was going to have four solid friends. But still to arrive were the real divinities: Andrew Deacon, Mahala Vale, the young leading woman, and Iris Pentire, who would be Bethel's own true twin.

The rocks looking on the Sound were their drawing room after dinner, and the twilit moment was complete as they lounged there—Bethel, Fletcher, Walter, Toni Titmus; tired actors (tired from scraping scenery), carelessly disposed in rest (but pretty careful about their attitudes of carelessness; the indolence of a knee, the angle of a face resting on a hand).

Toni screamed, "I've got to go up and write the loving parents. I wonder do we get any dancing lessons this summer? Oh, to be a Bernhardt, now that my stage career is here, and me not in the doghouse—not yet. See you soon." Walter Rolf sighed, "I've got to try and finish Stanislavski's *An Actor Prepares,* before we get down to real work and I learn that Stanislavski is all exhibitionistic nonsense. Good night."

Fletcher Hewitt stretched and demanded, "Your name's Bethel?"

"Uh-huh."

"Going to take acting seriously?"

"Oh, I am."

"I guess most of the apprentices are. For instance, a nice chap like Rolf—I'll bet anything he's got an uncle who's head of some factory and would give him a job, but Walter will gamble on earning fifty dollars a week twenty weeks a year, as an actor. Or an old bird like me—I'm thirty and I didn't have a job all last winter and I have to support my mother and prob'ly I could make two hundred a week in Hollywood, but I'd rather get sixty as assistant stage manager of a road show. Thousands of youngsters ready to starve if they can just have a chance on the stage, and no more permanent winter stock companies to train them, and so few touring companies—and that's the fault of the provincial audiences; they'd get the shows if they wanted 'em enough, if they knew their business as audiences as well as we know our jobs on the stage. So we flock to these theatrical Boy Scout camps—and we're making 'em into good theaters, too! Probably eighty-five summer theaters in the country solid enough to last through the season—probably two thousand kids, mostly from comfortable homes, that are willing to scrub floors and usher and shift scenery, with the thermometer a hundred backstage, to get a chance to act. If the theater's dead, we're going to revive it—we're reviving it right now! So! Well, I've got to go and have a fight with our electrician."

She was alone on the rocks when the oversize faun, Pete Chew, found her and crouched by her and automatically seized her hand.

"You like it here?" he said.

"Oh yes."

"And we'll have a good time, too. You stick by Uncle Pete, pretty-pretty. There's a lot of places where you can go dancing, and take a drink, but I'm liberal; I never insist on a girl taking a drink, unless she wants to. If we can maybe get hold of another fellow when the rest get here—I thought Walter Rolf would be a good sport, but he's a stuffed shirt —but if we can round up some live wire, him and Toni and you and I can have one swell summer. And swimming."

"I'm afraid I'm going to work most of the time."

"Oh, don't be that way. That kind of junk is all right in college, but we're artists—we can do anything we like and get away with it. Don't you know that?"

"I'm afraid I hadn't thought about it."

"Well, I see where old Uncle Pete has got to start your brain whirling. You come from a woman's college, don't you? And the backwoods?"

"Just a small manufacturing city."

"You see? How do you expect to be a high-class actress and act in plays about Long Island society if you don't hustle up and see the world? Why, I'll take you down to New Haven sometime, and we'll do Savin Rock. I got my own car. A Lincoln!"

Bethel tried to be tactful and retreat. "Do you want to act in society plays?"

"Well, I'll tell you, Bethel. I'm not so much on the charm

and social stuff, though my family is one of the best in
Bronxville. I'm more you might say a comedian. I did
Falstaff in prep school—the Ypsilanti Military Academy. I
had a row with a crank in the dramatic club at Amherst, so
I never got into that—oh yes, I'm an Amherst man, I went
there till I got sick of the place, so darn *provincial*—but I'm
a good comedian. And I'm thinking about doing a lot with
the financial backing of plays. I can be the biggest influence
on Broadway! That's why I want all this training this summer. You'll see me one of the hottest producers in town
someday. What I could do for a girl! I'd plan for her and
make her the biggest actress in America!"

"I see. Maybe you can do that for Toni Titmus."

"Her? That little tramp? She thinks she knows everything. I told her I was just interested in her artistically, and
she laughed at me. She claims she was a walk-on in *Our
Town,* and so she's a professional, is she! And when I asked
her if she liked presents, she says she only likes jewelry!
Nothing doing! No, no—but you and me would get along
wonderfully. I had a voice teacher in New York for a month,
Miss Lazla Lastigora—you know, the famous one that
taught Mrs Pat Campbell and Clark Gable and everybody
—and she said I was very sensitive. Come on!"

He patted her shoulder enthusiastically.

She achieved in answer nothing more than, "I—uh——"

"If you been stuck away in a girls' college, you probably
don't know anything about having a good time. And I certainly hate to see as lovely a kid as you wasted on a lot
of amateur hams here. Maybe you think it's kind of sudden, but I swear, I'm falling in love with you. Do you like
me?"

She spoke feelingly:

"I hope it won't happen to you, what happened to the last
boy that fell in love with me."

"What's that?"

"Yes. In Sladesbury. Oh, the handsomest, wildest, gayest

boy—Charlemagne Hatch. I *told* him I wouldn't be good for him. I *warned* him. But oh, why, why, why did he——"

"Did he *what?*"

"Just when I'd got so I couldn't live without him. I was always telephoning him when he wasn't there! Why did he do it?"

"W-what did he do?"

"Leaped right off the top of the City Hall."

"Gee!"

"Oh, ever so much worse than that old professor . . . Doctor Bickling."

"W-what happened to *him?*"

"Oh, not so bad, but I remember he talked so much like you. He was sensitive, too, the way you are. And just when I thought he and I were going to be so happy he—— I can't stand it!"

"What *did* he do?"

"He ran away."

"Golly!"

"They say somebody saw him afterwards in a low grog-shop in, uh, Mexico!"

"No!"

"Why is it, Pete? You don't think I'm insane, do you—am I a *femme fatale?*"

"A *what?* No, no, I don't believe you are. Well, I—gotta be getting along. I'll be seein' you!"

Bethel heard him shouting under Toni's window, "Hey, come on down and let's go summers and get a drink. I need one!"

She smiled, even as she sat among the ruins hearing her mother say, "Bethel Merriday, I'm sur-*prised!*"

But in the darkness she remembered Fletcher Hewitt's sermon about the children's crusade of the summer theater. She thought of the hundreds of other young people who were this moment dreaming of the theater, by the sea, in the cool hills, in the rustling woods, under the stars—boys and girls from factories and colleges and farms, from disapproving New England mansions and flats in the East Side ghetto, exhibitionists and sound workers, Communists and Tories and plain bored at home—an army of Gay Contemptibles.

How absurd must once have seemed the butcher's son from Stratford, piping on his penny whistle as he trudged to London, under the stars.

9

ON SATURDAY, her second day at Grampion, Bethel could not see what the tasks which Roscoe Valentine and Fletcher Hewitt and Cynthia Aleshire gave her had to do with acting. She helped the colored maid set the table in the dormitory. She answered the telephone in the box office for an hour. She sewed at heavy red curtains for the courtroom scene in *Night of January 16th* till her fingers trembled. She stitched and hung a new chintz curtain in the star's dressing room, to honor their greatest guest star, the famous Nile Sanderac (she ranked almost with Ina Claire in playing elegant young married women), who would be coming in a week now, to enact *Candida*.

Bethel's most theatrical duty was to drive the old Ford station wagon into Grampion Center and borrow, for the *Petrified Forest* set, a cash register and a couple of round tables from Mr Butch Stevens, proprietor and maître d' hôtel of the Lobster Pot Dance Hall and Dinery. Mr Valentine did not "believe" in buying such accessories or in renting them. It was a serious matter of principle. He loved a nickel with the same spirited and devoted passion that he devoted to God and Bernard Shaw.

"B-but suppose Mr Butch doesn't want to lend them?" protested Bethel.

Roscoe almost screamed: "Don't take any nonsense from him! You tell him I say he gets half his customers from my theater, and he won't need this stuff—second-hand junk; I know; I've used 'em before!—till mid-July, when the summer season's in full swing. Don't let him bluff you!"

Across the lunch counter of the Lobster Pot, Bethel smiled on the lumpish Butch Stevens and said briskly, "Hello!"

"Hya."

"I'm glad there's such a nice place to eat at in Grampion. I suspect I'll be coming here a lot this summer, with my bunch."

"You one of the theater girls?"

"Yes."

"Huh! None of you kids ever buy anything more than a malted milk."

"Oh, my bunch will. I'll see to it they do. Now Mr Stevens, I can see——"

"You can call me Butch."

"—I can tell from the way you look at me that you know I want to ask you a favor. You're the kind that can't be fooled."

"So what do you want to borrow for the theater this time? Summer 'fore last, they took all my Coca-Cola posters and brought 'em back torn. But last summer, one time I was away, damn' if Valentine didn't send some of the kids in here to 'borrow' four ham sandwiches!—and the girl let 'em have 'em, and that's the last time I ever see any of them sandwiches, and when I tackled Valentine about paying for 'em, he said he didn't know anything about it, and asked me which girls it was borrowed 'em, and Lord, I can't tell none of you actresses apart—you all look alike to me—all bare-

nekkid legs and sweaters and a lay-off-me look. So what do
I get stung for this time? . . . Just some tables and a cash
register? Does there have to be money in the cash register?
Because I suppose if Valentine wanted it, I'd have to give it
to him, or else these codfish-eating Yankees here would
say I didn't have any public spirit."

"Aren't you a Yankee?"

"Me? No, thank God! I'm a foreigner . . . from New
Jersey."

She returned to the theater, at noon, to find newly arrived
four members of the permanent stock company: Tudor
Blackwall, the second juvenile, sleek and doe-eyed and just
faintly effeminate; Clara Ribbons and George Keezer (in-
comprehensibly but always known as Doc Keezer), who
were both middle-aged veterans technically classed as "wise
old troupers"; and, at last, the baby of the stock company,
Iris Pentire, who was to be Bethel's own twin.

And she knew instantly that she would never know Iris.

That other twenty-year-old, Toni, the plump and pretty,
had been unhesitatingly friendly, but Iris, moving silkily
about the room she was to share with Bethel, putting away
salmon-colored silk pajamas and maribou-edged silver bed
jacket and scarlet pumps with gold heels high as obelisks,
cautiously smiling and musically murmuring, "Thank you for
letting me come in with you," was hidden with cloudy veils.
She was a Mystery.

And Miss Iris Pentire saw to it that she should continue
to be a Mystery.

The most nearly convincing stories about Iris that Bethel
was ever to hear were that she was the daughter of an Irish
nobleman, reared in a nunnery, still piously virginal and
viewing her stage career as a means of portraying the
austere beauties of virtue; and that she was shanty Irish,
from Wheeling, West Virginia, and had had only twelve
words, headed by "Okay," in her vocabulary until, at the age

of sixteen, she had become the sweetheart of Clum Weslick, the distinguished director, who had provided her with tutors and chiropodists.

Slender, fragile, with hair not golden but color of sunset gold reflected on a silver box, sweet eyes, and mouth that appeared sweet unless you saw it twisted in anger; silent, defenseless and slim as the child Elsie Krall; silent and sweet and never quite saying what she meant; silent and soft-moving; that was Iris Pentire; and one moment Bethel thought she was a statuette of gold and ivory, a charm to wonder at; and the next, a voodoo priestess.

"I—I don't suppose you care much for swimming?" said Bethel.

"No, I'm afraid I don't care much for swimming," smiled Iris.

"I hope you'll like it here," said Bethel—the Old Resident at Grampion.

Saturday noon, a young man who looked like a research scientist, and who may actually have been so but was now employed as one of the Deacon chauffeurs, flashed into the theater grounds and left Mr Andrew Deacon's favorite car, an English Rolls-Royce with a convertible coupé body, to await Mr Deacon's arrival as male lead in the Nutmeg company. It seemed that Mr Deacon's mother would be driving him down from Newport in a day or two.

All the apprentices, whether they came from Fond du Lac or New York's East Side, were expert and blasé about automobiles. But even their youthful American cocksureness was shaken now.

"Gosh, this Andy Deacon must be some actor. I bet if he chased Juliet in that buggy, he'd get her," said Toni Titmus, in a tone of vesper prayer.

Bethel wondered if Roscoe Valentine overmuch loved his partner, for, looking at the car, Roscoe muttered—even to her, the outsider, the raw recruit, "Huh! Andy doesn't hide his wealth much, does he—our theatrical playboy! But the fact is, all the money is his mother's, not his at all—and does the dear old dowager let him know it!"

Roscoe interrupted her stippling of canvas flats, for the adobe walls of the Black Mesa Bar-B-Q in *The Petrified Forest*, Saturday afternoon, and sent her on the illustrious mission of meeting Mahala Vale, the leading lady—she who had done so well, the past two seasons on Broadway, as a featured player in *Betty, Be Quick,* which lasted four months, and the sensational share-cropper play *You Cannot Dispossess Our Souls,* which had lasted four nights and one matinée—the second play having been a favorite of labor-union publications and the first play of labor-union members.

Mahala Vale descended from the dusty local train like a leading woman determined to be pleasant, and with a high handshake she caroled, "It was so sweet of you to meet me, Miss Merriday."

Mahala could not have been over twenty-five or -six, but she looked like a young woman who knew her job; carrying herself with authority, on the tall side, wide-browed, chestnut-haired, the true goddess; beautiful in a standard way where Iris was pretty in an exciting, perplexing way, and Bethel was either insignificant, or as tantalizing as music.

"A station wagon? How very exciting! Shall I sit up beside you? It smells of fish, doesn't it!" said Mahala.

Bethel was hereafter to hear her say a great many things in her cello voice, and never to know whether Mahala meant any of them, or what she was thinking, or whether she was thinking at all. If Iris Pentire was openly mysterious, Mahala Vale was mysteriously open; if Iris bewildered the frank heart of Bethel by her silence, Mahala baffled her by easy and indecipherable chatter.

All sixteen of the apprentices and most of the stock company had arrived by Saturday evening, and they sat all over the rocks by the shore, as vocal as a flock of blackbirds. Bethel again felt like a freshman—like a freshbird. She was an approachable fledgling, but a lone one, never quite willing to belong completely to the rule of any bevy.

She looked at the bumptious Pete Chew and the enterprising Toni Titmus snickering together—and sometimes, she felt uncomfortably, glancing over at her. She looked at Iris Pentire, alone, posed as a lone sweet goddess (small-sized) awaiting the mystery of the moon. She looked at Mahala Vale, being gracious and countess-like on behalf of a circle composed of the handsome Tudor Blackwall, Doc Keezer, the trouper, Walter Rolf and the rustic Harry Mihick; telling them what she had said to George Jean Nathan—though with a considerable avoidance of what George Jean Nathan had said to her. She looked at the honest Fletcher Hewitt being respectful—God knows why! —to Roscoe Valentine and to Cynthia Aleshire, the scene designer. Suddenly she preferred the honest guttersnipes, Pete and Toni, to all of them, and felt elated when she saw Pete (tonight incomparable in a cream Palm Beach suit with a white silk shirt and a crocus-yellow sash about his globular middle) rolling toward her.

"Look, Beth," Pete whispered hoarsely, "don't worry about your telling me about your Past."

"What are you talking about? I haven't *got* a Past!"

"You can trust me, Beth. I'm like the grave. I haven't told a soul."

"Except Toni!"

"Huh? Oh. Her. Well. Yes. Maybe. She don't count. How about you and me going to Clinton to the dance tonight?"

"Aren't you afraid to go with me?"

"Well, I think a fellow ought to have experience, if he's going to be a star. In school I didn't hardly have a chance to see any life."

"How about that little waitress?"

Now Bethel knew nothing whatever regarding the relationship of Pete Chew to any waitress. Something inside her had told her to say that; and she was as astonished as Pete, who gasped like a carp, and begged:

"How the dickens did you ever—— Honestly, that didn't mean anything at all. I fixed it all up. Oh, sure! I learned about women from her. But Beth, you got to remember, you *got* to remember that I've always been kept down by a whole slew of rich relatives and profs. You got to teach me. Golly, you and me could be such friends. Would you like a snake-skin belt?"

"I would not!"

"I know where I can get an elegant one for you, cheap. I mean I want to give it to you. I mean a present. You know. I mean just as a present."

"No, thank you, Pete."

"And you won't go to the dance with me?"

That intrusive inner voice was again speaking: "Don't be such a blasted prig to this poor Bronxville Casanova. He's an amateur even at that. Even with the best tutors and the best champagne, he'll never be a good flirt—not a real specialist." Thus warned, she said almost tenderly:

"Not now, Pete. Maybe sometime."

"And could I give you a box of candy? Two pounds!"

"If you'd like."

"I'll drive right into the Center and buy it."

It was the first of the assaults on her virtue which, as an actress, she had the right to expect, in tribute to her charm and beauty, and she was alarmed to find that she felt rather proud of it.

Pete gone, Bethel saw Toni Titmus scampering toward her. If Toni was not as fat as Pete Chew, there was no reason why she mightn't become so. Bethel could see them, forty years from now, as an admirable old married couple, devoted to food, the theater and the rights of immorality.

Toni said cautiously, "Well, how do you like it here, Beth?"

"Oh, fine."

"Well . . . I guess you find it pretty tame, though."

With huge gratification, Bethel saw that someone was in awe of her. She felt beautiful, languorous, and a little weary of strange sins. All of that she put into her line: "Oh, it's good to get away to the quiet country for a change."

"Tell me, Beth—honestly, I've never had a chance to ask any girl that knew: Do you think it's better, when you've had a row with the boy friend and you're in wrong but of course you don't want to admit it—should you call him up or wait for him to phone?"

This fundamental social problem—one that Bethel had, actually, never encountered—she solved airily: "My experience is, you better wait and keep him guessing. If he doesn't phone, then you haven't really got him captured anyway, and so you're safely out of it. These men! You have to be brutal with 'em."

"Are you brutal with 'em, Beth?"

"Oh, always!"

"Are you really, sure-enough?"

"Certainly. Anyone with experience is."

"How do you handle 'em if a boy comes home with you and makes a pass at you—one that you don't *want* to have make a pass at you, I mean."

"Just look at 'em and smile sort of cynically."

"Cynically?"

"Yes, sure—cynically."

"Well, I don't know. Of course I haven't been much persecuted by really dangerous men yet." She sighed. "Oh, there's plenty of boys that chase you in the university, and back home in Fond du Lac, but that don't get far if you're living home or with a lot of girls. Of course when I get to New York and take a job on the stage, I guess I'll have a little apartment to myself—of course just a little one, not very big—and then I guess I'll have to cope with some pretty unscrupulous fellows, producers and playwrights and like that, old unscrupulous ones, forty or so, and I'll just have to cope with 'em!" She looked much brighter.

Swept by Toni's narrative powers, seeing her own self

facing a vicious old seducer of forty or so in the stilly perils
of a one-room apartment, Bethel panted, forgot the theme
of her own role, and stated with indignant virtue, "A man
like that, you just look him square in the eye and say, 'Now
don't be silly! I'm not your sort and you better know it
right now. Don't you try——' "

She stopped, realizing that Toni was staring at her, medi-
tative, then derisive; and after a pause was jeering, "Look
here now, Bethel Merriday! My Lord, and you fooled wise
old rounders like Pete and me! But I'll bet you're nothing
at all but a Good Girl!"

Bethel looked stricken.

"Isn't that true? Huh? Huh? Isn't it?"

"I'm afraid it is—more or less," whimpered Bethel.

Toni was triumphant, then forgiving: "Gee, I don't blame
you for fooling a dumbbell like Pete. He's asking for it. Oh,
he's had experience, all right, but just with waitresses and
heiresses and screwballs like that. He don't understand educated artists, like you and I! And—God knows if this got
known around it would ruin me—but the truth is I'm still a
Good Girl myself! Ain't that the limit!"

But they agreed that Iris Pentire, still sitting by herself
and smiling mysteriously, couldn't be anything so commonplace as a Good Girl.

They were the more certain of it as slowly Iris attracted
Pete Chew, Fletcher Hewitt, the blundering Harry Mihick,
and two newly come apprentices: Cy Fickerty, a curly-
headed, screaming, village clown, and Bruce Pasture, a
too-sensitive-looking boy from St Stephen's College.

The elegant Iris (who was Toni's own age and two years
younger than Bethel), was quavering to her pages with
faint, fragile dignity, "I said to him, 'It's vulgar of you to
remind me that I was once a chorus girl. I would stoop to
even that kind of work to get the training necessary for my
career, but now,' I said, 'I won't consider anything but the
poetic drama or a good part in a George Abbott play,' I

said, 'and it's about time that you agents learned to appreciate sensitiveness,' I told him."

Toni whispered to Bethel, "Oh, nuts!"

"You said it," remarked an entirely new version of Bethel.

"Let's grab off Pete and Cy Fickerty and go to that dance. That okay by you?"

"Okay," said Bethel.

10

IN GRAMPION CENTER, Sabbath breakers had once been exposed in the stocks, and householders had warmed their cakes on Sunday only by their pastors' eloquence about hellfire. But the Nutmeg Players, once their season had started, recognized Sunday only by the dress rehearsal of the coming week's play and by permitting all the apprentices to sleep till noon . . . after having spent all of Saturday night removing the scenery of last week's bill and setting up the new.

But with the first play not yet on, Bethel and her fellow wights had on Sunday the one only day of leisure they were ever to know at Grampion. She slept till after lunch, following the rather aimless dance at Clinton, so unenterprising an event that Pete Chew had tried to kiss her only twice. She was too late to join the various motor expeditions and, after a sandwich and coffee which the grumbling Johnny Meddock dug up for her, sat on the sea-washed rocks, facing the sun.

She did not greatly mind being alone. She liked people, but people noisy in a mass embarrassed her. No matter, she told herself; no actress was ever called upon to play an entire mob!

Here, in the Y.M.C.A. of the arts, she had hoped to find a friend, a love, an idol to adore. But she regarded the youngsters like Toni Titmus as babies—and the seniors like Fletcher Hewitt considered *her* a baby. Well, she would just have to be alone again and like it.

The theater grounds, so like the campus of a rustic college, were blankly peaceful; the water high colored and the sails flying. She was content, she was a grown-up and busy actress—and suddenly she was an excited small girl again, as the great car, a limousine with chauffeur, rolled up in front of her, and a young god, sunburned and smiling, with cropped brazen hair and strong bronze neck, a tweed-bearing god of twenty-eight or -nine, slipped out of the car and addressed her.

"Hello, hello! Anybody around? Roscoe been transported to heaven yet?"

"I think he's only gone to New Haven."

"Then God help Yale! And it was such a nice boys' school when I used to attend it!"

Andrew Deacon, the leading man and co-director and angel of the Nutmeg Players, may have depended on his decorativeness as a rather rich, rather handsome, very athletic young man, instead of on flexible skill as an actor. Perhaps he was too aggressively youthful and humorous, too relentlessly charming. He shouted his adoration of the theater and his determination to revive it in every town in the land—shouted and chanted and smiled it, at rehearsals and late suppers, so constantly as to cause older workers in the vineyard to growl, "Oh, curse the theater! I'm going to save my salary and buy a chicken farm."

But Bethel thought him the most magic person she had ever seen. She had found a diamond on the pavement. And unquestionably, the moment Andy Deacon arrived, the Nutmeg Players came alive and turned from a mob into a spirited army.

Things began to happen. Things—not necessarily sensible

or commendable—would bountifully and rapidly happen
whenever Andy was around. Everybody miraculously appeared from nowhere, greeting Andy the Sun God, the moment he stepped out of his Olympian mother's sixteen-
cylinder Cadillac chariot. The old troupers, Doc Keezer and
Clara Ribbons, arm in arm, rolled across the horizon, murmuring, "Glad you're with us, Mr Deacon." Cynthia Aleshire popped out of a dormitory living room that had certainly been empty three minutes before, crying, "Oh, Andy,
Roscoe won't let me try an expressionistic set for *Candida*,
and I know I can just get the quality of that stuffy liberalism."
Tudor Blackwall and Bruce Pasture, the violin-playing apprentice, came caroling, "Welcome, boss." Pete Chew and
Toni drove up with Pete's Chrysler practically rearing and
neighing, and looked approvingly at Andy's dark blue flannel
shirt with white tie.

In fact, the peasant chorus was entering, inaudibly chant-
ing:

> *"Hurray, hurray, it's festival today,*
> *Our young prince is arriving, from his court*
> *so far away."*

Then out of the limousine stepped the heavies—but they
were too serious for so bright an operetta: Andy's mother,
Mrs J. Goddard Deacon of Worcester and Newport, that
white-haired serenity who had done so well in keeping the
late Mr J. Goddard Deacon's munition millions (and she
was in her own right a Pilchard of Plymouth, and as such
entitled to sit on Plymouth Rock), and Andy's fiancée, the
lovely Miss Joan Hinterwald, of the Fall River and Gas-
tonia woolen millions. And suddenly appearing, facing these
two women and not liking them in the least, was Miss
Mahala Vale.

Andy kissed Mahala, crying, "Hello, darling, so glad
we're going to play together this summer. We'll show 'em
love's young dream!"

"You must have acted with Mr Deacon," said Miss Hinterwald to Miss Vale, with a short sniff.

"Andy and I played opposite each other for four months in *Gray Tide,*" said Miss Vale, with a fairly good imitation of a sniff.

"I see," said Miss Hinterwald.

Bethel perceived that the two young ladies, Joan and Mahala, were enough alike to indicate that this was Andy's fated pattern in the way of loves. Both were tall, broadshouldered, light-footed, chestnut-haired, wide between the eyes and politely contemptuous. But while Miss Hinterwald was the real thing in the way of Long Island and Newport plutocracy, pleasantly snobbish to the entire world, including Andy, Miss Mahala Vale wasn't quite certain whether there weren't a few people, including Andy and Roscoe, to whom she'd better not be snobbish. Bethel had been developing a quite healthy small hatred for Mahala, but now she enlisted under her, hoped that she would take Andy away from the Hinterwald girl and marry him immediately —though she saw that this would mean that she herself would never have a chance at the young Sun God.

She was startled. For the first time Bethel knew that she was lorn and lost in love.

When Andy's mother had said "Don't be an idiot and work too hard at your playing this summer," and had retired into the silken wolf cave of her limousine; when Joan had kissed him as though it were a habit and not a very good habit; when the chauffeur had turned the great car, looking scornfully at the grassy ruts, and it had slid away, in silence and disdain, then Andy woke up, and the Nutmeg Players woke.

He put his arm about Toni and Clara Ribbons, he patted Roscoe's back—Roscoe winced; he shook hands with Harry Mihick and Pete Chew and remembered their names for almost two minutes, and he shouted, "Tomorrow we go to work on *Petrified Forest.* Roscoe and God being willing, we shall rehearse twelve hours a day, and I expect to be a better Alan than Leslie Howard, and I know Mahala will beat Peggy Conklin all hollow as Gabby."

"I don't suppose your Miss Hinterwald will be coming down from Newport to see us, though," sniffed Mahala.

"Her? She will not! What's Newport? Ha' done with the tents of Shem, dear lass, we've seen the Newport seasons through, and it's time to turn on the old trail, the repertory trail, the strictly one-sixty-five-top trail, that is always new. Let's go!" And he kissed Mahala again—but this time as though he took a personal interest in it—and picked up his bags to carry them to the House.

"He's kind of coy, don't you think?" said Marian Croy.

"Oh no, just young," said old Bethel.

And later, passing the open windows of the House living room, Bethel heard Andy and Roscoe discussing the season's casting. Andy was talking now without whimsy, quickly, firmly, cajoling the querulous Roscoe but not bullying him— not quite bullying him.

She was convinced that of all the people she had known, this Andrew Deacon was the only one who was radiantly, unquestionably, good enough for earth and heaven.

Sitting alone on the rocks, brooding, that evening, and telling herself that she mustn't sit alone brooding—it was antisocial or something like that—she felt herself a small child, and rather silly in wishing that someday Andy Deacon would be interested in her, be able to identify her in the whole mess of apprentices. She would never have a chance against the luminous Mahala.

Oh, they were all pigs, these tall, demanding women like Joan and Mahala!

She was relieved when Pete Chew came bumbling up and told her that she was a remarkably intelligent woman, ever so much more Intellectual and Sympathetic than Toni Titmus. When Pete tried to kiss her good night at the dormitory door, she had no sensation about it whatever, not even anger.

She was excited to find that someone, if only a Pete Chew, considered her a woman. But was anyone ever going to consider her an actress?

11

THE FIRST WEEK of the Nutmeg Players, while they rehearsed their first bill, *The Petrified Forest,* and cleaned
the theater of its winter accumulation of dust and cobwebs
and the smell of mice, was not so wearing. It was merely
slightly hysterical.

There were so many characters in the *Forest* cast that all
the men apprentices had to be used, though their theatrical
experience may have been nothing more than singing "I
Love My Little Christmas Lamb" at the Congregational
Church at the age of six. So it was that Bethel and Toni,
themselves still uncast for a play, had the derisive agony
of seeing Pete Chew and the lugubriously artistic Harry
Mihick rehearsing as the two telegraph linemen.

During the moments when they could escape from errands
and from the School, the two girls, looking owlish and chewing gum, perched in the highest seats of the theater and
glowered at Pete, trying to look lounging and easy at a café
table (represented, during rehearsals, by a broken stool),
and repeating the line "Oh, is God a Russian?" as though it
were a funeral speech.

Roscoe Valentine, directing, was still patient so early in

the season. He didn't do anything more temperamental than pull his nose and flap his fingers like antennae as he begged, "Chew. Please! You're supposed to be derisive."

"Derisive? . . . I see. . . . *Derisive!*" whimpered Pete.

"God *is* a Russian, or he wouldn't let that hot-water bottle act! It's a plot!" snarled Toni.

The theater school was opened on Monday morning. It consisted of a barn, a platform, some chairs, the sixteen apprentices (as many of them, at any given time, as were not running errands or rehearsing) and the teacher. The teacher had arrived that morning and, sitting down in the barn, Bethel gasped to discover that she was Miss Maggie Sample, that handsome and bitter character actress whom she had seen seven years ago with the McDermids in *The Silver Cord*. Miss Sample would be all of fifty-seven now. The pickle had not sweetened in these years.

Bethel was not yet aware of the basic rule of the theater that if you ever act with anyone, you will act with him again; that if you played St Clair's daughter in *Uncle Tom's Cabin* under canvas on the Dakota circuit in 1893, you must not be surprised to find yourself cast as St Clair's mother in a Gotham Theater Alliance comedy by Molnar in 1940, with one of the original walk-on bloodhounds now advanced to a Pekingese in the boudoir scene.

Maggie Sample did not remember her; looked at her bleakly as Bethel gave her name.

"Where from?" said Miss Sample.

"Sladesbury! And I saw you in *The Silver Cord* and *Dulcy,* Miss Sample."

"Sladesbury? Where's that? And what was *The Silver Cord?* Oh yes. Was that the operetta about the Turkish harem? Where I tried to sing the part of the Oldest Wife? And got strangled with a silver cord? Was I lousy!"

"Between my own cultural view of the drama and the practical experience of my resident teacher and the numer-

ous visiting lecturers, I think I may say that every aspirant
in our School of the Theater acquires a complete and at
once emotional and scholarly concept of acting as an art,"
Roscoe Valentine was saying, just then, to a reporter from
the New Haven *Journal & Courier*.

And he may have been right. Maggie Sample knew her
craft as thoroughly as she hated it. If only, Bethel sighed
from time to time throughout the summer, Miss Sample
wouldn't find it a consolation to assure all young actresses
that they would soon be as old and lonely and wretched as
herself, with breath as short and hearts that pounded with
like terror.

Bethel was never going to be that old—not at ninety,
she swore.

After a five-minute speech, which consisted entirely in
directing them not to be fools and particularly not to suppose that, because they had been stars in little theaters or in
colleges, they could act, Miss Sample assigned to the students detached portions of plays to present next Friday.

Bethel was to play Fanny in *Hindle Wakes*. She went off
to study, and Maggie Sample to sleep. Maggie had spent
the night, till five A.M., in sitting up with her mother, who
was eighty-three years old, in a gas-smelling one-room flat in
Harlem. She had supported her mother for forty years, and
every day for forty years her mother had told someone or
other that Maggie was a success and sent her so little money
because she was keeping two lovers. Maggie hated the
stage. Maggie's mother loved the stage. Maggie's mother
hated Maggie. Maggie had always been too busy to think
about whether she hated her mother. She had also been
too busy to remember ever having played, in *The Silver
Cord*, a part about too much mother.

The part of Second Lineman, to be enacted by Mr Peter
Chew in *The Petrified Forest*, contained exactly eighty
words. But to Pete the part was longer than Hamlet's, and

more confusing than the Theory of Relativity. The one speech, "Sure! Go ahead, Pop. Change the subject," he could, without half trying and in the space of not over five minutes, render as, "You bet, Dad, go on and change the subject," and "Sure, Pop, go the subject," and "That's right, pop the subject," and sixteen other versions, all fascinating.

Naturally, he cried for a lot of cuing. He got Bethel, Toni Titmus, Iris Pentire, Anita Hill, and four other girl apprentices, all young, to cue him, and with each of them (so they treacherously reported to one another, with details, laughing as women do) he found that it strengthened his memory to put his arm around her.

Between cuing Pete, avoiding Pete, going out to borrow chairs for the set, going to the bank and to the station for Roscoe, and learning her practice lines in *Hindle Wakes,* Bethel was hurled forward to Friday. Only once did she feel that she was getting something. She listened to a conference between the company electrician and Cynthia Aleshire and Fletcher Hewitt on the setting for *Petrified Forest.*

"You got to give me a better light than that bastard amber," wailed Cynthia. "I want more pink in it. I want to get the feeling of the whole, lonesome desert through that window."

"Window too big anyway. Whole right wall of a barbecue lunchroom one big window. 'Tisn't realistic!" complained Fletcher.

"I don't care if it isn't. I want to get the feeling."

Bethel crept backstage and looked at the ground row of cut-out cactus and mesas standing against the half-circle of the cyclorama; at the bank of lights on the floor of the stage and the border lights overhead. She peeped into Cynthia's thumb-greased manual of lighting and read, as though they were the names of the five sweet symphonies, about Opalescent Lamp Dips, Sprayed Coatings, Glass Color Caps, Gelatin Color Media and Sheets of Transolene. She looked up at the scenery hanging in the fly loft—a canyon turned upside down. She remembered, embarrassed, that she

had been content in *A Doll's House* with scenery that had
served before that for the interior of a Washington mansion in *The Witching Hour.*

She hadn't even known just what lights Miss Bickling had
used. She remembered, guiltily, that she had thought then
that the actors were all that mattered in a play. Now she
saw all the people of the theater—director, scene designer,
actors, electricians, stagehands, stage manager, musicians,
author (though she wasn't yet enlightened enough to in-
clude the audience and the wicked producer)—as a fra-
ternity, the sincerest democracy in the world, united to
create in a troubled world an illusion of strength and
beauty and hope and honor and noble wrath that were more
real than reality. In that mangy little wooden theater by a
pebble-scattered beach she was confirmed in her faith.

On Friday afternoon was the school recital from *Hindle
Wakes,* with Bethel as the Lancashire mill girl, Fanny, who
has been off on an illicit week end, and with Harry Mihick
as her worried father, Marian as her shocked mother.
Bethel had no notion of the Lancashire intonation, but then
neither had the others, and they all played it in cockney, with
overtones of Kansas and a dash of dry Vermont.

The set consisted of five chairs—two of them repre-
senting a table and a dresser—up on the barn platform; the
audience, of Maggie Sample and five apprentices, all looking up with idiotic blankness, like six Supreme Court jus-
tices rehearing a tax case. Bethel did not mind. She carried
her own fire and applause.

She had been devout in her study of the role; she had
not merely learned the lines, but had, she believed, come to
know Fanny and to love her. She had been surprised to
encounter an English girl so independent and forthright,
loving her family but directing her own life. Everyone said
that only American girls were like that, and Bethel wanted
to let the world know about this social discovery.

From the moment when she entered (from behind a chair)

with a cheerful "Well, you didn't expect me as soon as this, I'll bet," she was Fanny, not Bethel Merriday; and as Fanny she desperately justified her right to hide her sweetheart's name. When Roscoe Valentine and Fletcher Hewitt stumbled in and solemnly added themselves to her audience, she was not above the vulgarity of noticing them, but they made her only the more zealous to present her case.

What threw her was Harry Mihick.

Marian Croy was good enough as the mother, but as the father, Harry was King Lear played by a Marx brother in a red beard. He moaned, he staggered, he slapped his forehead. Bethel was so fascinated that she forgot to be earnest, toward the end, and merely fed in her lines, and did not realize that she had let down till it was over.

The three aspirants sat and prepared to be admired. Maggie Sample sighed, put on eyeglasses, sighed again and spoke:

"Miss Croy, you weren't bad. But a little less elocution and sweetness and melody. You're not a Y.W.C.A. secretary or a lobbyist for free tariff on canary birds. You're a Percheron-built housewife in an industrial town, and you worry about the taxes and the price of beer, and your feet hurt.

"Mr Mihick, I take it that you know you can never get on the stage, anywhere, in anything?"

"Y-you think so," groaned Harry.

"Don't you?"

"Well, maybe I can spread the gospel of the theater through Missouri and Kansas."

"Yes, you stick to that. . . . And now you, Miss——"

"Merriday."

"Miss Merriday. . . . Where were you born?"

"In Sladesbury."

"Where's that?"

"Why, right here in Connecticut. I told you. Don't you remember?"

"I do not remember! I'm surprised to find that you are a Yankee. For all their faults, such as suspicion of everyone that doesn't smell of wood mold and furniture polish, the Yankees do have a nice reticence. But you played this like an up-and-coming Middle Western girl who thinks the purpose of life is to yell at men and poke them in the ribs and keep on getting everything she can out of them—from Wrigley's gum and pineapple ice-cream soda to marriage lines and a trip to Los Angeles."

Bethel looked down at the unsmiling apprentices, the kind but now expressionless Fletcher Hewitt, the rococo but now expressionless Mr Valentine. She couldn't believe that this was happening to her. Her lifelong career as an actress was being ended, and her old friend Miss Sample was going on:

"You were too pert. You thought too well of yourself. Here you're supposed to be a North Country millhand who's independent only because she had to earn her living, but you acted as if you were a WPA investigator scolding a 'case.' Oh, Miss Bethel Merriday, you were ba-a-a-a-d!"

Into the gray silence swam Roscoe.

"Bethel, let me give you a few practical hints. Your voice —your projection. Don't try to do it all with your throat; use your lungs; use your diaphragm for volume. Every day, for ten minutes, I want you to do this exercise. Stand straight, with your belly completely drawn in; take the deepest possible breath, and exhale it, with a good loud hiss, between your closed teeth, so it won't go too fast.

"And voice projection is just as much mental as it is physical. Look up at the top balcony, way, way up there, and make sure your voice reaches them, and forget the carriage trade down in the pit.

"And when you sit, don't slouch. Let the gallery see your face, not just the pretty top of your head. No matter how relaxed you are, keep your spine firm, as an axis that you can revolve on in any direction. Picture it as a flexible steel rod, going right up through you and supporting you.

"But the biggest lesson in acting is never to do anything except for a psychological purpose. Don't walk over and open the door just because it's in the script. Why are you opening that door? Are you sore at somebody and walking out on him? Are you going uptown to buy some face powder? Are you afraid there's a dead man lying out there in the hall? Never do anything unless you understand *why*."

Roscoe had risen. He whirled now on the five apprentices in the audience, who had all been staring at Bethel, half amused. "And that goes for all the rest of you, d'you understand? Bethel was terrible, but the rest of you are just as bad. You're all terrible. If any of you want to go back to the soda counter, that will be all right with Miss Sample and me. Good day, young ladies and gentlemen!"

Fletcher walked with her to the dormitory.

He was to her the man who would always be there when she needed him, who would be always a little more understanding than anybody else and sometimes more intelligent, who, as stage manager, knew everybody's part and everybody's sorrows, whom she could almost love, and whom she would always forget the moment any more demanding male came in sight. She knew him deeply after this one week; she could never know him any better after thirty years.

"Well?" said Bethel to Fletcher.

"I thought you were going to be idiot enough to say 'Here's where I go home,' " said Fletcher.

"I did say it! But then I decided that's what I was here for—to get hell—to get training."

"Good girl. Maybe someday you'll be an actress!"

12

SHE HAD QUARTER-HOURS when she was free to sneak into the theater and watch rehearsals of *The Petrified Forest*. As Alan, the gentlemanly, the poetic, the rather seedy hero, Andy Deacon doffed all his humorous briskness, and in every word and twitchy movement of his hands was the wrecked dreamer. As Gabrielle, the lunchroom waitress who believed in François Villon, Mahala Vale was smaller than herself (but that wasn't so hard; even Bethel knew about flat heels versus high ones) and harder and quicker and more avid of love.

It was strange to Bethel, and a little embarrassing, that while she pored on Andy, he really did not know that she existed. She guessed that to him she was merely a smaller face than most among nine blank faces of girl apprentices. He had never addressed her by any more intimate form than, "Oh, darling—look here, sweetest," and in the world of the theater, that constitutes ignoring a person.

But Bethel could sit in the auditorium and hate Mahala

and her preenings toward Andy and her dove calls and her wrigglings and her scarlet smiling lips, as large as a clown's, just as comfortably as though Mahala—or Andy— knew it.

Pete Chew had the persistence which, in the American credo, must bring success. If for twenty times a girl shrank and bleated when he tried to kiss her, it was his belief that on the twenty-first she would seize him around the neck and faint in beatitude.

So the Bethel who had never before learned the maturity of making a snug bundle of her secret thoughts and throwing them at somebody's face was driven into learning it quickly.

The precise time was at 7:25 P.M. on Sunday, June 26th, between supper and the beginning of the Nutmeg Players' first dress rehearsal, and the place was the workshop, whither Roscoe, in panic, had sent Bethel to try and find a prop shotgun which was, actually, still in the Grampion Center Hardware Store & Undertaking.

On her shoulder she felt the familiar soft hot paw of Pete Chew. She turned.

"Will you quit trying to manhandle me? I'm sick of it!"

"Why, Beth, I'm shocked at you! I always thought you were a college woman and a lady, and here you bellyachin' like a Polack hired girl."

"I'm just learning it. You wait till I get it rehearsed!"

"But I thought you liked me."

"Pete, I think you ought to be the first to know. You see, I'm in love with—with——"

"*Who?*"

"With John Barrymore!"

It was a very good dress rehearsal, promising a successful showing of *The Petrified Forest*. Roscoe and Andy had for cheer the facts that: (1) nobody knew any of his lines—any whatsoever; (2) Mahala was, just now, discovered to believe that Gabby was false and pretentious, whereas she should be simple and real; (3) none of the property guns would go off; (4) the curtain stuck; (5) the prop whisky bottle, Jason's Sam Browne belt, and one shotgun were all missing; and (6) three times during the rehearsal, Roscoe screamed like a switch engine.

So the wise veterans like Doc Keezer knew that at the opening, twenty-four hours from now, everything would be perfect; they so assured the almost weeping Bethel; and on Monday night, so it was.

Along with Toni and Anita Hill, Bethel was drafted as an usher that week and had her first chance to study an audience. All the girl ushers discarded their shorts and slacks and wore their best afternoon dresses. As ushers they did not feel servile, but like hostesses and just a little superior to the superior summer theatergoers who never really looked at them. Doubtless, hundreds of readers of this history will have been shown to their seats at Grampion by Bethel Merriday without their now remembering it.

There are only three classes in the audience in a city theater: those who can afford to go—of whom some really like the play; those who want it thought that they can afford to go—they are too engaged in hoping they look like regular and expert theatergoers to have much attention left for the play itself; and the students up in the gallery, who love the play savagely or hate it volubly.

But at Grampion, in vacation time, the country audience was as mixed as an aquarium: the young station taxi driver and his beautiful wife, and old Mr Chamberlain Brewster Boles, the banker, from his castle on Crab Neck, tobacco growers and apple growers and dairymen from up the river, the Cap'n who took summerites out fishing in his motor dory, a flutter of young married couples from New York, on vacation, the Grampion Center doctor, gray, and his young wife, pink and stage-struck, a garage proprietor, and the Baroness Pont d'Evêque (née Quimby). They all thought fairly well of themselves as individual human beings, each with his prides and secrets and sins; they felt patronizing in attending the little theater; and they did not notice the neat, quick, dark-eyed thin girl who ushered them to their seats. But she was sorry for all of them, that they should be such laymen, such pathetic outsiders, and not allowed backstage.

She hoped, on behalf of the poor heathen souls of the audience, that they were sufficiently advanced toward salvation to be able to see that this was, approximately, the greatest performance of the greatest play in the greatest— well, anyway, the best-managed—playhouse in the history of the theater. She trembled with desire to tell somebody how privileged she felt.

There had never been such a stage-set as Cynthia's: the whole desert, thousands of shining miles of it, did come through the right-wall window. There had never been so touchingly lost a vagrant as Andy, so brave and mad a girl as Mahala (and if Bethel could admit it, how exquisite Mahala must have been!), so coldly terrifying a gang leader as Tudor Blackwall, so comic an old Westerner as Doc Keezer, impersonating Gramp. Bethel proudly knew that she mustn't disgrace her high office as theater usher by guffawing, and she stood at attention at the back of the little hall, hands clenched with a mirth that scoured through her like fever, as Doc cackled, "Don't think he really meant to do me any real harm. Just wanted to scare the pants off of me."

This was life! At its highest!

So the ecstatic Bethel.

The theater audience, driving over a sandy side road and parking in long grass which wet their delicate patent-leather slippers or white buckskin shoes, saw an old brown wooden church, not very well repainted. They might still have expected to find a pious meeting except that on the broad stoop were box trees in wine jars from Italy, and over the grained front door an arclight illuminating the sign:

ANDREW DEACON
MAHALA VALE
TUDOR BLACKWALL
in
THE PETRIFIED FOREST
A Desert Melodrama

The entryway had been turned into a lobby by the installation of a box office that was a bright blue coop, in which the apprentices took their turns sweating and fidgeting and misrepresenting the excellence of the tickets. In the country, every ticket buyer felt it only neighborly to explain, "I didn't know 's we'd come tonight—looked like rain all this week—but I said to Cousin Edie—from Elizabeth, New Jersey—she's staying with us for a couple weeks —I said to her, 'Oh, let's go and see a real bang-up theater show for once,' I said. . . . Is a dollar sixty-five the lowest you got? My! Just for a theater ticket!"

The lobby walls were lined with gray celotex, on which Mr Valentine had hung prints of Degas ballet girls.

The inside of the theater auditorium, all in slate-painted pine, with a peaked ceiling, was frankly a wooden box; and the seats were aged opera chairs, on steps. But from Bordeaux, Roscoe had brought, as traveler-curtain, an impish, gay tapestry with knights and dryads and long-necked greyhounds among intricate blue-and-saffron boughs, and it proclaimed, "Forget the drab box of the auditorium, forget the drab boxes of your daily lives. Here is the gate to imagination."

The metropolitan newspapers had for years found it a very sound and illimitably novel joke to refer to the summer stock theaters as "the strawhats" and "the barn theaters." Well, if the Grampion structure was not a barn but a decayed church, it did at least have, backstage, something like a mess of old horse stalls. The dressing rooms, the toilets, the property room, the costume room, the storage room, they were a honeycomb of thin coops, made of old boards with dark nail holes dotting them, and repaired with bits of old lath. They were in a crazy planless plan, so that you could, even in this tiny theater, get lost. And Bethel loved those dark passages between rickety walls. They were the alleyways of a crazy city of dreams.

When the curtain had opened, tonight, the spectator (other than Bethel) would have seen a fairly good stock-company performance of *The Petrified Forest,* distinguished by the facts that Mahala was beautiful, in a stately, benign way; that she was so unsuited to the role of poetic desert rat that the director must have done his casting in the cellar, by touch; and that Doc Keezer, as Gramp, was a really good character actor. The rest was silence.

Bethel went backstage once during the show, for no other reason than to assure herself that she could. All she said was "Hello" to Iris Pentire—so successfully made up to look thirty-five, as Mrs Chisholm, that she looked fifty.

During the intermission she stood at attention, but she looked out at the strolling audience and vigilantly listened for comments. When a vacationing New York stockbroker said "Not too bad," Bethel wanted to bite him. When the taxi driver's wife gurgled, "It was lovely—I was so scared," then Bethel almost kissed her.

In intermissions they walked blissfully not on a New York side street, of coal chutes and high dusty stoops and Chinese beaneries and thin evasive hotels and Greek bars and clammy persistent packs of autograph hunters, but on the dandelion-starred grass, under the elms, in sea breeze. It was the linden trees of Weimar to Bethel, and Stratford in Maytime.

There were some seven reviews of the play in the New Haven and New London papers. Bethel still has all of them in her scrap album. Her prize among them was written by a red-faced man who, under the name of Black Bart, did sports and harbor news for the New London *Era,* and who wanted to write plays:

If New York theatrical producers could occasionally persuade themselves to give up going to Hollywood to try to get jobs, or to London to try to meet a duke, in between their spasms of actual producing of plays, and if they could be persuaded to have a little interest in their own future careers, they would take a few days off and look over the summer theaters, at which they scoff but which, as a matter of fact, are about the only source, outside of some dramatic schools, for the Eugene O'Neills and Walter Hustons of tomorrow.

That was brilliantly seen last night at Point Grampion, in *The Petrified Forest,* the opening gun in the Nutmeg Players' theatrical barrage for this summer. If perhaps some of the actors weren't yet as heavily loaded as the Broadway big guns, a lot of them are going to be. The play had the speed of a clipper, with humor and poetic qualities well emphasized. Andrew Deacon, who last summer pleased all hands by his robust characterization of Ethan Frome, is now winning as an English poet in hard luck, and the new leading lady, Miss Mahala Vale, is exquisite in the role of an Edna Millay in a dog-wagon. Interviewed afterwards in his dressing room, Mr Deacon, who hopes to find time even in his eighteen-hour day in the theater to enter the New London Tennis Tournament this summer, having been one of the best players for Old Eli some six years ago . . .

But Bethel cared less for the end of the report, in which it was stated that—

Young Miss Iris Pentire who, seen in her dressing room, was exquisite as a skein of corn-colored silk, is indeed a find, for so clever is she in make-up and impersonation that this lovely child gave all the impression of a stuffed-shirtwaist female in the dubious thirties. She is a wow.

Bethel reflected:
"Maybe Iris is better than I am.
"Maybe she's better than I'll ever be.
"She is *not* a wow!"

13

THE APPRENTICES were permitted each to appear in three plays during the season. Not till the fourth play, *Stage Door,* by Edna Ferber and George S. Kaufman, which opened on July 18th, did Bethel have her chance.

The sensation of the two weeks after *The Petrified Forest* was the appearance, like a transitory comet—a rather old and tired-out comet that had gone a long way—of Miss Nile Sanderac as guest star in *Candida.*

She was the first really distinguished actress that Bethel had ever seen in the flesh—the exquisite flesh, shining, age-less, more than human.

Everybody in the United States—"everybody" indicating that 00.05% of the population that cared a hang about the theater—knew that Nile Sanderac's real name was Nelly Sanders; that she was half Irish, half Yankee. Her career had been energetic. She had appeared in eleven witty plays about London society, ten plays about Park Avenue society, nine plays about Long Island society, and one play about the wrongs of lap dogs. She had been married four times. She was a friend of Gene Tunney, Grover Whalen, Dwight Fiske, the Duke of Westminster, Heywood Broun, Professor Millikan and Representative Sol Bloom. She was forty years old. At least. Her hair had, at various epochs, been mouse, chestnut, black, gold, gray, platinum, and gold again. She had given away, to various worthless but pleasant males, over $42,000. She owed, to various jewelry shops, dressmakers and hotels, over $48,000. She had a bad temper and a kind heart. Her pure shoulders enabled her to wear low black evening gowns to advantage. She spoke French absolutely, and she had never read one book clear through.

Incidentally, she was a very good actress.

The Nutmeg Players did not see much of Miss Sanderac, outside rehearsals. She didn't stay even in the exclusiveness of The House, with Roscoe and Andy and Mahala and Tudor Blackwall, but at the tapestry-brick mansion of the rich Jeddabys, in Grampion Center. Always, Miss Sanderac was half shabby, in gray suits or spinsterish dresses of gray crepe de Chine. She seemed to Bethel to have no personal life whatever: she didn't even scold her silent colored maid or shriek at Roscoe for shrieking. Just once did Miss Sanderac come alive for Bethel and betray that she had private life in plenty—when Bethel saw a puffy man with puffy eyes and a gray mustache pouring out champagne for Miss Sanderac in her dressing room, and, afterward, taking her off in a limousine. It all dated 1906, sighed Bethel.

Yet every apprentice on the lot, particularly Bethel, loved Nile Sanderac and hoped to be able to die for her. For she smiled at them, a special smile reserved for actors, not the mock-humble grimace she gave to barbarian outsiders; not a stingy smile, but a large one, that showed all her excellent teeth. The smile said that they were all comrades and fellow mummers, rogues and vagabonds, and that laymen were pretty funny.

But that smile was a wall, too, that protected her. Day after day, while the fledglings expected her to go farther and say something cheerful and intimate, like "The rehearsals aren't going as bad as you'd think," it became more evident that she had a low opinion of Mr Roscoe Valentine, a high and lively opinion of Mr Andrew Deacon, a fellow-workman liking for Doc Keezer, and of the others, no opinion at all.

Poor Andy, blundering as bountifully as any other young collegian, tried to persuade Miss Sanderac to like his Mahala, who was not in the *Candida* cast and therefore sulkily invisible for a while. Sitting in the grass before the porch of The House, Bethel heard Miss Sanderac crying to Andy, "Oh, Andy, don't you want to drive me to Clinton for dinner? We can get back here before you have to make up." And heard Andy loyally trying to drag in his pet gazelle, with:

"I'd love to go, Nile. How about taking Mahala with us?"

"Oh, I guess we won't have time, after all," sniffed Miss Sanderac. And still Andy did not learn. He cried to the great lady, "I do wish you could have seen Mahala in *You Cannot Dispossess Our Souls*. She was swell—absolutely like a young prophetess!"

"In *what?*"

"In *You Cannot——* Oh, you heard me. I won't say it again."

"I should think not, darling. 'You Can't Possess Us.' What a title! What is it?"

"It's a play about share croppers."

"No. You're kidding."

"Oh, quit it. And she *was* swell!"

"Who was swell?"

"Mahala Vale."

"Who's Mahala Vale?"

"Oh, dry up."

"That's right, darling. Go on. Use me as you will. Yell at me. Beat me. Divorce me. You never did divorce me, did you?"

"I would, if I had you."

"Of course you would, my pie-lamb. Wait! Aren't you the young man I just met this week? We haven't been married, not ever, have we?"

"We have not, darling. Not yet."

"And you've never even married some little number like Mahala? Oh, dearie me, you *have* been busy with the Career!"

Andy Deacon could not have known that the slight, pleasant dark girl, sitting on the grass, chin in hand, her back to them—Bess Meredith her name was, or something of the sort—was not only devouring their words but scolding him ferociously:

"Oh, Andy, my dear boy, what a fool you are. . . . And so sweet. . . . And so dumb! . . . I know, dear; this Sanderac woman is ten or twelve years older than you are, and she's hard-boiled and she's extravagant, and she doesn't care any more for the spotlight than she does for heaven. But how much better it would be if you could fall in love with someone like her, that is honest and stands on her own feet and that can *act,* instead of these camellia-scented sharks like Mahala or Joan, that 'll get everything they can out of you, that 'll never stop acting off stage or start acting on! . . . I'll bet Mahala has never kissed you—or anyway, she held onto the kiss and snatched it back. And of course you'd never know that a really nice girl like me even existed!"

Since she was not rehearsing for *Candida,* Mahala had the daytimes this week vacant, from her favorite rising hour—noon—till early supper. Bethel innocently wondered what this young actress, not without experience and ambition, would do with her freedom.

Read? Exercise? Go and be noble about something?

Well, Mahala slept. And she also sat on the beach and looked sorry for herself.

Bethel too was lonely—when she had time to think about it. The offended Pete Chew had taken Toni away from her; she could never get through the veil of sweet, shining nothing that surrounded Iris Pentire; and Fletcher Hewitt and Walter Rolf were as pleasant as the west wind and just as impersonal. But she understood loneliness. She was used to being lonely; she always had been, always would be, unless Fate flourished the one miraculous lover . . . who would surely look extraordinarily like Andy.

She watched Mahala looking for a confidante to share her free week; poking a mental finger into the ribs of Iris, Toni, Marian Croy, Anita Hill, and giving them up as too commonplace to appreciate her. At last, rather obviously for a lady actress, she decided that Bethel would have to do, as servant of her bosom. Bethel told herself that she wasn't at all flattered—and was thoroughly flattered and excited by the favor of this wise, experienced old actress of twenty-six.

They sat yawning or laughing on the beach, Mahala in a bathing suit so tight, so white, with such handsome long white legs, that she would have seemed embarrassingly naked, had she not too much resembled an unbreathing marble statue.

"Oh, this place is such a bore," whined Mahala. "I think I'd of done better to go out to Southampton, on Long Island—Mrs Fribble invited me to go out and spend all summer—you know, the Montgomery Fribbles, he's the banker; they got scads of money and a yacht. Roscoe is too pixie—he couldn't direct swatting a fly—and the stock company are all such hams."

"Oh, not Andy, Mahala!"

"No, he's a pretty fair actor—if he doesn't tackle any parts that require subtlety. I had the most awful time carry-

ing him in *Petrified Forest*. He would play Alan, who ought
to be all delicacy, like a Yale basketball player. And he's
not so young—he's older than I am; not so young that you
can excuse him for falling for an old jalopy like Nile, who'll
be playing Irish grandmothers in Hollywood in another
year."

"Mm," said Bethel.

"You're lucky, Beth. Of course it doesn't make any difference to you what second-raters everybody here are, as long
as they're fun to play around with. I notice this Chew boy
is interested in you (oh, I never miss anything; that's my
business, as an actress!). He's a little dumb, but he ties
his ties well, and I know he's got lots of money. You better
grab him and marry him—or else you might have to go back
to your home town, wherever that is. You're lucky not having the kind of irresistible leaning toward a stage career that
I'm cursed with.

"It's all very well for me to get a lot of silly flattery about
my talent and beauty—and honestly, I'm so honest with
myself, I don't think I'm especially beautiful—but they're
like chains—they bind me to the theater—people just won't
let me go and retire and live a quiet life, the way I'd like to.

"Still, I'll admit there are rewards, when—only it
doesn't happen very often—these playwrights are such
dopes!—when you can get a play that's really worth
interpreting. I wish I were back in *You Cannot Dispossess
Our Souls*. Maybe it didn't run so very long, but the praise
we got—you never heard anything like it! Oh, the professional critics ganged up on us, of course; they always
do; they're jealous of all brave new experiment. Brooks
Atkinson said in the New York *Times* that it was 'dull
though doubtless worthy,' and Dick Watts said in the
Herald Tribune that it was 'worthy though doubtless dull,'
and the second-string critic on the *Sun,* he wrote almost a
whole column—he said it wasn't a play at all, but just a
Communist attack on the Governor of Oklahoma, and the

New Masses—*they* said it was a Trotskyist attack on Communism and Abraham Lincoln! But they *all* said *I* was all right, and Ward Morehouse, he had a note in his column that said I looked like Joan Crawford."

Mahala stopped, scratched her knee, looked at the sea, apparently decided that all this water was pretty useless, and sighed:

"I loved my role. I had such a good costume change. Here in the first act I was the wife of the local doctor and I wore a cocktail gown from Bergdorf Goodman's—it cost two hundred bucks! The director kicked like a steer—he said it wasn't suitable to an Oklahoma small town, but the producer was kind of sweet on me—he was a Communist and *awfully* rich, his father's a New York banker, he was a sweet boy, only kind of a screwball—and he let me have it. And even the director came to admit I was right, because it made such a swell contrast when my husband gets bumped off and I'm a poor widow and living in a share cropper's shack and I'm all in rags and barefoot—and thank God I've got feet that will stand showing—look; see how regular the toes are and what a high arch—and I was kind of the queen of the share croppers, you might say—you know, with my hair loose and a spotlight on me —and I led the revolt—wow, it was colossal! Oh dear!"

Bethel was a skillful listener; always had been; and until Nile Sanderac was gone and Andy again delivered to the arms—or at least, the conversation—of Mahala, she was Mahala's heart's-ease and swimming companion.

Mahala Vale was neither a fool nor entirely vicious. She was a handsome young woman whose mind was flexible enough to give her a high stand in the stage army—she would certainly someday be one of the best of the second-rate actresses. There was one small trouble with her: she could not conceive that any person or any play or any historical event or any dollar in legal minted coin could have any importance except in its relationship to her.

Bethel had to admit that Mahala taught her several bits of stage craftsmanship—all of the lowest and trickiest. You must always assume, even if unfairly, insisted Mahala, that almost any old trouper was at any moment likely to do anything, short of creeping up behind you and clapping on a red nose, to turn the audience's attention from you to him.

He would stand facing the audience, with his back to you, during your long, tear-dripping confession, and you could see that he wasn't moving, not doing anything to throw you—no, he was merely looking comically lugubrious, and twisting a coat button, or running his fingers along the edges of his lapels. And the dear old lady, the mother of the company, seated way down right-stage—it wasn't her fault that you always got a wrong laugh when you were gazing into the hero's eyes; all the old darling had done was to light a cigarette as though she had never, never smoked one of the horrid things before, and give a dear little pussy sneeze.

Mahala said righteously: "People that do lousy tricks like that, they ought to be kicked off the stage. They have no appreciation of the fact that you all got to work together to make a perfect performance; and there isn't any one actor, no matter how perfect he is, that's got a right to grab any spotlight off anybody else. So when you run into scene stealers like that, you just do something to throw 'em, and maybe that 'll teach 'em something!

"I remember once—it wasn't so long ago, either!—I was playing *There's Always Juliet* in stock with a born kleptomaniac. His ducky little trick was to pause before the last three-four words of a speech, so you didn't know whether he was going to give you your cue or not, and then if you jumped it, he'd give you the cue after all. I fixed him! Middle of a speech, I'd start to powder my nose, and just held it and stared at him. I got him so embarrassed he used to blow every night!

" 'N' of course—and here's something you'll never learn from Roscoe or any of these dramatic schools or those amateurs: the way to cure upstaging is, if a guy starts going upstage, on account of he thinks you'll turn your back to the audience and follow him, why, you just deliberately go right down to the foots, giving your lines to him over your shoulder—and if you think the producer ain't around to catch you, you can even kind of half wink at the audience so's they'll know what's up. That 'll show 'm!"

"I see," said Bethel.

Mahala had often spoken of the wealth and other charms of a young Mrs Tzirka who in summer lived at East Haddam, ten miles from Grampion. Her husband was a stockbroker—but artistic; she was the daughter of a wholesale jute dealer—but a very wholesale dealer in the best of jute; one of the men who had given jute its social significance.

On Saturday, Mahala permitted Bethel to borrow Pete's car and drive her to the Tzirka villa.

"They won't want to see me," Bethel had hesitated.

"Betty Tzirka 'll most especially want you. Her brother, Jock, a grand kid, 'll be there, and he'll think you're manna from heaven."

This, felt Bethel, was going to be her first real "society party" (she called it that) and a foretaste of the refined exuberance, the beautiful people, she was going to know. She pressed out her best silk print dress in the dormitory kitchen and dared try some flowers in her hair.

When she saw the Tzirka house, she suddenly knew what sort of a retreat she would have when she had become a reigning actress. It was simple enough, a white salt-box cottage at peace with a landscape of river and small hills and apple orchards, but it had been made frivolous with a green-and-white awning and a crazy-paving terrace, with green wicker chairs and glass-topped small tables, concealed by an old stone wall above the roadway. Here the Famous Merriday would read, rest and talk with friends . . . talk about the stage, of course.

Mrs Tzirka, thirty and slim and quivering and chemically blonde, met them at the flight of stone steps up from the roadway. Bethel was conscious of being regarded without favor.

Mahala bellowed, "Betty! Darling! Priceless! I've brought you a lovely date for your imbecile Jock. Beth Merriday."

Mrs Tzirka crooned at Mahala in answer, and doves at twilight were as nothing beside her: "Oh, Maggie! Duckie! Darling! I'm too-too sorry. Jock, the monster, has gone up to Hartford to see the polo. But I'm enchanted to see you, Miss Merriday." She glanced at Mahala over Bethel's shoulder, with a distinct lack of enchantment.

And now did Bethel find herself on-stage in a play with a charming set of sun-speckled awning and wicker couches and glasses of gin rickey and maple trunks, expected to snap up her cues and give her lines at fever tempo. But the cues were in some foreign language and she didn't know any of her lines. She didn't even know what the play was about.

There had been provided, for Mahala and Mrs Tzirka, two slightly rancid young-old men, aged some indistinguishable where between twenty-five and forty-five, both with double-breasted gray flannel suits, black mustaches, meaningless yelps at the names of meaningless people, and a way of looking at her as though she were a milkmaid. (*"Two* villains in the damn play," sighed Bethel.)

The four Sophisticated People were amused rather than annoyed when she carried her rusticity so far as to refuse a gin rickey, and they plunged into a colored pool of gossip, of which Bethel understood not a word:

"Simmy's going to divorce Natalie—he ran into her with Tom at El Morocco and—you know how quick on the trigger he is—he said, 'Sweetie-pie, if you want a round-trip Reno ticket, I think Tom and I ought to split the cost.' "

"I don't believe a word of what she says about Joe always

nipping outside the house. I know for a fact he's completely domesticated. It's the parlormaid at home he's interested in."

"Xavier isn't broke. He's still got his annuity. Why, he's got a Scotch grouse moor. No—fact—he's laid it out in his own back yard."

At what time in this feast Mahala rose with the younger of the two beaux—or maybe it was the older—muttered "Be back in a moment," and drifted off with him to the birch grove beyond the house; at what time Mrs Tzirka followed with the other prize, Bethel was not quite sure; but presently she was entirely alone on the terrace, and she was alone for half an hour.

It was a half-hour of growing and healthy anger. She suddenly knew that these slick people, with their references to polo and yachting and Meadowbrook, were fakes; that they hadn't much even of the one thing they worshiped—money. It was good that they had not buttered her; their rudeness had made her less likely ever again to mistake insolence for good manners.

It didn't much help her temper that they would have to drive wildly back to Grampion and have only a sandwich for dinner, if Mahala was to be in her dressing room on time.

Bethel spent part of her isolation in imitating Mrs Tzirka's tricks of chain-smoking—taking five puffs of a cigarette, exactly five, lighting another from it, and crushing out the first with a nervous sidewise brushing motion; of showing her knees and nervously, constantly, pulling down her skirt; of arching her right big toe in her half-sandals; of widening her eyes with glad surprise every time she looked at a male.

When Mrs Tzirka galloped back, gushing "So sor-ry—we were looking at my espaliered pears," Bethel bowed quite amiably and in silence.

In the car Mahala shrieked, "You were very rude, not even saying good-by to your hostess."

Bethel was pleased to hear herself saying nothing whatever, and pleased that, whether Mahala knew it or not, there was war between them now, and no sex loyalty need stop her if she should ever be able to protect Andy Deacon, her god and reckless child, from the man-eating Mahala.

14

Dᴜʀɪɴɢ ᴛʜᴇ ᴡᴇᴇᴋ of July 11th, while Nile Sanderac
was playing *Candida* in the evenings, Bethel was rehearsing for *Stage Door,* along with the whole stock company,
all the apprentices, and a few summerite outsiders from
Grampion Center, so large was the cast.

It was the first time that she had ever played with professional actors, the first time she had tried to play comedy,
the first time she had had, to devour and treasure, real
professional typed "sides" instead of a book; and in all, the
first time she had been entirely away from the pleasing
school of extempore acting, as demonstrated in Russian
schools, in Point Royal College, and on the bench in the
Prindles' garage in Sladesbury.

Andy was David and Mahala was Terry in *Stage Door;*
Iris was the Kaye who committed suicide; Toni was Jean
Maitland, who went to Hollywood; Pete Chew was the
Texas student of acting; while Harry Mihick suffered
clear down to the bottom of his sensitive boots as the
colored houseman.

Bethel's own role was that of Bernice Niemeyer, the

curiosity-driven girl who was the pest of the theatrical boardinghouse. She was glad that it wasn't merely a pretty ingénue part. She would have to represent a person as alien to herself as Cleopatra, and that was the training for which she longed.

She had heard from Doc Keezer an old stock-company belief that an actor ought not to learn his part before rehearsals, but during them, so that he might tie up lines and business. But two days before the terrifying Tuesday morning when they ran through *Stage Door,* in the orchestra pit, in front of the *Candida* set that stared down superciliously at their ragged beginnings, Bethel knew all of the Bernice part, and she had studied such speeches as "I'd rather go out with the handsome one" as though they were the last words of Fanny Kemble. . . . She *was* Bernice, sharp-nosed and brassy and a little touching in her predestined failure. When Toni demanded, "Shove over the box of shredded hay" at Monday-morning breakfast, Bethel looked sleepily at her, sighed and murmured, "With the handsome one."

Whatever she did, remembering the stripes and afflictions she had borne over Nora, Bethel was not going to overplay the role. Her chief concern was that she had the very first speech, opening the play.

All Saturday night she worked with the other apprentices removing the *Night of January 16th* set and erecting that of *Candida*—good work, for all its weariness; laughing and clattering on and off the stage together; the boys in undershirts and belted trousers, their shoulders glittering with sweat, the girls in slacks or babyish gingham rompers, allowed to stay up till dawn, feeling that they were doing something pioneering, something important for the drama; never stopping their boasting about what great actors they were going to be, and swapping faith for faith. Yet again on Monday night, after the *Candida* opening, Bethel stayed up till three, studying her part at the dormitory dining table, under one economical light (Roscoe saw to that), her legs twisted around a table leg, her small tongue poked out of the corner of her small red mouth. She was, in fact, so thorough about it that when she came to the first rehearsal of *Stage Door,* at ten on Tuesday, she couldn't remember a word, and had to read her part, like all the others.

At the beginning of the play, set in the jumbled living room of a boardinghouse for girl aspirants, one Olga is at the piano. The busily intrusive Bernice stops her letter-writing to ask about the music. So, beginning the rehearsal, looking not at Olga but at Mr Roscoe Valentine, who sat in the front row of the orchestra, scratching one fat calf, his usual resemblance to a ripe olive heightened by a dark green hunting jacket, Bethel gave her first line, "What's that you're playing?" like a plunging sparrow beholding a very small worm. All the while she sat rigid at the writing desk. . . . She wasn't overplaying *this!*

Roscoe bellowed.

Usually, Roscoe would only squeak, pipe, pullulate, whine, whimper, bleat, blat or blether, but this was a man-sized bellow.

"Bethel, have you by any chance looked at the role you're supposed to play? Have you taken one single moment from the golden joys of swimming and amorous dalliance to read maybe a couple of Bernice's speeches? Did anyone tell you that they can be procured in manuscript, all nicely typed? Also in book form, at all literary emporia? Have you looked at the play? Do you even know which character you are, by the wisdom of Mr Deacon and Miss Sample and myself, elected to portray?"

"I know it by heart." Bethel wasn't sure whether she sounded dangerous or blubbering. She felt both.

"Then you have no excuse. Or maybe no heart. Now let's save a lot of time at the beginning, by getting your concept of the part right. Bernice is supposed to be an active, inquisitive busybody—a sort of oversized blue jay. When you give your line—what is it?—'What's that you're playing?'—make it as fresh and irritating as you can. And don't sit there lolling. Get up. Make a cross. Look at

Olga's music, over her shoulder. Breathe down her neck. Make yourself as generally objectionable as you can. Understand?"

"Yes, sir, I'll try to be very objectionable."

"On-stage, I meant."

Roscoe Valentine was a skyrocket; heated-looking for a time, but cooling with celerity. For the first three or four out of the twelve half-day rehearsal periods (including dress rehearsal, on Sunday evening) he was savagely on time, and fussy as a watchmaker. He would spend ten minutes in discussing whether, in view of the fact that she was later to commit suicide, it would be more significant for Kaye Hamilton—that is, Iris Pentire—to turn right or left, when she sat down.

But each day Roscoe was later at rehearsals, each day he was angrier when actors were even later than himself. By the end of the week, when an actor would ask, "Don't you think I ought to cross here?" or "What about my standing up before I answer?" Roscoe would clasp his breast and moan, "Hasn't anybody told you the news? We're not rehearsing ten weeks! We're playing stock, with six days for rehearsal! I'm directing for tempo and mood, not for business. Can't you work out *anything* for yourself?"

At his best, Roscoe could take out enough time in explaining that he hadn't enough time for directing to have directed a mystery melodrama.

Yet, with it all, Bethel learned more about the drama than she had in four years of college library and of Miss Bickling. The week was an idyll. Whatever foam from Roscoe had to be wiped away, she was working with professional actors: Andy, Mahala, Clara Ribbons, Doc Keezer, Tudor Blackwall, Maggie Sample. Whenever she was sent up to Grampion Center on an errand, though the bright waters and dancing boats in the harbor beckoned, and the fresh watery odor, she hastened back to the dark interior of the scrubby theater—a sacred chamber more illuminated than the sun-washed ocean. Through the open doors she could see one gay little pine tree against blue open sky. She felt that it was her friend, her totem, and for her, just now, it was forest enough.

The whole business of rehearsal had an exasperated fascination. She had early noted that the actors who had the fewest lines were those who were least likely to be ready for entrance, and that the less they had to memorize, the less likely they were to know it. Clara Ribbons never fully knew her lines till the Wednesday of actual playing—with the pleasant result that she threw everybody who played with her.

Bethel had resolved not to be one of these slovenly workmen, doomed to dreariness, and yet—you waited so long for your line to come; you sat out on the step, sniffing the air; someone came and spoke to you; or perhaps, alone, you were going over and over, over and over just the line you were waiting to give, and then, in horror, you heard Roscoe yelping, "Bernice! Where the hell is Bernice? She's on now!" And you bolted into the rehearsal space so rattled that you forgot the line that you had been repeating till you knew it better than your own name! And Roscoe scowled, as you stammered and felt sick and could remember nothing at all. And Fletcher's kind voice gave you the first words, and you said, "Oh, of course!" And afterward, you laid your forehead on your elbow on the upright piano and looked as though you were weeping, but you were again repeating the line—over and over, over and over.

The acutest twinge of rehearsals, always, was to be going on smoothly, feeling that you were giving a speech perfectly, really becoming Bernice Niemeyer, and then to be jerked out of the superreality of the actor's unreality by Roscoe's sharp, "All right! We'll go back to David's entrance again." That was like stubbing your toe when running. And you stumbled thus, and your heart stopped, twenty times an hour.

But the moment came, the last day, when you weren't

saying lines, weren't rehearsing, but playing, lost, absorbed, and that was the second when you left the earth and were flying.

During rehearsals the democratic comradeship of the theater was at its surest. While they were awaiting their scenes, they sat back together, young and old, veteran and raw apprentice; Andy in white flannel trousers unelegantly extended over the top of a seat; Doc Keezer, as the Dr Randall of the play (he would always be playing doctors and ministers), sitting back with closed eyes, so indifferent to everything but his own lines that it is doubtful whether he knew what any of the play was about; Iris with a small, set, misty smile ignoring the fact that Pete Chew was gaping wistfully at her from the circle of Toni, Tudor Blackwall, Mahala and Cy Fickerty, who were squatting on the stage and shooting craps, while Harry Mihick looked on them in sorrow at such desecration.

At rehearsals they were given to fantastic clothes: Walter Rolf to overalls, sneakers and a lumberman's green-and-yellow flannel shirt; Tudor Blackwall to mauve or maroon lounging pajamas. But whatever they wore, almost every man carried his brown-covered part in his back pocket.

They were all serious children; very childish, very serious, and apparently the only people still existent, in a world of Hitler and Buchmanism, who enjoyed life. At every mistake, at every dropped line, they laughed, and laughed together. And together they shared the one, profoundest misery that a rehearsing actor could know: that in a wooden summer theater you were not permitted to smoke. Oh, you *did* smoke, of course, and flattened the butts with your toe, and kicked them under chairs, but it took away the relaxation.

All over the theater grounds, as they lay studying lines or reading Steinbeck and Hemingway and Noel Coward or plain sleeping and acquiring a sun tan, and at rehearsals, when they sat slouching on their shoulder blades, listening, there was a flaunting of brown legs of girls in shorts, but they were very nice legs, and so numerous that they became as modest as noses. Some of the students were aloof and arty, but most times they were a gay crew—shouting at each other when they met for rehearsals, goading those who were late—Pete Chew had the disease of chronic, inevitable lateness—smiling generously when a speech had been said with spirit, and fiendishly when an apprentice had earnestly given the line "How do you justify your terms?" as "How do you tustify your germs?"

With the most beautiful, baby-like absence of self-consciousness, they were to be seen standing in corners, glaring at a wall, and to it addressing hysterical lines of love. At rehearsals the actor tossed an entirely imaginary cloak about his shoulders as though it were heavy brocade, courteously removed a hat made of air, and seriously set out on a suppositious table a nonexistent dinner, after sedulously cooking it on a kitchen range that was a chair. In everything was the spirit of children's play—not the rule-ridden, time-killing play of adults that is a preparation for death, but the busy and credulous play of children that is a preparation for life.

She was rehearsing with Andy! She had a scene with Andy alone!

He came on as the young movie producer—not only handsome and rich but the donor of jobs; and as the desperately pretentious job hunter, she pretended not to see him, preened herself, and babbled to an imaginary auditor off-stage: "Yes, Mattie, an actress's life is such an interesting one. . . . For example, an English actress came into the office today. 'My dear Harry, how definitely ripping to see you. Definitely ripping!' "

She worked desperately at acting Bernice desperately misacting an Englishwoman, and when (on the stage!) Andy looked at her with irritated pity, she was content.

Their relationship had now progressed so far that Andy usually remembered her name.

The company were beginning to pair off: Andy and Mahala, Doc Keezer and Clara Ribbons. Walter Rolf and Marian Croy read plays aloud; Roscoe Valentine and Tudor Blackwall and Bruce Pasture were usually together; and Bethel and Fletcher Hewitt, who was as busy with script at rehearsals as he was with off-stage noises and curtains during performances, were accepted as uninspired friends. The only active triangle was of Pete Chew and Toni Titmus and Iris Pentire.

Mr Chew was a fool and Mr Chew was noisy, but Mr Chew had a kind heart and lots of money. And Toni seemed to have a good time with him and to like his dancing. It is doubtful if Iris ever thought of having a good time; in her spun-glass quietness she cared for nothing more vulgar than being admired. With Pete, as with Cy Fickerty and Walter Rolf and Fletcher and Bruce Pasture, she was always delicately amused, waiting, unmoving.

Whenever Pete invited Iris to a dance—that must have been, on an average, nine times a week—she refused with pallid sweetness, "Oh, not tonight, I think, but it's so kind of you." Whereas Toni always accepted, and always accepted with a whoop of "Oh boy, ask me, *ask* me!" So, naturally, Pete fell out of love with Toni and into love with Iris, as devastatingly as he had fallen in love with Bethel, long, long ago—days and days ago. He gaped at Iris during rehearsals; he lolled at her delicate feet on the shoreward rocks; and when she fluted such revelations as "I think committing suicide on the stage is quite dramatic, don't you?" Pete rumbled, "It certainly is—you bet your life—it certainly is!"

What the feline Iris would do with her plump boy-mouse, Bethel did not know. Perhaps Iris herself did not know. Perhaps Iris merely enjoyed waiting and stretching her claws and feeling the quickness in them.

Gravely tearing a lobster claw to pieces, at the Lobster Pot, where the Nutmeg apprentices swarmed after the

evening show to drink beer and coffee and to play that
monstrous form of charades called "The Game," Fletcher
Hewitt studied Bethel, and said slowly:

"Pete—Iris—Mahala—all those amateurs—they spend
too much time working up an artificial sex stimulation. It
takes up the energy they ought to give to acting. I think
you're free of it."

"So are you," said Bethel.

"Me? Huh! I have to be. I have my mother to support
—bless her. Beth! Are you falling for Andy Deacon?"

"How ridiculous!"

"Why are you?"

"Oh, you know. He's so lovely and childish and beaming."

"He's a nice fellow, Andy, for a rich young man, and
he might be a fair actor if he ever got any training. But
you better duck under shelter when he turns on that golden
smile of his. All you kids fall for it. But it's no use."

"I know, Fletcher."

"In fact someday, Beth, when you and I have been
sufficiently licked in this insane gamble of the theater, we'll
retire and get married and go keep a summer hotel. *That'll*
give us enough people to fool with. Okay?"

"Yes, okay, Fletcher."

She wasn't sure but that both of them half meant it.

Between them, Bethel and Cynthia Aleshire made much of
the Bernice Niemeyer costumes, and Bethel was so excited by
them that she forgot her meals . . . well, she forgot one
meal. Bernice was to flaunt sleazy satin frocks and to paint
her face like a gasoline pump.

When, at the dress rehearsal on Sunday evening, Bethel
stood up from the desk to reveal herself in an apricot-
colored tea gown, with purple panels, slightly torn, with
a chain of carved imitation-ivory beads, a chain of crimson
glass beads, a chain of coins, a souvenir bracelet hung with
small silver animals, and a broad chased bracelet of plated
silver, with her lips widened and (under Cynthia's tutor-

ship) her temples and cheeks hollowed, she received a tiny hand of applause from the Grampion theater sponsors, and she heard Roscoe whimper to Cynthia, "Why, she looks the part pretty well."

Ah, that was heavenly praise! Ah, that was praise enough for Bernhardt! Dear youth!

15

BETHEL WAS SHY ENOUGH; in any mob of more than five people she was so uneasy that she chattered, and hated herself for chattering. Yet exposed before the four hundred and seventeen people at the first night of *Stage Door*—and that was a large audience for the Nutmeg Theater—she was, after the agony and trembling of waiting for the curtain to go up, as placid as a bishop. For she was not Bethel Merriday at all; she was Bernice Niemeyer, and very intrusive.

In her dressing room, between scenes, she felt sure of herself. It was a real dressing room to which she had now climbed. Though it was a large, jammed, low-ceiled den, which she shared with three other apprentices, and with Iris, Clara Ribbons and Maggie Sample, it had real dressing-room shelf-tables, narrow enough so that she could study her make-up in a mirror enchantingly rimmed with lights.

At the final curtain line-up, she got a reasonable share of the hands, and knew that if she had not been brilliant, she had not been bad. Fletcher Hewitt cried, afterward, "You were magnificent, baby"; Andy Deacon beamed, "Nice work, Miss M-Merriday"; Roscoe Valentine so far extended himself as to croak, "You were all right, I guess"; Iris Pentire, as they undressed (no elaborate task in the days of three-piece robing) caroled, "Just be careful and don't jump cues, dear"; and Mr Black Bart wrote, in the New London *Era:*

As it is probable that off-stage she is a very charming sloe-eyed young woman, a new friend, Miss Bethel Merriday, is all the more to be praised for having made Bernice so objectionable and flashy that she made you itch, and yet so pathetic when she busted down that you changed your mind and decided to just shoot her instead of boiling her in hair oil.

That review is on page seven of Beth's scrapbook, just after her dance programs, the program of a Universalist Church cantata in which she sang two lines, the stub of her ticket to her first basketball game at Point Royal College, and the program of *A Doll's House.* And just before it appears the first opening-night telegram that she ever received; it came from Charley Hatch, Alva Prindle and Ben Merriday, and read "All wish you thousand good wishes tonight good luck wish were there." That had made her homesick, on first night, for at least two minutes.

Through the week, all the evenings after the strained first night, it was pleasant to slip out of doors between acts for one of her few cigarettes.

You could do that, in a summer theater, under the trees —though also you had to endure the inquisitive spectators, city brokers feeling superior on vacation—millionaires for sixteen days a year—who sneaked around back of the theater to stare at the actors as at a zoo. Some of them even had the bad manners to ask for autographs between acts, but this did not annoy Bethel—she was not yet notorious enough to be dunned, or to hate the whole tribe of autograph hunters, the thick-skinned devotees of the one hobby in the world which consists in turning into brazen beggars and annoying innocent strangers, preferably by interrupting their talk with friends just at the moment when they are most weary and relaxed. To Bethel the theater-goers were still heavenly visitors who, out of pure benevolence, were permitting her to act.

Through the week while she was playing *Stage Door,* Bethel was rehearsing all day long for her second role, that of the maid in *George and Margaret.* Iris should have had this lively bit, but Iris was to take part in a broadcast in New York on an evening this next week—a fact which made Bethel, who had come to consider Iris as a pink papier-mâché sphinx, to hold her again in awe. Was Iris not one of the magicians who could make twenty million modern Americans listen to such bodiless beauty, such skylark melody, as the shoplifter in a radio drama lilting to her mate, "Grab your rod and scram—it's de G-men"?

Now, first, Bethel knew something of the labor of the real theater—a toil which was already persuading Anita Hill and Harry Mihick to talk of Roscoe Valentine as a slave driver and of doing the stage an irreparable injury by renouncing it. She was working violently, sixteen hours out of the twenty-four. All day she rehearsed in *George and Margaret,* in the brown, stuffy, spicy heat of the theater, which she loved above the sea foam and sea gulls and silver-channeled sea outside. All evening, and at Wednesday matinée, she played *Stage Door.* Till two o'clock she sat up studying her new lines and helping make her costume as maid. She was afraid of mixing up the two plays, so that as the bounding Bernice from the Bronx—standing out there, helpless, fanning the air for her line—she would be able to say nothing to her fellow job hunters beyond "Very good, moddom."

She was always a little dazed, always surprised to find that she had, without having for a second heard her own voice, got clear through an evening of *Stage Door* without making a fool of herself. Roscoe was wearing down, and beginning to shriek all through rehearsals, but Bethel was too numb now to resent it.

Then, on Saturday morning, the spell was broken, and Roscoe became her enemy.

Roscoe had become edgier every day through the week, and last night he had fully attended a Chianti party among the artists at Old Lyme.

Gladys the maid, who was Bethel, was supposed to enter in the third act of *George and Margaret* with a smartness befitting her new God-given station as the fiancée of the oldest son of the family. It was morning, and Bethel had slept, and she knew her lines, and at rehearsal she was one with the gods as she blithely tripped in, chirping "I'm going now, Mrs Garth-Bander."

"Oh God, Bethel, don't you know anything about your part?" yelled Roscoe. "This wench is supposed to be scared to death of the old hag. Try to act, even if God did make it impossible. Take that entrance again."

Bethel looked at him silently, unhappily. She thought that Andy Deacon, perched on the back of a seat far back in the auditorium, seemed annoyed and smoked rapidly.

Again she came on, through an imaginary door between two chairs. She smiled wanly at Clara Ribbons, who was yawning as she tried to wake up enough to impersonate Mrs Garth-Bander, and said "I'm going now" timidly.

Roscoe yelled again, and hysterically: "I didn't tell you to play it like a funeral, you fool! Get some lift into it, d'you hear me, *d'you hear me,* D'YOU HEAR ME?"

In the quiet after this shrieking, Andy came down the center aisle, blank as a sleepwalker, and spoke to Roscoe, flatly, "Don't talk that way. I do not like it. I do not like your screaming. Do not talk that way, Mr Valentine!"

And clumped back to his seat.

Bethel had never before really seen anyone turn purple. Roscoe turned purple. He glanced for a second at Andy's broad back, he glanced at Fletcher and Doc Keezer and Clara, who had made their faces expressionless, he glanced at the trembling Bethel, with poison pouring out of his red eyes and loose mouth. He pushed forward his neck like a turtle. He spoke calmly enough.

"I am sorry, Miss Merriday, if I have been too enthusiastic in my directing, as Mr Deacon seems to think. We will go on now. Try your entrance again. You come in gaily, but your courage begins to ooze when you see the old woman. All right."

He never called her "Bethel" again.

She appeared in one more play, in the tiny part of Eva Blake in Noel Coward's *We Were Dancing,* and in that Roscoe directed her with just as much interest as if he were winding a watch.

When they had sifted out for lunch, after this fatal rehearsal, Andy patted her back, grinned, said casually, "I'm afraid I just made you the more uncomfortable by blowing up and bawling out poor old Roscoe. He'll forget it by tonight. You're doing swell work—uh—Bethel."

This voice from Eden did not console her. She took Fletcher aside after lunch:

"What will I do? I've made an enemy of Mr Valentine, and I didn't mean to. Honestly, it isn't because I'm scared about his keeping me from getting jobs and so on, but it makes me sick to think of him looking at me that way . . . as if I were a bedbug."

Fletcher was cheerful. "Beth, I'd be unhappy about your future if I didn't think the spiteful people are going to dislike you. That's one test of success. And—I'm afraid I know better now why girls adore Andy. He didn't jump on Roscoe just because he can afford to. He would have jumped just the same if he'd been a walk-on with holes in his soles. While I sat back and didn't say anything. Sorry."

Fletcher turned away quickly.

The Nutmeg Players were going to hold their first party this Saturday evening, the end of the run of *Stage Door,* and Bethel felt high.

Rain was threatening, and they would have the party in the dormitory instead of on the beach. In the dining room Japanese lanterns were so blossoming by suppertime that the place looked more like a Baptist lawn festival in Sladesbury than like a temple of Chekhov.

As Bethel crossed to the theater, before evening performance, she was excited by the omens of the storm. It was unnaturally dark, and incessant distant lightning revealed whitecaps and shaken sailboats out on the Sound and turned the sedge grass to a poison green, while the whole shifting air was filled with uneasiness and the brave last fireflies were menacing points of flame.

The audience was small, and it breathed hard at the occasional thunder, yet it was a good audience, quick to laugh, quick to be stilled in sympathy. Already Bethel had learned to be conscious of audiences; not to fawn to them, but to feel them. Tonight she was playing well enough—or it may have been badly enough—so that she didn't care whether anybody else thought she was playing well or ill.

She was annoyed, from the wings, at Iris's mourning and handclasping as the suicidal Kaye; she felt somehow responsible for her roommate. But at the end, when the audience stopped even in reaching for raincoats and rubbers to applaud and scream "Bravo" as the cast assembled for curtain call, Bethel felt ten feet tall, in golden armor, and ran into the communal dressing room emitting happiness like a cloud of steam.

If Roscoe pettishly stayed away from them, Andy looked in to shout, "You were all on your toes tonight, kids. You're all Margaret Sullavans, the whole lot of you."

They were all stripped to dressing gowns, rubbing cold-creamed faces with wads of tissue, when an unknown voice, like that of a young Scotti, rumbled at the door, "May I come in?"

The owner of the voice plowed in without waiting.

He was a belligerent-looking, square young man, with tousled brown hair and a face, healthy and slightly rough of skin, that turned instantly from impish impertinence to sorrow and back again. He might have been a butcher, a Communist poet, a fundamentalist evangelist, a prize fighter or a researcher in physics. His bare head, his thick brown sweater, his khaki trousers dripped rain.

"Hello, girls," he said. He stopped beside Toni Titmus (she had played the Hollywood hussy) and grunted, "You weren't too bad—you had some hint of oomph, sister."

"Whadya mean 'sister.' I never saw you before," bristled Toni.

"You will. Plenty. On Broadway. With Maurice Evans *and* the Theater Group, someday. I'm Zed Wintergeist, of the Dory Playhouse—Jerry O'Toole's select summer sisterhood down the coast. Not playing this week. Took the night off to give your masterpiece the once-over. . . . God, most of you were bad! I should come out in the rain to see *you,* sweetie!"

Young Mr Zed Wintergeist had plodded over to Iris Pentire now and was looking down at her, amused, apparently not overcome by the sight of her delicate shoulders. "It didn't look as though it was economic inequality that made *you* bump yourself off in the play, but just plain bellyache."

"Really!" said Iris.

He proceeded to Bethel, dripping all the way. His glance, bold but good-humored, impertinent yet honest, made her too uncertain for any Sladesburian retorts of outraged ladyhood.

"You were pretty fair, Bethel—I take it from the program that that's your pious name. Lemme look at your eyes."

"Really!" said Iris again; and Toni, "Of all the nerve!" But in silence Bethel let the young bully jab his forefinger under her chin, tilt back her head and stare at her eyes. "Yeah. I guess so. You got some perception. You got into Bernice's hide—made me understand how much that poor gutter pup longed for a chance to parade, and yet you didn't do much tear-jerking—you made her as intrusive and offensive——"

"As you are!" yelped Marian Croy.

"Exactly. That's what I was going to say!"

"I suppose you're casting us all for the play you're going to produce in 1968," cried Iris. (It was the first time that Bethel had ever seen Iris yanked out of her frail aloofness, and for that she could have loved Zed Wintergeist.)

"Yes, sweetie, and maybe I am, at that. Be good, girls. See you all at the party. Don't let Mahala Vale put anything over on you. I saw her once, in an awful piece of tripe about share croppers. She was lousy. She peeled potatoes with kid gloves on. Andy Deacon doesn't know it yet, but he's going to invite me to your party. See you there, Bethel! Be good."

They all begged her not to take the monster's attentions seriously.

She told them that she didn't intend to take them at all—only Zed wasn't really a monster—not really—just a "fresh kid"—couldn't be over twenty-two—just a baby——

"In sin and impertinence, he's ninety-two," groaned Marian Croy. "His heart is black with vice. He thinks he can act! I know he was the prize scholar in a progressive school, and got the works of John Dewey bound in ooze calf for graduation."

"That's just what I was going to say!" said Toni.

"Yes! So was I!" said Iris.

"Were you, darlings?" said Marian.

As all of the apprentices had appeared in *Stage Door,* Roscoe made only four of the more docile among them miss the party and work all of Saturday night changing the sets. He even hired two men to work with them; Doc Keezer alleged that this must have cost Roscoe all of ten dollars, almost the only money that he had ever been known to pay in wages without compulsion.

Before the *Stage Door* set came down, Bethel went on to stare at it with more nostalgic love than she had ever given to her wide-porched home in Sladesbury.

On a stage twenty-one feet wide between the proscenic pillars, Cynthia had magicked a forty-foot apartment. That was Bethel's real home, that canvas-walled, canvas-ceilinged, littered den, with its fourth wall made of air: the handsome stairway out in the hall, the fireplace with white wooden columns like a small-sized edition of a national bank, the huddle of couch and piano, the handsome double doors that led to a festive dining room, off-stage left, where she had eaten so many meals with her companions of the Footlights Club.

She murmured to Doc Keezer—now changed from a frail country doctor back to a short, grizzled, somehow unidentifiable trouper. "Oh, Doc, won't you miss this set? Don't you think it's terrible it has to come down after only one week?"

Doc Keezer looked startled. He said mildly, "Set? Don't know 's I noticed it much. Any set's all right, if you can get on it without stooping through the doors and barking your shins, but otherwise, they all seem alike, after thirty-five years of it—I started at fifteen—my father and mother were in burlyque. No, dear, I don't think I'll miss it!"

She heard the bumptious invader, Zed Wintergeist, just off-stage, greeting Andy Deacon.

"H're you, Andy? Remember me?"

"Why—oh, of course! Zed! See the show tonight?"

"Yes. Ran up from the Dory. I'm doing time there this summer."

"How did you like us?"

"Oh—well—you know. Can't expect much from stock."

"I see."

"Look, Andy, what you going to do this fall? If I had your money—and your patience—yes, and talent, too—I'd produce something experimental."

"Maybe I will, Zed. Look me up in the fall—if you're interested." But Andy did not sound too cordial.

"You bet your life I'm interested! I'll look you up. Say, uh, understand your gang is having a spirited little gathering this evening."

"Yes. In the dorm. Come along, will you? And can I put you up tonight? Rain's pretty bad."

"Yes to both. See you later."

She stood with Andy at the stage door, awaiting a halt in the rain before they should scurry over to the dormitory.

"I heard you talking to that Wintergeist boy, Andy. Is he a good actor?"

"Excellent. I'm not sure but that Zed'll turn out to be another Burgess Meredith or Van Heflin or Dean Jagger."

"He seems so bumptious."

"Young people of talent often are. I haven't had the chance to get much acquainted with you yet, my dear—not my fault, I assure you!—but I haven't a doubt that you're just as cocksure of yourself——"

"Oh, I am not!"

"—only you have more ladylike manners. You wouldn't want Zed to be ladylike, would you?"

"Who *is* he?"

"Nobody—yet. He's conceited and destructive. He'd be perfectly capable of telling Guthrie McClintic or Tony Miner that their direction is rotten. But he's honest, and he's got ideas, and he doesn't want to be an elegant connoisseur —like me!"

"Oh, you're not!"

"I played with him on tour in that English mystery melodrama, *The Light Goes Out*. He was the English captain who'd murdered the Rector of Mittyford, and he made even that phony part believable. You could almost smell the mess port and the machine-gun grease. And I, my dear Beth, will have you to understand that I was a chief inspector of Scotland Yard—*chief* inspector, not a plain one!—and I was so realistic that in Pittsburgh, Harold Cohen wrote that I made him homesick for the Camden, New Jersey, police station. . . . Yes. I'm a better organizer than Zed; I'm more punctual and I can keep expense accounts more accurately; but I'll never be able to act as well," said the honest Andy.

"You just mean you'll never be able to act as noisily."

The great man was looking grateful.

"Thank you, my public! Zed's a biological and biographical sport. I'm afraid I'm too standardized. He's one half Virginia gentry, and a quarter German and a quarter Irish, I suppose with some good Jewish blood for flavor. I suspect his real Christian name of being Ezekiel. He's about twenty-three, I guess. He came from a Montana ranch to Broadway via a country newspaper in Minnesota and a medicine show and a year in Dartmouth College and a few months in the New York School for Design and six months playing Shakespeare in the Old Vic in London. God knows how he got into any of 'em, but it's easy to see how he got out of all of 'em. Well, Iris, darling—oh, I'm sorry! Bethel darling, I mean!—let's forgive him. Look! Rain's let up. Let's scoot."

Somebody—Bethel suspected Andy—had for the party provided cold chicken, lobster salad, English sweet biscuits and champagne—oh, a very little champagne, of a very little domestic brand, but it was the first Bethel had ever tasted, and on tasting it she decided that it wasn't half as good as cider. Nothing so obvious as alcohol or nicotine would be the downfall of Bethel Merriday.

At the party they played The Game, inevitably, and Maggie Sample astounded them by coming to life and riotously enacting the advertising slogan, "A skin you love to touch."

Zed Wintergeist went around being superior to these puerilities. In a corner he muttered again to Bethel that she really hadn't been bad—that she might have a chance to become a real actress, if she worked like a slave.

It was the warmest attention she had ever had from a fellow priestling. "They say my danger is overplaying," she confided.

"Nonsense! Bunch of amateurs! Overacting *did* used to be the tradition. Then the Provincetown Players and the Theater Guild came along and made acting more natural. Now we're going too far, underplaying too much. Can't you see from the words themselves that *under*playing must be just as bad as *over*playing. I'd rather be a scenery chewer than play so far down that it ain't playing at all. *Playing*, that's what you'll do!"

Maybe she was being taken seriously! breathed the ecstatic Bethel.

Andy and Mahala were burlesquing their last scene in *Stage Door*.

ANDY

By the way, you *are* my girl, aren't you, Maggie? You know I'm co-director of the Nutmeg Players.

MAHALA

Okay. Here's where I kiss you—only I don't—it's after eleven-thirty and it 'd cost you time and a half overtime, Equity ruling.

ANDY

Roscoe would never stand for that, so we'll just pay a spiritual tribute to your great future on the stage.

MAHALA

No, 'tis something else I want, too—a room of my own.

ANDY

And that's your curtain line? What kind of an ending is that for a romantic play!

Everybody laughed very much—except Bethel and Marian, who felt embarrassed, and Roscoe, who glared at the reference to his parsimony, and Zed, who snarled to Bethel, "That's the worst piece of irreligiousness I ever heard! To burlesque a part you've just been playing, no matter what part, is my idea of a damn blasphemous sacrilege!"

"Oh, dry up, angel," said that seasoned woman of the world, Miss Merriday.

He looked offended and stalked away, and she was certain that he had none of Andy's warm humor. A quarter of an hour later she beheld Zed squatted on the floor by Iris's chair and gazing at her rapturously, while Iris dripped down upon him all her frail sweetness.

"And to think that young man dared to criticize Andy! Mr Jerry O'Toole and the Dory Playhouse can keep him!" snorted Bethel.

THE NUTMEG PLAYERS
Pt. Grampion, Conn.

Roscoe Valentine, Director

Present

for the week of July 25th, 1938

GEORGE AND MARGARET
by *Gerald Savory*

The Characters

(in order of appearance)

GLADYS................Miss Bethel Merriday
MR. GARTH-BANDER...Mr. George Keezer
MRS. GARTH-BANDER..Miss Clara Ribbons
DUDLEY................Mr. Tudor Blackwall
FRANKIE...............Miss Mahala Vale
CLAUDE................Mr. Walter Rolf
ROGER.................Mr. Andrew Deacon
BEER....................Miss Marian Croy

The action takes place at the Garth-Banders' house on the out-skirts of London during February.

Act I   The dining room, breakfast time.
Act II   The drawing room, two weeks later.
Act III   The same, next morning.

Settings designed by Miss Cynthia Aleshire

Staff for Mr. Valentine

Stage Manager	Fletcher Hewitt
Publicity	Elizabeth Jeddaby
(care of the Grampion Courier)	
House Manager	John Meddock
Treasurer	Nora Bronson

NEXT WEEK

Three Charming One-Act Comedies

by NOEL COWARD

WE WERE DANCING
FUMED OAK
FAMILY ALBUM

with Andrew Deacon, Mahala Vale

and as Guest Star

BROADWAY'S FAVORITE ROMANTIC COMEDIAN
DAN DAUGHERTY

16

THAT THURSDAY AFTERNOON, the fourth of the *George and Margaret* run, Bethel had a letter from her father:

DEAR DAUGHTER:

It is fairly cool for July up here, I always say the sea may be all right but you cant beat the hills for real nice summer weather, we took out the car last evening & had a nice joy ride to Norfolk to see Cousin Mary, you wont remember her she is the daughter of old Squire Patten, still has her teeth @ eighty and eyesight as good as a girl's. Well, you have only 5 weeks after this week in summer theater & am sure you realize none better that you must now give some solid thought to question of what you will do in the fall.

We have an idea you will be wanting to fly off to N Y and look for a job in the theater but we have been talking a lot to Mr. Sampson you remember him, though now in mercantile business he had a lot of experience with the stage, vaudeville & Shakespeare & so forth when a boy, he says

N Y is a terribly dangerous place for a young girl, gets more so every year with all these immoral shows & dance hall and so on.

Now Bethel we want you to do whatever you think is right, we have every confidence in yr good sense & if you absolutely feel you must go on the stage, shall stand back of you always. We have decided we can manage to let you have $25.00 a week till you get a job, though as you probably know business is bad & collections simply terrible I swear they are almost as bad as in 1930.

But we beg of you to stop & think if you are not still pretty young to try & cope with the temptations in N Y & if we couldn't persuade you to stay home for a year & then tackle the city. We are not getting any younger though thank God we are both still hale & hearty but we are both at a time of life when we can never tell how much longer we will have a chance to see our daughter & visit with her & of course Ben has a girl friend, several of them I guess, & we don't hardly ever see him except at breakfast, & while we certainly do not complain & enjoy the radio & occasional movie as much as anybody, it sometimes gets lonely here & it certainly would brighten up this household a terrible lot if we could hear our bright girl chatting & entertaining her friends here in the evening, maybe our last chance to see anything of her, but dear, you must decide, we honestly don't want to put any pressure on you. The dog was sick last week, too much whoopee, I guess. Well, I must close now & hope you are enjoying every second of your stay with all those clever people.

With all our love,
Yours faithfully,
Your loving,
FATHER AND MOTHER.

She cried.

She saw them, alone in the evenings, waiting, talking about her; she saw their eyes, so cautious yet so kind; timid dull eyes that she could so easily brighten with her chatter. Surely the least she could do for them was to give them a year of her life——

But she had to hasten to the theater.

After the play, Fletcher stuck his head in to drawl, "Gent to see you, Beth. Looks to me like the boy friend from back home. Charley Hatch."

"Oh, dear!" wailed Bethel. "Tell him to wait!"

Already it seemed to her natural that Fletcher, Andy, Roscoe should see her in loose dressing gown and bare feet. They belonged to the sacred order of wandering vagabonds. But Charley was an outsider—how dismayingly an outsider she perceived now.

She flung on a skirt and sweater and sandals and scrabbled her hair into some sort of a knot and crept out. Before she could face him with the gaiety and poise suitable to an actress, she had to halt inside the dressing-room door, her throat throbbing. She was not insincere; nothing so masterful as that. She was plain frightened by the kind demand that she return to babyhood and the back streets and the evenings of loving vacuity.

"Why, Charley! This is too divine! Did you drive down to see the show?"

"Yes, I guess so. Well, no, I drove down to see you, mostly, I guess."

"But you were out front?"

"Uh?"

"I mean, you saw our play?"

"Oh yes—yes, sure."

"Why didn't you let me know and I'd 've had a ticket for you."

"Well—— Kind of thought I'd better buy my own. And I wanted to surprise you."

"And you certainly did! In such a lovely way, I mean."

"Let's go somewhere and talk."

"Oh yes, Charley—oh yes, of course. Uh—have you got your car with you?"

"Sure."

"Then we might drive to the Lobster Pot. It's a ducky place."

"Is it?" Nothing more from Charley, as he escorted her to the car. She felt as frothy as Mahala Vale. She became very geographical about the neighboring estates as they drove into Grampion Center.

At table in the Lobster Pot, Charley, very virile and dominating, demanded, "Want a drink, Bet?"

"No, I don't believe so."

"You can have one if you want to. I'm getting wise to the world. You got to, if you're a streamlined salesman. You don't have to conceal any vices from me."

"I haven't got any to conceal."

"No? Well, that's all the better."

"They have lovely waffles and chicken here."

"Kind of late at night for waffles, isn't it? Well, all right. You can only be young once!"

"Charley! Here's a funny coincidence. I heard from Mama and Papa this afternoon. Did you know anything about it?"

"Why yes, in a way. I kind of got to talking with them, yesterday. Listen: I don't know 's you ought to go off and leave 'em all alone. You certainly owe them some gratitude for having brought you into the world, and giving you such a swell education."

"I know. They've been wonderful." She spoke wretchedly, in a vision of returning home and, evening after evening, listening to her father chuckling, "Almost time to hear Amos and Andy on the radio. Don't know how they ever think up all those comical things." But—yes, she must do it; she couldn't be selfish.

After all, what was a mere year?

"You oughtn't to be so selfish and sacrifice them."

"I know."

"And they've been so patient with your notions about acting—even let you come here to this crazy place."

"What? What do you mean? 'Crazy'?"

"Why sure. Isn't it? Lot of grown-up people kicking around on the stage and kissing and Lord knows what-all instead of working for a living."

"So you don't call acting working?"

"Do you?"

"You don't think it's important like your work—like selling coffee percolators!"

"I certainly do not! That's what you could call a real Mission, and not kid yourself either—thousands of households getting better coffee——"

"And quicker!"

"—yes, and quicker, every morning! And you got no idea what sales resistance there is, these days. It takes guts and scientific training to make folks change their brand of percolator. It's a real man-sized job—not like painting your face and putting on a lot of fancy clothes and pee-rading around in front of a lot of women."

"I see your idea."

"Yes, and you'll adopt it, too, when you grow up and realize your responsibilities. Now, Bet, I'm no poet or no actor, but I guess you know I've always stuck to you like a limpet."

"What's a limpet?"

"Huh? Oh, you know. It's just a kind of expression. And as I say, you're never going to find any of these pretty boys that 'll be devoted to you, and forgive all your wild ideas, the way I do. I watched 'em tonight! Bunch of acrobats!"

"Charley Hatch! You look at those two men at that table! Andy Deacon, the big fellow, and Fletcher Hewitt—the Yankee—he's our stage manager. Either one of 'em could lick his weight in Joe Louises. Either one of 'em could build a set out of cardboard, and tour it carrying the set on his shoulders, and play with a fever in his bones. I suppose they're pretty boys! I suppose they're acrobats!"

"I didn't mean to get you sore. I just mean——"

"And what did you just-mean, may I ask!"

"Ah, don't get sore! I just mean things are going fine with me. I'll be making fifty, in less than two years, if you could wait. We could get a dandy little three-room flat, looking right out on the high-school grounds. And a convertible coop with a top that it goes up automatically when you push a button. You've seen 'em? They're dandy." Wistfully: "We could have an awfully nice time, driving around to Waterbury and Hartford and every place, on Sunday, and take a picnic lunch along—I'd get a thermos jug. We'd laugh a lot together. I don't laugh so much, now you're gone, Bet."

"Oh, I'm sorry, but—— Oh no, no, no!"

"Not good enough for you, eh? I hear that Deacon fellow has all kinds of dough. I suppose a fellow has to have a Park Avenue apartment and a chauffeur to interest you in him!"

"You see here! I expect to have a hall bedroom, myself, in New York——"

"So you *are* going there!"

"I certainly am . . . now! I expect to walk my feet off looking for a job at minimum. I expect to model or wait on table while I'm waiting for it. I'm going to act. You've made me see that, no matter if it makes me feel wicked and ungrateful and selfish, no matter even if I fail, I'm going to act. I know now!"

"Well, it's kind of too bad. You and I might've had a good time. Of course you aren't pretty, like Annie McLaut —remember her?"

"In school? Lots of teeth?"

"She's got the finest set of teeth in Sladesbury, let me tell you that! And she doesn't want to go helling around New York and Hollywood. She'd be glad to stay home and keep house. She thinks it's important to increase a sales quota. I think I'll see a lot of her. I don't guess you'll be sore, will you?"

"I certainly won't!"

"Then I guess she and I'll be married in the fall."

"Oh, that's splendid; that's perfectly splendid."

She tried to make it enthusiastic, but she had dropped ten thousand feet and landed on rock. She had discovered that she was much worse than wicked; she was dispensable. As Charley babbled about the wonders of Miss McLaut, apparently rather relieved at his freedom to enter a new slavery, Bethel was a very little girl whose family had forgotten to call her for Christmas dinner. It was all of five minutes before she could get up a self-respecting bad temper again.

"You say this Andrew Deacon is quite a husky guy," said Charley.

"Oh yes. He got his football letter at Yale, and he was Skull and Bones, too, and Phi Beta Kappa."

"And rich? Don't some guys have all the luck! I don't think he's good-looking like these fellows in the moom pictures, though."

"Of course not, thank heaven!"

"He ever make a pass at you?"

"Don't be absurd! Mr Deacon doesn't know I exist, except as the dark-eyed kid among the apprentices. He isn't sure whether my name is Bethel or Elizabeth—or Mehitabel."

"But your name isn't anything like Mehitabel."

"No—no—it isn't."

"Well, I guess it's all to the good he don't care for you."

"But he does!"

"But I thought you said——"

"Oh, never *mind* what I said!"

"Gosh, Bet, this play-acting life is certainly getting you hysterical. Well, never mind. I hear this Deacon fellow's mother lives in a regular high-toned castle, in Newport. He's out of our class entirely."

"Ours? Charley, I never realized it: you're perfectly

content to go on living on a side street in a side-street town!"

"Aren't you?"

"I've never thought much about it. But I guess there's no position in the world that I won't demand—if I can earn it."

"You're going to let yourself in for a lot of trouble."

"I hope so!" She was exuberant. "Yes. I hope so."

Andy and Fletcher Hewitt were leaving; Fletcher stopped by their table and spoke to Charley:

"I envy you for being an old friend of Bethel. We're very proud of her. I don't believe she knows it herself—she'll probably scratch me for calling her a good Puritanical influence—but I assure you, Mr Hatch, she's the kind that keeps us all working harder and drinking less and going to bed earlier."

Charley—her Charley, who so recently had been nothing but the scrubby little boy next door—answered condescendingly: "Glad to hear that. Guess it's pretty hard to go straight and take care of your health when you associate with a lot of crazy actors that stay up all night."

"You make me sick!" said Bethel.

But Fletcher answered Charley with gravity: "Yes, it is. The stage is a good dream, but I long for a little reality sometimes. Good night."

"Any time you're in Sladesbury, just drop in and see me—the Flamolio sales offices," said Charley.

"Oh, thank you, that's very kind of you," said Fletcher.

And what made Bethel glad to see the last of Charley, to feel free when he had gone, was his patronizing summary afterward:

"Well now, that's not such a bad guy, that Mr Fletcher. I wouldn't hardly think he was connected with the stage. He looks like a regular guy."

"Yes—yes, dear—I think he might be a regular guy. Will you forgive me, Charley? I'm so sleepy."

Only she felt that it was her youth, and everything she had loved and trusted, that was driving away that night with Charley Hatch.

Iris had not come in yet, at one in the morning—as Iris was likely not to come in, these days, now that the auriferous Pete Chew was fascinated by her. Bethel sat brooding:

"I would go home and stay—oh, not a year, but for months and months. But they wouldn't like it. They wouldn't like it any better than Charley did, when they find out how restless I really am.

"So I'm 'out of Andy's class!' Not good enough for him. I'm slightly crazy about you, Mr Deacon. I like your funny, bristly hair. I like your solid jaw. I would very much like to pat it—except that you would probably sock me. I think your voice is like a whole flock of organs all playing Bach suites. I like your childish grin. But a Merriday of Merriday Grange is as good as any powder-making Deacon and any Mrs J. Goddard Deacon and your Aunt Victoria Cabot Lodge Sedgwick Lowell Brewster Deacon, if there is one. I come from a very fine family, Mr Deacon, and my mother's brother is the best accordion player in the state of New Hampshire.

"Anyway, I'm not one of these brats that want to go on the stage just to escape from a beastly home, as Toni does, as Pete Chew does . . . as maybe Andy does. Dear Andy.

"Dear Andy. . . . I *am* so sleepy! . . . When I come in crying, as Gladys the maid—if I just stopped and stood with my mouth open, like an angry cat, not making any noise . . . I'll try that tomorrow evening. That ought to go over big."

17

FIVE MORE WEEKS of summer theater, and of school for Bethel: voice projection; building up a laugh; answering cues with not a tenth-of-a-second wait. In the last week, Miss Sample unwillingly hurled at her the laurel wreath: "Well, you may have a chance. You better try New York once, before you give up. You never can tell. I read the other day that the Shuberts are giving tests to an Eskimo."

And in odd hours she was sent back again to building scenery. Now that she had had to act before it, scenery was no longer a stupid mass of mechanism but a living part of the action.

Toni, Iris, Doc Keezer could not see why an actor should know anything about scenery. Even Walter Rolf grumbled, "No more need of it than there is of an author's learning printing and binding." But Bethel saw that the scene designer could ruin the actor—swamp him in flamboyant form and colors, or make a whole scene dreary by too drab a background—or help him by making it clear, as the curtain went up, just what sort of person he was, how rich or poor, how precise or slatternly.

And the actor could use the scenery; he could really look out of that window and see the Kentish downs there—though if he was not an actor, he would behold, through the paneless windows, nothing but Toni Titmus, in dirty linen overalls, sitting on a kitchen chair in front of a melancholy pile of furniture all on end, humped up over the play script, and passionately attacking gum.

The actor could, if the script demanded it and Roscoe had screamed at him enough times, remember to shut the door when he went out, so that it wouldn't be standing open when Lord Blenkinsop was to be discovered standing behind it. And it made a difference whether the door was so situated that the actor could slip off the couch and out, or had to walk between the two violent lovers. Even technical details mattered, perceived Bethel. You couldn't be properly gloomy in a darkened room if a streak of light was shooting in between two badly fastened flats. And, useful or not, she was plain curious, like a squirrel, about everything in the theater.

She learned how to make an entire flat; laying out the thin battens of white pine on the workbench (which, loving all technical terms and loving to be able to annoy Iris and Toni by using them, she was zealous to call a "template"), fitting the battens together—stiles on each side, top and bottom rail, the enchantingly named "toggle rail" in the center, with butt joints reinforced by corner blocks and corrugated fasteners; turning it over, stretching canvas (which she had learned to fireproof, with borax, sal ammoniac and water) across the frame, tacking it, gluing it, then on the back attaching the hardware, brace cleats, and lash cleats for joining flat to flat to make a complete wall.

She even learned to make mortise-and-tenon joints for the shutter of a doorframe unit, and that is the jewelwork, the higher metaphysics, of stage carpentry.

They did not make many new flats in a summer theater,

however; and Bethel was expert at washing off the glue-mixed paint from old flats and turning a section of a cottage wall into a satin panel for a château drawing room.

She liked the smell of new pine; the honest workshop floor, rough, scurfy with dried paint in a hundred faded tones of red and green and gray.

To citizens like Charley Hatch, who pictured all actresses as lying, in scandalous negligees, on chaise longues, to all the girls of her own age whose bibles were magazines about Hollywood, it would have been incomprehensible to see Bethel, in vile old basketball bloomers and a cardigan, with blue paint on the end of her nose, red paint on her knuckles, and a painful clot of glue in her tangled hair, noisily sawing a miter joint, yet all the while whistling "Old Man River," and looking up to see the dusk grow soft on the eel grass, the golden pools of water, at the edge of swamps across the bay.

Andy Deacon stopped by to wonder, "Aren't you working overtime?"

"I didn't know."

"Like it?"

"Lots."

"But why the passion for carpentry?"

She plumped down on the template, stared at him—the late light shone through his coppery brush of hair—and thought aloud:

"I honestly don't know. I just want to be able to do *anything* in the theater."

"That's—that's swell!" said her poet hero. "Maybe someday, pretty soon, I'll have a theatrical unit of my own, independent of the old-line producers, and if I do, you're the kind of kid I'll want."

And he looked at her as though he might actually know her again a month from now.

The season wound up on Saturday night, September 3rd, with a gargantuan beach picnic: with hot dogs, roasted corn, tamales and beer, and an enormous mulligan of beef and veal and chicken and goose and oysters, that had been boiling on the shore all day long, attended by Pete Chew—the best theatrical activity he had found yet.

There was a quarter-moon, and quarter-music: Johnny Meddock, the grounds custodian, on the accordion, and Butch Stevens, of the Lobster Pot, on the mouth organ. They were, unfortunately, more successful than that fairfaced young apprentice, Bruce Pasture, with his violin. It was no night for Brahms. They rioted, and sang "Coming Round the Mountain," and danced in long, wavering, handclasping lines along the sand, to conceal the melancholy of parting. They all confessed, tonight.

Harry Mihick and Anita Hill and four other apprentices were giving up the stage. (But they explained that it was only temporary.) Pete Chew was giving up and going to work for an uncle in Zanesville, Ohio, and Bruce Pasture was giving up and going to Paris (Left Bank) for practically the same reason: Bruce because the Nutmeg Players spoke such primitive American that he couldn't stand it; and Pete because they spoke such pedantic Oxonian that he couldn't understand it. None of them, you understand, were giving up because they hadn't proved to be very good actors.

Marian was to try Broadway for one year, but in her eyes you could see a vision of a summer theater back in the Nebraska cornfields. Toni Titmus was doubtful; she hinted that the Theater Guild was begging her to come in and see them for a part in the Lunt-Fontanne tour, but also that an extremely rich aunt was imploring her to spend the winter in Santa Barbara and that there she would practically take charge of all the Little Theater groups.

Five apprentices were definitely going to plunge into Broadway—they spoke, rather, as though they were enlisting in a revolution—and one of them, Walter Rolf, actually had a job . . . reading scripts in the office of a manager who had almost produced a musical show in 1932 and who still had a telephone number to prove that he was a manager.

As a surprise to them all—probably it was rather a surprise to her—Andy had invited his more-or-less fiancée, Joan Hinterwald, down from Newport. She appeared at a moment when they were particularly rackety. Three of the men, who had been having a moonlight swim, wore coats and old trousers over wet bathing suits; Anita Hill had dressed up as a woman of the French Revolution, and Doc Keezer as a clown, with red nose and flour cheeks; two girls were in evening clothes and two in voluminous white slacks; and all of them were dancing in a circle about Johnny Meddock, standing by the fire and playing "Pop Goes the Weasel" on his accordion. The bonfire was painting them into pirates and their molls.

They were aroused from their private frenzy by the hortatory sound of a motor horn, and out of her pale green roadster, airy in a pale green knitted suit, tripped Miss Hinterwald, waving amiably; the princess amused by her peasants.

They froze. They all became, instantly, free strolling players, the honorable company of rogues and vagrants, resentful of secure and prosperous outsiders, whether nobility or dusty shopkeepers. They could admit the cynical Johnny Meddock, worthy journeyman of broom and dust-pan, or Butch Stevens, oyster huckster, but not the too-well-bathed young lady from Newport. They forgot internal feuds; they became one harshly loyal company: Roscoe with Bethel, Mahala with the scornful Cynthia, Harry Mihick and Bruce Pasture, Iris Pentire and Maggie Sample. Arm in arm, they froze and stared at Joan—for whom Bethel was sorry, as she watched Joan freeze, too, and her white-kid cheeks become stiff and her eyes turn hostile.

But instantly Bethel was sorrier for Andy, who stepped out cheerily to greet the royal fair one, then felt around him the hatred of his companions for her. . . . It was *As You Like It* rewritten by Strindberg.

They were silent enough to hear him hail her, "Come join the dance. This is a very special dance of triumph over all critics and creditors."

"Oh, thanks, but I think you can do it very nicely without me. I'll just watch."

Miss Hinterwald perched on a decayed boat and, while they tried to resume the gaiety of the dance, she looked as though there were no doubt in her mind that they were all, including Andy, the loosest fools in Connecticut.

At suppertime, at one in the morning, sitting beside the wretched Andy, Joan nibbled one hot dog, but refused the noble mulligan, and immediately afterward walked toward her car and sourly waved good-by. But that was, for Andy, merely the beginning of trouble. He came back to Mahala, perched on a slightly wet rock, but Mahala did not welcome him.

"Hello, Maggie dear. Haven't had a chance to talk with you this evening," said Andy.

"Why should you, when you've had elegant Newport society yearning over you?"

"Poor Joan! She felt out of it. I wish you knew her better. She's really a good sport."

"She wouldn't care to know *me* better. Don't kid yourself, Andy, my bright young friend. I'm a poor working girl —I don't act to show off, as Joanie would, but to make a living. But you and that young woman are rich, so why do you try and patronize me?"

"Oh, please, Maggie, don't you go and get complicated, too."

"No. Of course. So sorry. Working girls have no right to get complicated. That's reserved for women that haven't anything else to do."

It went on. But in concentrated venom, in off-stage staginess, it was no better than the rival show that Bethel was watching over to her left. And that was the spectacle of Toni Titmus watching Pete Chew drawn by Iris Pentire's magnetic emptiness into a fascinated circle: the rowdy Cy

Fickerty, the bumbling Harry Mihick, Doc Keezer, who was old enough to know better, the morocco-bound Walter Rolf, who certainly did know better, and even the esthetic Bruce Pasture. They were all squatting on the sand at Iris's feet as she throned it on a noble beer barrel.

Tudor Blackwall was looking on in delicate reproach, but in Toni's watch over her straying Peter, there was nothing delicate whatever. She stood, arms akimbo, like a plump model of a pioneer woman facing a bear. She was unconscious of being observed, and when she had stood enough, her yell of "Pete! You come here!" was the pioneer woman communicating across five miles of prairie. Pete weaved over to her sheepishly. Whatever Toni said, it was punctuated by pounding her hand with her fist.

"Oh dear," sighed the lorn lone Bethel. "I wish I had anybody as much interested in me as Andy and Mahala are in each other, or Pete and Toni, or Iris and the Seventh Regiment."

Pete and Toni came to her arm in arm, and it was Pete who looked proud, as though this had been his idea all along, Toni who was shamed and halting.

"We want you to know—nobody else," caroled Pete. "The kid and I are going to middle-aisle it. I convinced her that our contribution to the stage will be to back shows and encourage actors. As soon as I can get the rich uncle in Zanesville to let us, we'll have a flat in New York and— wow!—will we catch ourselves a Time. We'll have a lot of actors and writers and bohemians. You must hang out there a lot."

"That's fine," said Bethel.

Fletcher Hewitt had been stage-managing the picnic. While the rest made suggestions and looked helpful, he stirred the mulligan, kept the hot dogs hot, bribed Butch Stevens, with forbidden whisky, to play his mouth organ, and soothed away five several quarrels between Roscoe Valentine and Cynthia Aleshire. But the food was gone now, at half past two, along with the moon, and Fletcher had coaxed the apprentices to lug the plates and pots up to the dormitory instead of waiting till dawn.

Mahala had gone off to bed. Sadly Bethel had seen Andy bid her good night—he so pleading, Mahala so patronizing. Why couldn't he pick someone more appreciative?

Fletcher wearily dropped on the sand beside Bethel, scratching up a little pile for a pillow, looking up at the stars, holding her hand casually, and speaking at his most casual and cool and calm.

"So, Beth, it's Commencement. When do you go to New York?"

"After a week or ten days home. You'll be on Broadway before I am."

"No, I won't be there at all. Beth! I'm going to quit the stage."

"You're what?"

"I can't face another winter of tramping from office to office, till the snow leaks in through the soles of your shoes, looking for a job. I don't care for making much money, but I do want to buy a few things for my mother—she's so little and sweet and pretty—and for you."

"Eh?"

"More and more, every day, watching you, I've decided you're extraordinarily like her, and then I knew that some-day you and I would be married."

"Eh?"

"Yes. You'll remember me when you're sick of hunting for glory."

"But I thought you felt the stage was sort of sacred to you and me."

"I do. And you're to have your shot at it. But I've done my bit. And when you're tired, you'll come back to me. You see, I'm really the hometown boy that every young actress has waiting for her—I'm him, and not this Charley Hatch you had here. Neighborhoods don't matter, houses next door don't matter, playing with the same air rifle as kids doesn't matter, *time* doesn't matter. It's all imagination. In these ten weeks I've become your old schoolmate, that lent you the bandanna handkerchief when your nose bled at the party, haven't I?"

"Yes but."

"Good. And I know what I'm going to do now. Mother and I have been phoning. I'm going to lease a grand old inn up between Millerton and Lakeville; swell summer business, and I think if it's run right—and you know I *do* run that kind of thing right?"

"Oh yes."

"I think I can keep it full all winter. And someday I'm going to try and turn the big old stable there into a first-rate summer theater. So you see? We won't be giving up the holy cause! And anyway, Mammy and you and I will be there, and we'll have a good serene life. Sound like fun?"

"Yes but."

"But what?"

"Darling, it's hard to tell you."

"But you do like me."

"Oh yes, Fletcher."

"You know that I think you have the most beautiful eyes—for a skinny chick—and the most graceful walk in the world? And incidentally, if that interests you, a shining soul. And you'd like me better and better. I think you could depend on me."

"Darling, I just can't."

"Afraid of my mother complex?"

"I don't believe so."

"In love with Andrew the Anvil King, Galahad the Grail Hound?"

"Oh, what would be the use of *my* caring for him?"

"Plenty! He's not such a fool, even if he does let emotional usurers like Mahala tie him up. He'll wake up someday to the fact that you're solid—solid silver—solid gold. Mahala's plated. He'll really see you. Would you be in love with him then?"

"I might be. But I don't think it's Andy, at all. I've always wanted the stage. I can't imagine myself without it."

"But I told you, we'll try to make a summer theater. Maybe we'll even do some exciting experimental things. I know you and I are the kind that could—and you'd be surprised how sound Mammy's advice is—she's the best sport —of course you are, too."

"No! I want training. Professional training. The hardest kind. I mustn't fool myself. In the theater I'm of the mental age of three. I want to have some real hard-boiled director give me the devil. I want to do one-night stands. I want to act twenty different roles in a year."

"Well, judging from the number of shows that close in four days, now, you'll have a chance to. And then maybe you'll be willing to come back to hometown boy, that'll be waiting. I've never once kissed you. I'm going to!"

He did. She was rather astonished.

As the older actors began to make home-going motions of yawning and kicking at the sand, Roscoe Valentine chased Iris off her beer-barrel throne, climbed on it, and spoke:

"Boys and girls, this is our last feast of unreason together till next summer. I now descend from my temporary grandeur as director and become an eccentric old gentleman toying with an arty magazine and a gilded theateria in Boston. But I want to tell all of you, *all* of you, that if I have ever seemed to ride you, if I have ever been temperamental or unreasonable, it's only been because I love you, and love the theater, and have wanted to wed these twain and—God bless you all!"

Maggie Sample, standing beside Bethel, muttered, "Wouldn't you know he'd manage to get the curtain? I wish I'd thought of that. Anyway, Merriday, here's your chance at me. I'm no longer your loving teacher, and you can get back at me for all my grouches. Shoot."

It is possibly a little sad, but Bethel didn't even hear her.

She was looking at the passing Andy, with firelight in his hair. Andrew the Anvil King, Andy the Grail Hound, Andy the Paladin.

Everybody drifted away. Bethel, in her dormitory room, now light with dawn, listened to Iris snorting that she was sure *she* didn't want Pete Chew hanging around her and Toni could *have* him, for all she cared.

Bethel decided that she couldn't sleep. She crept downstairs, stole a horrible cold griddle cake and wolfed it, and slipped out to the beach again. And there, solitary, looking out to the dreary dishwater of morning sea, his back to her, squatted with hands on knees, was Andy.

She came up to him cautiously. He looked up and snorted, "Hello, kitten. What you doing up?"

"I couldn't get to sleep."

"Neither could I."

"Andy! What's the trouble? You look unhappy."

"Hell, I am! I'm sick of running around with garlands in my hair yelping that I'm artistic and happy. It's all a mess."

"People?"

"Eh? Oh, I don't mean my lady-loves. Mahala and Joan are good girls—though I do sometimes wish that they could take out their undoubted powers in work, as apparently you can, Beth, instead of in getting their little feelings hurt. But it's not that. It's career. Work. Art. Ambition. Purpose. Looking at the apprentices tonight, I've been thinking: nice bunch of kids, but what have they got out of this summer? Picnickers, that's what they are—that's what I am. What have Roscoe and I done? Good plays, but not one new one in tryout—not even one unusual one, not one profound characterization in the acting, mine or anybody's. I've been doing my parts on my head. That Zed Wintergeist that came up here from Dory Playhouse said we were Boy Scouts. He was right. The genial Mr Andy Deacon! Why does he waste his time so, Bethel? Why does he?"

She patted his hand, and together they looked out as a young rosy light quivered on the slaty waves.

"Andy, I've learned to relax here, and feel at home on the stage, and I learned it from watching you, so sure and so easy, and not from listening to Roscoe shrieking."

"Maybe both you and I need more shrieking at. But—— You really have enjoyed it?"

"Incredibly."

"I'm glad."

And already, with the rising flood of light, the spirits of the mercurial Andy were rising. He rose, lifting her up, and cried, "We have left undone the things we ought to have done, but this coming season, we'll be swell! On to New York, kitten! We'll have our names in electric lights there before spring! Absolutely!"

She wanted to wail, "But I'll never see you, once you get to New York." Violently she kept herself from it, as he chanted on:

"You saw *Our Town,* didn't you? Remember the end:

" 'Everybody's resting in Grover's Corners. Tomorrow's going to be another day. You get a good rest, too. Good night.' "

18

R<small>ED—THE COLOR OF REVOLUTION,</small> the color of anger, of angry eyes, of vigorous dawn and wild sunsets, of battle smoke, of rubies on the breast of courtesans—red, acid red, carmine, crimson, scarlet, madder, vermilion, flaunting rose.

From the window of her minute room, high in a hotel-for-women in the East Fifties in Manhattan, Bethel saw the whole welter of city turn red as the evening rain began. In the country the wet lonely night would have dissolved in shifting gray, but New York, in the late-October rain, was the pit of a volcano, and more insistent, and more dreadful.

Atop the white mountainous cliff of the R.C.A. Building, in Radio City, a crimson aeroplane-beacon was rotating, crossing a white shaft of light that shot straight up to the illimitable heavens, to be lost in the orbit of the farthest star. The sloping top of the General Electric Building (not of the DeMedicis or Plantagenets or Barbarossas were these high castles, but of the lords of radio and electric heating), like a jewel casket of the giants, turned from alternate crimson to pallid gold.

Backing these prickly towers, the light from Broadway was a dome of writhing fire, until, unwarning, a menacing billow of fog enveloped the burning sky, and the fantastic sanguine spire of the distant Empire State Building was wiped clean out. In the streets below her the red glare still pierced the melancholy rain. On the wet pavement the motors whirred more loudly, the taillights mimicked the scarlet of the stop lights, and when Bethel looked to the left, to Lexington Avenue, she was uneasy at the flaming neon signs aggressively thrust out above shop windows.

Ten thousand cherry-lighted windows piled up in tier on tier in office buildings, and behind them were a hundred thousand windows unlit, and weary with memory of the day's toil. It was a mighty, proud and terrifying city, an Orient city in red lacquer lit with red lights, a crimson barbaric city, and it was all hers—to conquer or be crushed.

It was after ten; she had napped for three hours of the evening, and she was hungry in a thin, petulant way, and her head ached, her legs felt shaky from want of food. But she sat on by the window unmoving.

She couldn't rouse the energy to go all the long way down the hotel corridor, down in the elevator, whose cheery young woman pilot would with depressing inevitability remark, "Pretty wet tonight," out through a lobby explosive with young women being emptily merry with dreary male visitors, down the soaking street to a fish-stinking hole of a cheap restaurant. She was afraid to go out. She couldn't, not again today, face the heartless, anonymous, moving human detritus on the sidewalks. She was lonely, up here in this bright coop, but she was less lonely than scared.

Her little room was a miracle of compression. It must have been planned by an architect trained in designing prison cells, folding picnic baskets, and combination vanity sets and cigarette cases. To enable it to offer what was known in the circle of girl job seekers as "a good respectable address on the East Side, just off Park Avenue," at only ten dollars a week (without food; jobless girls didn't need food;

just addresses and silk stockings and a kind word), the
builders had imaginatively got the furnishings of a two-
room apartment into the space of a hall bedroom.

Everything conceivable to the genius of American
gadgetry was here, but reduced below tolerable human size,
and fitted together without six square inches of the waste
space that could be used only for walking, relaxing, dreaming or any other merely human need: bed, reading lamp and
bedside table, upholstered armchair, combination bookcase
and desk and radio and bureau, and a dressing table so
elegant that in the advertisements it would be referred to as
"milady's." And a bathroom. It was nearly possible to sit in
the tub and reach out and write a letter, open the hall door,
open the window or answer the telephone.

It was Modern enough for any Merriday. Only, daily,
Bethel was becoming less Modern and more insistent about
getting an old-fashioned job on some old-fashioned stage.

She was daily more timid about her dream, phonograph-
engendered, of appearing not in the bare, pine-platform
simplicity of Grampion, but on a great stage, jewel-lighted,
lofty as Canterbury, with Noel Coward and Yvonne Prin-
temps. Now she wanted any stage, with anyone.

Her timidity and tiredness won over her undoubted common sense, and for the third time in ten days she did not
go out to dinner at all but, after nibbling at a chocolate bar
and drinking a glass of water from the tap in the tile-and-
nickel bathroom, she sat down to type the script of Tudor
Blackwall's play—and that script typing was the nearest she
had yet come in New York to being associated with anything theatrical.

At Grampion, Tudor Blackwall, second leading man, had
never paid her any attention beyond murmuring, "How are
you, blessed?" and borrowing a match. But he was the first
of the Nutmeg Players that she encountered in New York.
She ran into him at lunch at the Olde Roanoke Drug Store,
at Broadway and Forty-sixth Street, which is the chief club,

restaurant, news bureau and matrimonial agency of all young actors looking for jobs.

He invited her to his flat for dinner. She had heard about the horrors of going alone to a man's flat, but Tudor seemed to her extraordinarily safe, and she took a chance.

He cooked dinner for her—a very good dinner, and very well cooked: onion soup and kidney stew and profiterolles with chocolate sauce. She discovered that he, who looked twenty-five and prosperous, with his sleek waistcoats and shoes fitting like gloves, was thirty-five and very hard up indeed, and that a part of his lovely glass-smooth black hair was a toupee.

He laughed about it all, and told her how unsuccessful he was, as though they were two girls together, and admitted that the silky superciliousness with which he had treated the apprentices at Grampion had been to keep these innocents from discovering that he was sickeningly uncomfortable with all strangers, and that his average yearly earning was two thousand dollars.

And he didn't borrow money.

She knew enough now to be prepared for that; she had even done hasty calculations indicating that five dollars was all she could afford. But he did read her a play he had just finished—he finished it every year at about this time—and he begged her to copy it for him.

It was a good play. It always has been, and when it is written by Noel Coward, S. N. Behrman, Philip Barry, or Samson Raphaelson, it even gets produced, to considerable glory. The hero was Cecil Gisthorpe, and he was a playwright, and he was witty, and he didn't really care a hoot when his girl was taken from him by a flannel-mouthed radical—but also witty—named Steve Grimston. There were cocktails and cigarettes in it, and an eccentric maid—also witty.

Bethel thought it was "simply lovely," and said so, and Tudor said she was the nicest kid he had met for years and they would be great friends, and she said yes, and he bowed over her hand, and she took the script back to her hotel to copy it.

That was a week ago, and she had almost finished.

One of the few things on which her father had ever insisted in high school was that she should learn typing, and by the touch system. She blessed him now—though that was nothing sensational, for she usually did bless him. She was aware, after these six weeks of job hunting in New York, that she might not find any theatrical job whatever this year; that if she did get one, it would be an accident; and that she could not endure her family's going on stinting themselves in order to send her twenty-five dollars a week.

Probably she would have to be a stenographer till her dramatic miracle happened . . . though by now she was beginning to see that the employers of stenographers, too, were not excited by the chance of hiring young ladies with B.A. degrees, nice ankles and modest manners.

If she was going to get an office job, she told herself, she had to be *good* (not meaning it, apparently, in any moral sense, but only in reference to words-per-minute, a memory for telephone numbers, and such unpoetic slave virtues). Very well, she would be good!

Her typing was already tolerable, and her vocabulary was unusual, she concluded, after talking in employment bureaus and the anterooms of offices with candidates for stenography who seemed rather proud of themselves as exhibits of the renowned American free public school system if they could type anything so flawless as "We acknowledge yours of the 5th instant and wourd asure you that we are shiping yours consinement at once to Niajerrer Falls."

An hour a week, she was taking shorthand lessons with her one lone hometown acquaintance in urban wilds—her mother's cousin, a spinster secretary from Sladesbury, who was always parched with longing to hear from Bethel the details of the glamorous, naughty parties to which, as an actress, she must be going. And to practise the black art of shorthand, Bethel took down the free lectures in the schools, and sermons and political speeches on the radio.

Her back stung at last from typing, and she arose from the aphorisms of Tudor Blackwall's script and achingly undressed and crawled into the narrow sheath of her bed.

She was, normally, a cheerful person, and no hermit. She told herself, as she twitched into shallow sleep, that she must look up the other Grampionites here. She had not looked them up; she didn't want to impose on them. She had had one letter from Pete and Toni, now married in Zanesville and married to Zanesville. Toni talked airily of "hitting the Big Town in a big way this winter," but she also wrote so familiarly of "her" riding master and of the country-club dances that Bethel felt that all of Toni's dramatic genius, all that talent for dancing the rhumba and the Lambeth Walk (the favorite mumbo rite of late 1938), all that ability to remain awake at three A.M. even after eight highballs, all that emotion-colored memory which enabled her to recognize Franchot Tone and Loretta Young and Jessie Royce Landis and W. C. Fields on the street and to recall at what hour Edgar Bergen could be heard on WEAF, those uncommon glories of smooth knees and rounded breast, were lost to the artistic world forever, and what was Broadway's tragedy was Zanesville's delighted gain.

Once Bethel had talked to Marian Croy on the telephone and, hesitatingly, had refused to share a room with her.

Bethel had a formless, confused notion that it would be better to read plays (borrowed from the Fifty-seventh Street Branch Library, the young actor's British Museum) than to listen to a boiling of Marian's friends chattering all evening about: "I got it straight from a man that knows John Mason Brown personally, and he says Jed Harris is going to put on a radical revue, and they'll be hiring forty-two girls for bits and walk-ons right away."

Once, in the Olde Roanoke's mammoth basement restaurant, Bethel had seen Iris Pentire, alone, delicately nibbling at Blue Plate Luncheon №5 (chilled tomato stuffed with egg salad, garnish of whole olives and radishes, rolls, butter, and beverage, 45 c.), and waiting to ignore some young male as soon as one should notice her enough for her to ignore him.

Of Mahala Vale and Doc Keezer and Maggie Sample, she had heard nothing whatever; of Andrew Deacon, nothing beyond a note, in Leonard Lyons's column in the New York *Post,* that Andy, with his mother and Miss Joan Hinterwald, had been staying at a Great Neck château, and telling some very funny stories about summer theaters.

Flushing as she lay there trying to sleep, Bethel hoped that none of the funny stories had been about her.

She was out on her gaggingly familiar round of job hunting at ten next morning, after the actress's toilet of bathing and powdering and manicuring and hairdressing and choosing between the blue silk frock and the gray suit, and after saving ten cents by having only orange juice, toast and nice refreshing hot water for breakfast. (She was young rather than fundamentally imbecile.)

She walked to the office of Equity, the actors' organization, and, with a milling of other girl crusaders, studied the bulletin board with its notices of who was casting, who was organizing a road company.

She was not a member, and not supposed to intrude there, but as she couldn't join Equity till she had a contract, and as she probably never would get a contract till she was a member of Equity, such trespass as hers was tolerated. The paradox which ruled all young actresses was that you couldn't get a job if you hadn't the experience, and you certainly could not get experience till you had a job, and so you just weren't going to *get* a job.

Bethel started another day of high artistic hopes with the usual matutinal conclusion that there were no jobs left in the world.

She walked—every dainty young flower of the stage walks far enough every day to disable a hairy infantryman—to the palatial offices of Hochwohlgeboren & Schnitzel. In the outer room was a sign "No casting," and a twitter of young ladies who were trying to ignore the sign. She walked to the offices of Sam & Rufus Kitz, and got no farther than a cold-hearted girl reception clerk who gabbled, "Wha's name any-experience cnleaveyrtelephone number." She walked to the offices of Thorncroft, Inc., where a graceful young man mur-mured "Cast's all full for *California Cavalcade* except big rangy blondes, and that lets you out, darling." She walked to the office of Cyril Sassoon Solobar, and found that Mr Solobar was his own secretary and office boy. A round man, bald in layers, he sat hunched at a scarred desk, held her hand, pinched her side and whined, "No, I haven't got the script of *Towers of Teheran* yet. The author's holding out on me. How's for lunch, babe?" She walked to the office of a new agent of whom a girl waiting at Kitz's had said that he took beginners and got them nice jobs.

He didn't.

And now, at one-thirty, she walked for her one compara-tively substantial meal of the day to the Olde Roanoke Drug Store.

Forty years ago, two bustling pharmacists from Maine named Rowen and Oaks, opening a drugstore in the wilder-ness at Broadway and Forty-sixth, were moved to be facetious, to pretend that they were from the flower of what they called Ole Virginny, and to combine their names in the designation Ole Roanoke.

It is an urban version of the Rex Pharmacy of Sladesbury, and, even in alien New York, it is as American as flap-jacks.

It still has a kingly trade in perfumes and soaps and face powder, and a small rush of prescriptions, but its glories are the lunch counter upstairs, where the least prosperous of would-be actors deceive their miserable stomachs with sand-wiches and jumbo malted milks while they listen anxiously to the news over the theatrical grapevine, and, downstairs, the vast restaurant, which fills the basement floor, where, in daily hundreds, the not-quite-so-impoverished actors meet to look at each other, to show off their new costumes and make-ups, to hear the labor-market news and subordinately to eat.

The basement room itself is of battleship gray, and the ceilings bristly with water pipes, but the proprietors have craftily covered the walls with mirrors, so that, as they talk, the young things can stare at their images, study their own experiments in the Arch Smile, the Appealing Smile, the Wistful Regret. They eat in booths along the wall, or at tables elbow to elbow out on the floor. The waitresses, showy in white-and-cherry uniforms with green berets, are hostesses, comforters, reconcilers and free employment agents.

Alone, rather alarmingly filling up on the "Hot Spot Special: salisbury steak, julienne carrots, whipped potatoes, lemon chiffon pie, coffee, 40 c.," Bethel watched and, since they were at the next table and not at all shy about their humor, listened to one "Bunk," a young man with gray, double-breasted jacket, green, purple and brown checked shirt, and red plaid handkerchief, "Ally," a girl with a wolf jacket and a tall, cone-shaped lettuce-green hat with royal blue streamers setting off a chartreuse-colored dress that disdained her knees, and "Peg," a child of nineteen with yellow hair to her shoulders and a cartwheel straw hat hung with a black ribbon on the back of her neck.

Bethel, in gray suit and frilly jabot exquisitely ironed (by Bethel, in her bathroom), felt a cool and collegian superiority to these plush flowers until she remembered hearing a handsome girl in black, at the Roanoke, snarl, "I'm a B.A. of Vassar and an M.A. of Columbia and I'd swap 'em both for a two-line bit in a show that opened in Cain's Warehouse."

"Gee, you got a lovely tan, Bunk," said Ally. "Where you been? Steal somebody's Alpine lamp?"

"No. I'm an actor, b' God. Been stealing applause!"

"Quit it or I'll wake up."

"Fact. I've been out on the Borsch circuit all summer. Nineteen dollars a week and coffee and cakes and a nice bed over the garage—three in the bed. We had a swell bill: the six dirtiest scenes from the six dirtiest plays in the last six years. Symbolism, heh? We played a seven-hotel circuit, one a night. I can't kick. I come back engaged to the daughter of the biggest kosher butcher in Schenectady—if I can find her address—and I got a swim every day."

Bunk studied Ally in a bright, sexless, beaming way and jeered, "I see you've got new lashes and a new mouth."

"Yeah, my complexion's been bad, so I've been giving up make-up for a while and concentrating on my eyes and mouth. Maybe some producer will see me here and say, 'I never knew Ally had a mouth like that. We ought to be able to use a mouth like that for something!'"

From Peggy, jeering, "You know what he'll use the mouth for now that you've gone coy and got your hat out of the way of kissing."

From Bunk to Peg, "That 'll be all from you, you heel. I swear to God, you *like* appearing with the Y.W.C.A. non-professional groups! Go on back home!"

From Peg, "Not me! I was there all summer. In Elmira. God, was I bored! The folks had a fit if I wanted to sleep after ten. They wanted me to play tennis and marry a lawyer—calls hisself a lawyer!—he's a clerk in a law factory with six partners! So I come back looking for a job where I can prove what bums Kate Hepburn and Tallulah are. But I dunno. My big trouble is I'm too individual a type—a marked ingénue and yet sophisticated. My sister's got more sense than me. She's taken up Physical Ed. She's already got a job. She's safer than I am, in this lousy theater racket. I dunno. Yesterday I got to see this bum Mack Pzister that calls himself a producer. He's new to the show business. I think he makes his dough out of some kind of mine promotion."

"He's a heel. He's an exhibitionist," said Ally. "It peps up his dirty little snow-white personality to think he's a real the-at-ri-cal producer. He just lu-loves the dray-ma, and see-ing he can't act and he can't direct and he can't write and he's too lazy and dumb to shift scenery, that makes him a producer, the sweet potato that puts up the money—only I understand Mack ain't got any money either. I know for a fact, six times in the last two years he's sent out a call for casting and interviewed about a thousand bright young things and kept 'em coming back, and nobody ever heard anything more about the show. Did he make a pass at you, Peg?"

"Huh? Don't be silly. And I could almost like Mack. He's got such a cute mustache. Of course he's got a wife and children. Maybe she's cold. I dunno. You been in summer stock, haven't you, Ally?"

"Yuh. Up at Whale Hollow, upstate, and did I get a raw deal! I knew that director, Carv Bledaud, was a heel. Oh, last spring, I was nuts about it. My first real job. Remember I came into the Roanoke here yelling 'Today is a very big day. Today is a day that will go down in history. The history of the theater will star this date along with the death of Joe Jefferson and the birth of Shirley Temple.' But all the time my intuition told me it was the bunk. When my intuition tells me something, I always know it's right, but I'd do *any-thing*—except let a lot of screwballs make love to me—to get on the stage. Well, I got up there, and I found Bledaud was a washout. He never read clear through a script before he started 'directing,' and there were only 278 seats in the house, and the stage is so small that when they put on a chariot race, they use carpet sweepers. Oh, I stuck it out, but I never had a part more 'n six sides. I was disgusted. . . . Where you living, Bunk?"

"Three of us got a furnished room with a kitchenette, in the West Fifties."

"I'm going to stick it out at the Y.W.C.A., though all the bosses there try to persuade you to go back home to your beautiful home in Scranton and marry the boy friend. *My* beautiful home's next to the Adventist Church—you can hear 'em singing all Saturday morning, when you want to sleep—and the boy friend is a grocer, but even if my folks lived in a penthouse, I'd stick it out here. Nobody can keep me from succeeding on the stage! If I get just a little more busted, maybe I can get on the Federal Theater Project. They don't take you there for how well you can act but for how badly you can earn a living. But anyway, I'll stick it if it takes ten years."

Bunk half rose. "I got to get out and chase a job. I'm an actor. As beautiful as you two dolls are, I'll never make a dime here."

Said Peg, "Don't take all the jobs today. Keep a few for another day. You coming back from the Borsch circuit with all that dough saved up! I knew you were in the chips the minute I saw you. You had your face washed and your hair combed."

Bunk settled down again and ordered a coffee. "Saved up? Listen! The minute my old man found I had a job, he started panhandling . . ."

Bethel knew that the three would stay here all afternoon, talking of nothing but the stage—nothing but their particular chances of positions on the stage; that they would be back here at their café of futility tomorrow and the next day, next year and the year after, till they vanished into that undiscoverable limbo where, dead or still living, float all the young actors and novelists and prize fighters and promoters of billion-dollar sun-power plants whose exhibitionism was too great for their talent and whose talent was too great for farming.

Bethel had been reared to the solid American Protestant belief in the glory and efficacy of human will power. If anyone wanted enough to do anything, he would unquestionably do it, and his resoluteness was somehow very beautiful, even if his ambition was to devour the moon or become the Queen of Sheba.

Every minute, among the young things seated in rows in managers' waiting rooms, Bethel heard them bravely and just a bit noisily vowing, "I will make good on the stage, and nothing can stop me."

That was inspiring. That was how we built the Union Pacific.

But she saw that a number of those who were most courageously willing to give-up-everything for their careers believed that the giving-up-everything automatically extended to their families and friends, and that it was the natural duty of their fathers to go on sending them funds and of their barest acquaintances to go on "lending" them money, while, year on year, they sat in restaurants and enjoyed their artistic martyrdom.

This was all very confusing to Bethel. Was she a real worker, or just another soft little faker in a funny hat? Um. Well, she'd prove herself. She wouldn't forever let her father go on supporting her. She'd type or wait on table or model or *something*. Meanwhile it depressed her to see that there were hundreds of authentic, nonboasting aspirants who seemed to be as good as she. If she ever did have her chance on the stage, it would be mostly by accident.

A horrible dislocation, this present theatrical situation. No wonder the young Communists at the Olde Roanoke were able to be eloquent! For every actual stage job, there were ten brilliant young actors being considered, a hundred who ought to be considered, and a thousand heartbroken youngsters, ranging from good to atrocious, who thought they ought to be. And when someone out of the thousand, anyone, finally was signed for the role, all the other nine hundred and ninety-nine wailed that this was the blackest example of favoritism, incompetence and sickening bad taste in all the history of the arts.

Why, she sharply asked herself, did she go on being huddled in this herd, as just one of the thousand?

As she paid her check and wearily climbed up from the

basement, Bethel decided that she would never go to the Olde Roanoke again.

There was a standard debate among the job hunters as to whether it was better to try to see the producers in the morning or in the afternoon. Bethel did both. This afternoon she knocked at the granite portals of two more theatrical tombs, then turned to that new heaven and high ambition, that putative new bed and bread and butter of the young actor: the radio.

To apply for tests for broadcasting, that ethereal art whereby the sweetness of the human voice is wafted to the listening seraphim ten trillion light-years away, she went not to a star-capped and venerable master of the air waves but to young men, in advertising agency offices, who would —just possibly—tell older men in the agency that, look, here's a kid that prob'ly she's no good but we might let her have a test.

She sat across a desk from a young man with eyeglasses and premature baldness.

"Come back in about a week. There might be something doing on the Cadgbury Health Salts Hour. How about coming out for a little dinner with me some night, Miss Dairyvale?" said the young man.

By now there was less pious horror than ritual boredom in her refusal.

She could not afford to, but at six she stopped in at a chain restaurant, where doughnuts were served on Medici tessellation, to have tea and toast, and to ask her waitress about a restaurant job.

"You got to have experience, and there's a long waiting list, anyway," said the young woman.

Back home in her hotel, Bethel asked of the girl elevator runner, "How do you go about getting a job like yours?"

"Busted, dearie? Then you better go home. No chance on the elevators. There's only a few buildings in town use girls

—mostly hospitals and medical buildings—and when a girl leaves, she usually gets the job handed on to her lady friend. And of course you got to have experience before you can run an elevator," said the operator, as the floors slipped downward past them.

"How do you get experience running an elevator if you don't get a chance to *run* an elevator?" sighed Bethel.

The young woman looked at her with dark suspicion. "I don't know. But that's the rule."

She was safely home again. She wasn't sure what had happened to her artistic integrity this day, but she did know that her feet were sore.

Again she slept till after nine in the evening.

She woke up and sat waiting for the telephone to ring. She imagined Walter Rolf, Marian Croy, even Iris Pentire calling her up, inviting her to some vague, exciting theatrical party; she imagined Pete and Toni, unexpectedly arrived in town, demanding that she come to Twenty-One or Sardi's. She was so lonely that she was frightened. The sound of the city blurred in one relentless mumbling.

She forced herself to get up, pat her face with witch hazel, go downstairs past the elevator girls, the pages, the clerks, who, she fancied, were suspicious of her idleness, and walk ten blocks to a Chinese restaurant, where for thirty cents you could dine lavishly on chow mein and rice and tea and spicy fruits floating in pale syrup. But she fled back to the refuge of her bright lone room.

Thrice a week she went to the Class in Acting conducted by that lanky Polish demon, Sol Gadto; an echo of the Group Theater discipline, with memories of Stanislavski. The students had most of them been inconspicuously on the stage already; they were afire with the purpose of great acting; they looked down on the Olde Roanoke loafers almost as much as the Olde Roanoke free souls looked down on their father and brothers.

The class cost five dollars a week. Bethel could not have afforded it, but Mr Gadto, a theatrical fanatic who lived on brandy, hope and rich widows, told her with jeers and objurgations that she could pay him when she had her first engagement.

Gadto had assigned to her the part of Laura, the girl in *Men in White* who could not keep her lover. Bethel went through the lines with spirit, trying to reveal Laura—spoiled, a good sort, demanding, filled with a plain decent honesty. Bethel was rather proud of the gestures she had devised to illustrate the character: the airy circles with her cigarette holder when at heart she was agonized; the mouth upturned in luring.

That red-eyed buzzard Sol Gadto, as he listened to her, curled in his chair in their bare rehearsal hall, with both elbows against his belly, as though it ached, moving only to tap his teeth with a lax right hand in which drooped a cigarette.

When she was finished, he droned:

"That's a little better. But you're getting into a lot of fancy little movements that decorate action—oh yes, they decorate it, all right, and make it interesting—if you tied a pink ribbon on an archbishop's nose, it would make him interesting enough.

"How often have I got to tell you that every single movement of your whole body has got to grow out of your realization of what the character is feeling and thinking at that moment, and not for the sake of doing something? Now I want you to go and sit down and do what's sometimes called 'sense memory.' Put yourself back in some moment when you wanted to keep some boy and you felt at once sore and like a fool. Quit trying to act for the next ten minutes and put yourself in charge of that emotion. And sit still while you do it."

Bethel could not recall any incident in which she had been a lady left and lorn. She had been rather glad when Charley

Hatch had blithely turned her down for a girl with teeth. She thought of Fletcher Hewitt; she realized that she had not answered, for a week now, a letter in which Fletcher had told of painting their dilapidated inn, building bookcases, putting in plumbing. It was idiotic that she couldn't adore Fletcher, the while she worshiped at the shining feet of an Andrew Deacon who considered her merely a little chit to be kind to. In six weeks now he would have forgotten her name.

Andy . . . His small-boy grin. His rigid, President Coolidge insistence that Roscoe Valentine pay the theater bills and answer all the letters. His bellow as he swam out through the tide rips, the sun-stroked hair on his arms like golden mail. His patience with that gilded shrew, Mahala. His beautiful coarseness in *Fumed Oak* and his beautiful gallantry in *Tovarich*. And she had never heard from him—there was no reason why she ever should hear from him—if she could just once see him at a restaurant . . .

Gadto was calling her out of her trance, "Let's try it again."

She trotted up on the small platform, and it was no stage character, composed of paper and typewriter ink, that she was playing this time, but a muted, suffering woman who would have given anything to blow up in hysteria, to throw inkwells at the admirable young doctor, to yell, to tear out somebody's eyes . . . maybe Mahala's.

The director said "Good," and for Mr Sol Gadto, that was practically raving.

Mr Gadto lived in the "Village," and she returned uptown—to the Olympian groves of theatrical managers' offices and bus stations and Italian restaurants and hand laundries and grimy hotels—by subway. She was fascinated by the medley of people in the car: old Negro women with bundles, well-dressed, intelligent-looking young Negro women of the new urban colonies, old men mumbling into beards, resentful boys.

It tormented her that she could never know them, find out what they were like; that this young woman across the car, with her shocked, staring eyes, would in three minutes be leaving the car and be shut off from her forever by the iron doors and the relentless speed of the departing subway train. If she could better understand that woman, she could act all unhappy women, forever.

Here was a whole maddening city of people that she wanted to act—whom maybe she really could act—if she could ever get up on any stage to act anybody at all.

She lunched at a Coffee Pot Restaurant, where the only guest suggesting the theatrical profession was a sandwich man. In defiance of her budget she had bought an afternoon paper and, having been deprived of stage gossip for an entire four hours now, she turned feverishly to the "News of the Theaters" column.

Heading the column was the announcement, written with typical New York contempt for all places outside Manhattan:

Andrew Deacon, who last winter was the leading man and co-director in *The Best of Times,* is organizing a touring company to play *Romeo and Juliet* in modern dress. This is believed to be the first time that the play has been thus costumed. Mr D. indicates that he is going to use a number of his last summer's associates in the Grampion straw-hat aggregation of which he was co-producer. He is uninformative as to when he will attack Broadway, but he has definite bookings in a score of culture depots in the mail-order territory.

With a comic vision of Iris Pentire losing her Mona Lisa calm and Mahala her Ritz dignity and Tudor Blackwall his sleek superiority as, like herself, they dashed for bus and taxi, to reach Andy Deacon, Bethel left her steak sandwich unfinished and galloped to her hotel and to her telephone.

19

SHE TELEPHONED to the small hotel of Marian Croy.
No answer. She scrabbled through memoranda, found Iris
Pentire's address, telephoned again, and again no answer.
For weeks she had kept from going near Walter Rolf and
the small office of the small producer for whom he was
reading very small playscripts, lest Walter think she was
asking him to help her, but now she threw away her delicacy.

Walter was very kind; on the telephone he even said
something—something you couldn't quite pin down—about
their having dinner together; but he didn't know where
Andy Deacon was. Reckless then, she telephoned to *Variety,*
and the telephone girl answered, as though she had given
the same answer many times that day, "He's at the Hotel
Picardy, Park Avenue."

She kept herself from the frenzy of taking a taxicab, but
she almost ran across to Park Avenue, skimming a block
out of her way to an old-book shop, where she primly bought
a second-hand copy of the Tudor *Romeo and Juliet.*

She had realized that Andy represented wealth, but she

was so acquainted with him as a khaki-trousered beach-comber that she was shy when she encountered him as a bustling Man of Affairs. In the ducal Hotel Picardy he had two suites: his own duplex apartment and a smaller extra one across the hall as a concentration camp for inquiring actors. It was to this secondary, overflow suite that Bethel was directed at the hotel desk.

She entered a plum-colored drawing room richly filled with every sort of overstuffed furniture that a sensible person could not possibly want. Facing the door, at an incongruous metal desk, was a Miss Sally Carpet, a young woman made entirely of glass, typing so rapidly that it looked vicious.

"Yes?" said the glass lady.

She had clipped some of the normal sounds out of even that inextensive word, and pretty well got it down to "ys."

"I'd like to see Mr Andrew Deacon, please."

"Nappointment?"

"No, I'm a friend of his."

"Snamepls?"

"Bethel Merriday."

"Wastabout casting?"

"Yes, pleas ."

"Spearance " (Bethel concluded that this meant "Have you had any xperience?" but it may have signified "Do you expect me to approve of your appearance?" or "Do you spear your aunts?")

"I was with Mr Deacon at Grampion last summer."

"Oh. Another one! Well, I suppose he'll want to see you. Excuse me if I'm a crank, dearie, but nine tenths of the babies that come in here either were playing in *The Women* or *Our Town* last year—under the stage name of Marlene Dietrich, I guess—or they got soused once with one of Andy's sisters."

"Oh. Has he sisters?"

"*Has* he? *Ask* me!" With which mystifying demand, Miss Sally Carpet went across the hall to announce her. Days later, Bethel found that Andy decidedly had no sisters.

Andy himself met her in the entryway of the main apartment—yet was this Andy, this Hollywood creation in double-breasted blue suit, light blue shirt, dark blue tie, spats, sleeked hair, and a titanic seal ring with what she supposed to be armorial bearings?

He shouted, "This is wonderful that you've come, darling! You're just the girl I've been looking for! I want you to meet the greatest director in the world—Adrian Satori. . . . Adrian, this is one of my discoveries! Bethel—Bethel —oh, damn it, sweet, what *is* your last name?"

To meet Adrian Satori was, for Bethel, like being introduced to the Archangel Uriel at a cocktail party; Satori who had shepherded Molnar and Pirandello in New York, who had reintroduced Chekhov, and who was reputed to have been so impertinent to George Bernard Shaw that Shaw had respected him as a fellow dictator.

For no clear reason Bethel had expected the great Satori to be either gaunt like Jerome O'Toole and Sol Gadto, or plump and pixie like Roscoe Valentine. But, gaping at him, she was overwhelmed to find that he looked like a pipe smoker, a golfer and a commuter. He shook her hand with a paw like a boxer's.

"Come join us, Bethel," he said, as dryly as though he were ordering ginger ale. "You may have some interesting new form of insanity that hasn't occurred to us yet."

He was looking at her with bold dark Mediterranean eyes. She felt that he already knew her better than Andy did, and liked her more.

The living room of Andy's apartment was tall, it was very tall, it was taller than the great hall of the Grand Central Terminal, with a studio window on one side so tremendous that it should have framed a view of the entire range of the Himalayas. Across the room was a Gothic stone fireplace composed of an entire castle transported from Normandy. On either side of the fireplace were couches for giantesses, and somewhere far up in the smoky heights hung a balcony, with a collection of all the tapestries in the world dangling over the rail. Apparently there were a bedroom or two up on this airy, healthful mesa, and a kitchen and dining room under it.

The living room was full of practically everything: brocade-covered couches, marble-topped tables, harewood glass-topped tables, Spanish thrones, footstools, a grand piano, or it may have been two grand pianos, a portable bar displaying whisky, brandy, gin, Grand Marnier, Benedictine, vodka, arrack and Chinese rice wine, vulgar typewriter desks, eddies of punched playscript paper, delightful cardboard models of scenery, half-unpacked suitcases, typed estimates, lost vanity cases, variorum editions of *Romeo and Juliet,* phonograph records, copies of *The Billboard* and *Variety* and *Theatre Arts Monthly,* armchairs deep as bathtubs . . . and people. And the telephone rang without ceasing, in the subsidiary suite across the hall, and Miss Carpet could be heard being noisily frigid in answer.

And people. They were plastered over the expensive furnishings. Tudor Blackwall, wearing a checked gray flannel vest, dashed up to Bethel glowing, "Darling, don't worry about finishing my script. I know where I could get it accepted, but I'm going out with Andy in *Romeo and Juliet* as Paris."

Doc Keezer of Grampion was there, looking like a well-contented chicken farmer. He was to play both Montague and Friar Laurence. Seeing Doc was to Bethel like seeing Sladesbury. And, considerably less soothingly and home-comingly, Iris Pentire was on hand, being cryptic to a piano stool.

She was chastely clad in a black loose-woven wool skirt up to her bosom, a Nile-green chiffon blouse with black sleeves down to her knuckles, and a patent-leather hat like a newly polished stove lid. She had already been chosen page to Paris and understudy to the Nurse and to Lady Montague. She confided to Bethel that she was so rare a hand at make-up that she could conceal her extreme youth and beauty and be a hag of a nurse like—as she herself put it—"like no-body's business."

The throng made exits and entrances with dizzying swift-ness and meaninglessness. Bethel would not have been sur-prised to see Eddie Cantor and President Roosevelt enter, arm in arm, followed by a milk-white antelope with a starry crown. But through all the walk-ons persisted the voice of none other than Mahala Vale, very handsome in a blue suit with a chinchilla fur and a hussar cap, shrieking at Andy and Satori that *she* ought to be cast as Juliet, instead of as Lady Capulet, and that for Mrs Boyle to play Juliet was as sensible as to cast Madame Flagstad as Little Eva.

Boyle? Bethel wondered if this could be Mrs Lumley Boyle, the famous, beautiful and shockingly bad-tempered Aurelia Boyle. For Juliet?

Mrs Boyle was one of the highly competent English actors who, after working up a hatred for everything British, including fish and chips and the royal family, had come over to America chiefly because they could hate every-thing in these gangster-infested jungles even more. She was of the age called "not so young now." Perhaps forty. And she was really distinguished. . . . Bethel felt that socially she was now going a step even higher than Uriel.

She begged of Andy, "You're so busy; when may I come back and ask about a job—maybe understudy?" and he clamored, "No, no, no, no—don't you go, kitten—you stay —I need you," and she sneaked off to the security of a small pale armchair.

While Mahala bravely went right on denouncing her civil wrongs, and Andy cajoled, and Satori laughed and helped himself to a Scotch and soda, hundreds of thousands of other people popped in and, after having a free drink, sloughed away. Sally Carpet flashed in with telephone mes-sages from press agents and company managers and juvenile actors who were "at liberty," and from agents who had com-plete assortments of Shakespearean casts ready to deliver.

Seven feverishly competent young women came in to

present the merits of as many dressmakers and, as it had definitely been announced that this *Romeo and Juliet* production was to be in modern dress, they all brought drawings of Elizabethan costumes in velvet. There was a rush of dealers in rapiers, floodlights, cosmetics, printing. There was even a live process server.

In the House of Merriday, in Sladesbury, to be served with a summons for an unpaid bill ranked with divorce for adultery or the use of cocaine. But when Miss Carpet quacked from the door, "Process server here from Mintz, Dolce & Carr, Mist' Deacon," the hero laughed: "Shoot him in. . . . How are you, comrade? This the document? Thanks. Have a drink?"

"My . . . God! You bet I will!" yelled the tipstaff.

And all the while, through all charges and retreats, Mahala's golden voice pealed on:

"Boyle's too old and too conventional. She dates about Beerbohm Tree. Are you going to have J. Wilkes Booth for Mercutio? Why, this child Beth Merriday could play Juliet better than that old——"

From the door, Miss Carpet jeered, "Mrs Lumley Boyle to see Mr Deacon."

"——devil!" Mahala finished, and looked haughty.

A small, slight woman, all eyes, walked in. They were black eyes, full of life and anger; like the eyes of Bethel and of Adrian Satori, only more so. She wore a coat of which you could never remember anything except that it was old but had once been very expensive. She stood turning the eyes on Mahala, whose knees grew feeble and her voice puling as she intoned, "Oh, how do you do, Mrs Boyle? Raw day, isn't it? I've got to be running on, Andy—Mr Satori —Bethel. See you all soon. That's a wonderful picture of you in *Stage,* Mrs Boyle. Good-by, all—goo-oo-ood-by!"

Bethel slipped up to Andy to whisper, "Shall I go now?"

"No, no! Now least of all, dear. Adrian and I need somebody with sense in these troublous times that are about to occur right now."

But Mrs Boyle didn't really want many things—what she did want, she wanted earnestly and eloquently, but they did not go beyond:

A run-of-the-play contract, whereby she could not be discharged except for barratry, treason or miscegenation.

Billing—not at all on her own behalf, but for dear Andy's sake, to sell the play—as follows:

MRS. LUMLEY BOYLE
The world's most distinguished tragedienne
in
Romeo and Juliet
with Andrew Deacon, Mahala Vale,
Mabel Staghorn, Hugh Challis, and cast
of famous New York and London actors.

Dressing rooms A and B, both, in all theaters—B for her maid, her shoes and her dog.

Pullman drawing room for herself and section for her maid, on all overnight jumps.

And to be present at all interviews, to tell the reporters—since her modesty prevented her doing it herself—what Sir Johnston Forbes-Robertson had said to her.

No cuts in any of her speeches, no matter what cuts there might be in the lines of the groundlings.

Johnnie Walker whisky—black label, not red, remember, *black* label—provided and paid for by the management, to be present in all her dressing rooms, hotel suites and train drawing rooms.

But, as she was an old trouper, just an old trouper, just one of the cast and as democratic as a streetwalker, that was all she wanted.

When Mrs Boyle was gone, Andy and Satori stretched in chairs, their legs thrust out far before them, and were wan and silent.

Bethel was inspired to bring them whisky-sodas. "Poor darling!" she murmured to Andy.

"Oh, bless you, of course I remember now, it's Merriday," said Andy.

But he said nothing about a job for her. And she would have been so willing to go along on the tour, even without Johnnie Walker, black label.

The designer of sets and costumes was a Mr William Schnable, a businesslike person with a red mustache and eight-sided spectacle lenses. He marched in with a portfolio of scene drawings. The play was to have a unit set, with Romanesque mock-plaster portals and a number of balcony, archway and window units which could be shuffled for quick changes. Bethel wondered why, in a modern-costume *Romeo,* they should use the old, bogus, Shaftesbury Avenue-Italian for the sets, but, unbidden, feeling that she belonged here now, she brought Mr Schnable a drink and handsomely sat back and shut up.

Andy, Satori and Schnable showed that there was life in this stage venture by immediately falling into a derogatory argument about costumes. Schnable was for having Romeo wear a contemporary Italian army officer's uniform. Andy yelled that this would look like Fascist propaganda. Schnable said that anything else would look like Communist propaganda. Satori said, with what seemed like considerable reasonableness, that they were both crazy, and that Romeo should be the most elegant young clubman that could be turned out by the best Fifth Avenue tailors, and wear a dinner jacket and an opera hat for the balcony scene. Andy announced that he would be double-damned if he'd recite "Oh that I were a glove upon that hand, that I might touch that cheek" in a boiled shirt and a natty gent's bow tie. Romeo was so great an aristocrat that he could wear whatever he liked. He was going to wander through the play in gray flannel bags, with a tweed jacket and a soft shirt; maybe he'd change his tie from act to act, but he wasn't so sure about even that, and . . .

And weapons. The three stage maniacs came almost to

the use of weapons themselves as they debated what should
be used in place of rapiers, which would be absurd with
modern costumes. Revolvers—blackjacks—brass knuckles—
stray bottles and brickbats? And then stilettos; yes, Tybalt
would kill Mercutio with a stiletto. But the first fight between Tybalt and Benvolio should be with plain hearty fists.

They were still denouncing one another at seven o'clock,
when Miss Carpet indicated that she had to go home, that
she had had the telephone calls switched onto Mr Deacon's
suite, and that there still were three young actors waiting
across the hall, to read for the role of Mercutio.

"I've taken a look at them. No good. No good at all.
Why don't you chase 'em away?" said Satori.

"Oh, the poor devils, let's give 'em a chance, anyway," insisted Andy. "Besides! How do you know they're no good,
just glancing at 'em? The psychic Satori! Come on, let's
read 'em now—Bill Schnable and Bethel and you and I."

"Oh, please no! It wouldn't be fair for me to listen to
them reading," Bethel protested.

"You'll have a good fresh point of view," said Andy. "You
may beat Adrian and me all hollow. And can't you stay and
have dinner with me?"

"I'd lovetobut," said Bethel dutifully.

"So you think this batch are no good?" Andy sighed to
Satori. "Tempot, the agent, swore they were all three of 'em
better than Gielgud. We've got to have a Mercutio, right
away. Look, Adrian! I've got a brain wave. Let's see if Zed
Wintergeist is engaged. Know his work?"

"Yes. I directed him in a Shaw festival. He's a clever
actor, lots of power, intelligent, but he's a sea lawyer. He
criticizes everybody and everything. He's a mutineer."

"I know. I played with him in *The Light Goes Out*. But
he's not effeminate, and he can act—anything from King
Lear to David the Shepherd Boy. I'm going to give him a
call, anyway. Bethel, sweet! Will you please find Wintergeist's address—remember him?—the angelic roughneck

that came out of the rain at Grampion and invited himself to our party? His address is in my little red book there on the piano—no, I guess it's upstairs on the bureau in my room—no, I think I saw it last in the phonograph—well, anyway, darling, find it and get him on the phone for me, while I bring in the boys for the reading."

She did—chasing the little red book to Miss Carpet's desk across the hall, and then chasing Zed from his cheap-sounding address far over in the West Forties to the Tavern Restaurant to backstage at *Pins and Needles* to a small select dinner party of two hundred people in Sol Gadto's one-room-and-toilet apartment.

Yes. Zed would condescend to come and see Mr Andrew Deacon. When? Oh, nineish—if he was still sober.

Schnable had reasonably escaped, but Andy, Satori and Bethel dragged three deep chairs into line, as an audience, tried to look profound, and listened to three several actors trying in turn to read the most unreadable lines of Mercutio.

Inasmuch as you can tell nothing whatever about an actor by looking at him, and still less by listening to his first reading of lines, and inasmuch as these two are the only ways of choosing an actor, it is probable that nobody has ever yet been chosen for any role in any play.

Bethel and all the Olde Roanoke pilgrims had resented the fact that so few managers would ever give an unknown the chance to read, to be heard and seen. "It's their duty to give every kid that much chance, anyway," they had raged. Now she wondered if it wasn't less cruel to refuse even to see a job hunter than to let him go on reading, out of courtesy, when you were certain from the first sentence that he would not do.

She found the whole business of listening to the reading horrible. Two of the young men were too soft—they made Mercutio into a teashop proprietress; the third, though he looked like a young white-browed angel, was too tough. He made Mercutio into a battling longshoreman.

But to all three of them the three judges listened with glazed politeness. They were arbiters of life and wages and glory—and Bethel didn't like that at all. She suffered with the defendants, and wanted to help them, and didn't know how.

Through the ordeal by fire, the telephone kept ringing, relentlessly, contemptuously, and Bethel, cursing the name of Alexander Graham Bell, took over the answering. . . . Could Mr Deacon see a fourteen-year-old prodigy who would make the greatest Juliet in history? Would Mr Deacon be interested in buying, for two hundred dollars, a playbill of Salvini in *Macbeth* from a dear old lady with a mortgage? Would Mr Deacon see—right away, this minute —a dear old friend of Mr Deacon's, who hadn't ever exactly met him, but who had been at Grampion for two weeks, three years ago, and who was now generously waiting down in the lobby?

In all her life Bethel had never learned so much about practical perjury.

The young men finished reading. To each of them, in turn, Andy said with wretched politeness, "We'll let you know in just a few days. Will you please leave your name and telephone number with my secretary, Miss Merriday, here?"

And with equally phony hopefulness and gratitude each of the three young men bowed out—condemned again to a death of dreary waiting.

Satori had gone. Andy seemed not to remember anything about the promised dinner, and Beth could have used a good dinner just then. She had not had one for ten days.

Andy and she were going over and over the satin out-rageousness of Mrs Boyle and the huge demerits and few virtues of the three candidates, when Zed Wintergeist exploded into the room, without ringing, except as he was in himself a clamorously ringing bell.

But he was low tonight. Bethel had remembered him as a

combination of Jed Harris, Orson Welles, Richard Whorf, Jack London, Tarzan and Percy Bysshe Shelley, but tonight he was just a strong young man, broad-shouldered but not very tall, in need of a comb, sulky and rather pale; a plebeian who was inconceivable as Mercutio, the cavalier.

"Hello, Andy," he croaked. He stared at Bethel, scratched his chin, then snapped his fingers at her, infuriatingly, and shouted, "Wait—wait, I tell you! Don't prompt me!"

Indignantly, "I don't intend to."

"Hush! Oh, I've got it. Grampion. The nosy character in *Stage Door*. Beth Merriday! Greetings, pet. . . . What can I do for you, Andy?"

"I'm organizing a *Romeo and Juliet* company——"

"Why not *Uncle Tomeo's Cabin?*"

"I wouldn't mind. . . . We're going on the road for I don't know how long, and then come into New York if we're any good. I think you might possibly do Mercutio, if you're interested."

"I'm not. *Romeo and Juliet* was a good play once—hell-raising youth, cockeyed, funny, romantic, swell. Now it belongs with these knitting shops you see in old fishing shacks all along the New England coast. It's pure and noble and phony."

"But we're going to do it in modern dress—first time *Romeo's* ever been done that way, far as we can find out. That ought to be experimental enough for even you, Zed."

"Look here. I don't think a play's necessarily good because it's experimental. Maybe I did once—two years ago —two thousand years ago. Not now. Any provincial Little Theater that's run as an adjunct to the golf club, and that plays *Liliom* in front of a muslin cyc, does more experimentation in six months than the whole Abbey Theater in six years. Still . . . It *could* be interesting. Who's directing?"

"Satori."

"Mm. He knows his business. He's even heard of Lope

de Vega and of jackknife stages. Of course he's completely cynical and dishonest."

Bethel was foaming with indignation. This creature Zed, who had crawled out of the woodpile, to pick and chatter at the Sun God's proffered gift!

Andy was gentle as he hinted, "There may be a lot to what you say, Zed. What are you doing?"

"Starving."

"No plans?"

"Same answer: starving! I was out on the road for two whole weeks with that awful flop, *The Soul Clinic*. We didn't even bring it into town. But I did well financially. Two hundred and fifty a week! Two-fifty for two weeks makes five hundred bucks, and five hundred bucks divided by fifty gives me ten dollars a week for the whole year round, and you can live on that—in fact you can live on even less than that, in jail, I suppose——"

"Zed!"

"Huh?"

"You know you're coming with us! Make Mercutio contemporary. He's a good deal like you, anyway—crazy, poetic and bad-tempered."

"Well——"

"You know you're going to do it, Zed, if you can get enough salary out of me, so why waste time in all this unpaid performing? Mercutio in uniform—no illusions about immortality—sore because he's going to die. Heh?"

"Well," said Zed.

Andy took him into the entryway to whisper about salary —that was artistico-commercial etiquette, not to talk openly about money—and Zed returned to shake Bethel's hand and shout, "Good! Let's go! Streamlined Shakespeare with gyroscopic control! See you on the stage, pet."

Bethel painfully did not tell him that she wasn't of the company at all.

She was cross with Andy, though she felt petty in view

of the fact that she had seen him patting two or three bank-notes into Zed's gritty hand.

It was ten by the rock-crystal electric clock on the balcony railing. Andy, spreadeagled on a couch beside the fireplace, wailed, "I'm completely exhausted," and in a completely un-exhausted voice started what promised to be an hour's commentary:

"I'm glad we've got Zed. If Adrian will just beat him to death at the first rehearsal——"

He was interrupted by a very small voice.

"Please?"

"What is it, darling?"

"Dinner?"

"What?"

"Please? Dinner?"

"My Lord, what a sarcophagus I am, what a zany, what a gaby, what a doodle, what a dizzard, what a hoddy-doddy, what a tom-noddy, what a dunderpate, what a jobber-nowl, what a gowk! I didn't have lunch till four. I forgot people do get hungry. My poor drowned kitten! You shall have champagne and caviar and the sound of flutes."

She did, too—the flutes provided by the electric phonograph. He even cut off the telephone and, though once every quarter-hour a page would knock with a sheaf of telephone memoranda, they dined in almost matrimonial peace and drowsiness.

With a script of *Romeo and Juliet* by his plate, Andy droned about cuts for their acting version. He seemed to take her as his equal—his sister, his old trouping companion—she who was wondering if by direct interposition of Heaven she might get a chance to broadcast two lines four weeks from now as an Apache squaw in the "St Clair of San Antone" radio serial.

Andy was happily fussing. "In his Globe Theater version, Thomas Wood Stevens cuts out Romeo's 'They pray, grant thou lest faith turn to despair.' That spoils the sestet.

That first duet of Romeo and Juliet's a sonnet, you know.
. . . Oh, you *didn't?* Well, neither did I, till yesterday.
Well, what do you think, darling? I value your judgment
so much——"

"So much that—— Look, Andy, please! I guess I've got
to be a bold wench. You know—like Juliet. I want a job.
Won't you please give me a reading, too? For anything
from the Prince to the wardrobe mistress!"

"Darling! I'm so ashamed! As a matter of fact I was going to talk with you about that, but it slipped my mind, what
with the telephone calls from classmates and creditors and
cousins and all the nasty words beginning with C. I thought
last summer that you were the only student that had much
possibility. You need training. But then, so do I, and we'll
hope to get it, on one-night stands with Romeo and friends.
The play's mostly cast, now that we've got Zed: there's
only Benvolio, and a triple of the Apothecary and Sampson
and Second Watchman for some poor overworked ham, and
Juliet's understudy—who'll also play Mercutio's page. I've
read about a dozen ravishing young maidens for that last
part, but I haven't decided and—— Yes. Read Juliet. And
you better be good!"

The waiter had taken out the table. The room, in the
thirty-seventh story of the Hotel Picardy Tower, was quiet.
Andy thrust the *Romeo* script into her nervous hands,
switched on an electric hearth fire vastly more real than
clumsily burning wood, and flopped out on the couch in beefy
elegance.

She got herself a small coffee table and a straight chair,
laid out the script, leaned over it with her cheeks in her hands
and began to read. She became fairly calm. This was not a
manager considering her for a job; it was her friend, almost
her worshiped idol, Andy Deacon.

She was calm enough to forget him entirely as she read,
"O gentle Romeo, if thou dost love, pronounce it faithfully."
Her reading had no particular "modernity," no discernible
link with Freud and Adler. It was as old as cypress groves

and little rivers and the young moon, and if there was anything contemporary about it, for contribution to the Deacon Theatrical Experiment, it was that to her, just now, Romeo was not smoldered in an antique tomb, but alive and here, ducally lolling on the couch, his eyes (she peeped to see) tight-closed in the closeness of his attention——

And she realized that he had fallen asleep.

She was not angry long. Asleep, his face was so youthful, so weary. She sighed for herself and her lost opportunity, and then she sighed for him. "Poor Andy! Poor dear!" She softly drew a cover over him, tiptoed to find her hat and jacket, and tiptoed out into the hotel corridor, crying.

The telephone by her bed terrified her out of sleep. She was entirely convinced that she had murdered someone and that this was the police after her. Her breath coming harshly, she turned on the light and saw her little old bed-side clock. It was three o'clock.

"Y-yes?" she said quaveringly, into the hateful black maw of the telephone.

It was Andy—blast him! And he sounded as fresh and busy as at noon.

"Beth? You thought I fell asleep?"

"Yes, I did sort of think so."

("You know you fell asleep, you producer, you capitalist, you face-grinder, you spats-wearer.")

"Maybe I did. I'd been going hard since seven in the morning—or anyway since eight or eight-thirty. But I heard enough of your reading before I popped off. If I remember rightly, you have good legs, haven't you?"

"*What?*"

"You heard me! As Mercutio's page, you have to wear tights."

"Yes, I have!"

"All right. You're elected. You understudy Juliet and say the prologue and play the page."

"Oh, Andy!"

"You get forty a week, Equity minimum. Okay?"

"Oh yes, quite okay!"

"You're not an Equity member yet."

"No, I couldn't join till I had a producer's contract."

"Come around to the Picardy sometime this afternoon and I'll give you a contract. Rehearsals start Monday, October thirty-first, five days from now. We open in Belluca, Indiana, for a week's run, on November 28th. Look, Beth, what do you think of keeping the two pages in tights, as I said? It don't jibe with the modern costumes, but then, we haven't got anything corresponding to a gent's private page today anyway. I've been thinking about it—I tried to get Adrian and Bill Schnable on the phone just now to talk it over, but the dirty dogs have both cut off their telephones for the night, fine theatrical men *they* are, sleeping like commuters, and—what do you think?"

Twenty minutes later they were still talking, with Bethel pleased to believe that she could keep her voice steady and practical.

She did not go back to sleep. She read an act of *Romeo and Juliet*—sitting up in bed, solemnly sucking a candy bar, looking about ten years old in her pink-and-white knitted bed jacket. At dawn she had a shower, dressed, slipped through the hotel corridor, while the aged male night clerk frowned. She had coffee and corn flakes at the counter—of pine scrubbed down till the knots and the grain stood out like a relief map—of an old, cheap restaurant that was lined with pressed tin, so that she felt as if she were cooped in an old tin packing case.

As she sipped the coffee, which managed to be at once weak and bitter, she was still hotly reading *Romeo and Juliet.*

20

For the five days of waiting before rehearsals, Andy's apartment was her home, her temple. He seemed to like having her about; occasionally he kissed her cheek, though in an entirely absent-minded way and usually during a discussion, explosively carried on with from two to a dozen persons, as to whether Romeo, the blighter, should ever carry a tennis racket.

Regularly he insisted that she stay for lunch and dinner, at which you met a cross section of New York, London and Central Europe, none of them particularly invited to stay but none of them ever disinvited.

With no very definite arrangement, she became assistant secretary to Miss Sally Carpet, and by a judicious combination of her small shorthand and her large memory, she was able to take fifty letters a day—most of which began, "Dear Joe, When I arrive in Palace City with my show—oh hell, Beth, never mind; I'll phone him, long-distance, this evening."

Miss Carpet accompanied her when, with the grandeur of

a real theatrical contract in her pocket, she went to join the Actors' Equity Association. . . . The secretary at Equity seemed perfectly calm about it.

The apartment became hourly more disordered and insane. On the grand piano was a heap of scenery sketches, letters, script pages, theatrical pages torn out of newspapers, and proofs of advertisements. At any moment you saw Andy emerging from his bedroom in a maroon dressing gown over crimson silk pajamas; Zed Wintergeist sitting up on the rail of the balcony, legs dangling over the abyss, eating two ice-cream cones in succession; a completely strange man in morning coat and striped trousers, sitting vacantly hour on hour, holding his derby hat and seemingly having no purpose in life except to hold derbies; and Adrian Satori asleep five feet away from a poker game conducted by Andy, Zed, Tudor, Mahala and the stage manager—a competent standard-sized person named Nathan Eldred.

There were long conferences with a professor from Swarthmore, changing the names of Shakespeare's weapons, so that Benvolio's "put up thy sword" became "put down your fists," and old Capulet cried not for his "long sword" but for his "oak stick." During these solemnities Bethel and her typewriter retreated farther and farther, until one afternoon she quite happily put in two hours typing with the machine resting on a chair up in Andy's bathroom, while Iris Pentire was being helpful by sitting on the edge of the bathtub and repowdering her nose.

Iris was not there so often, but her ways were simple and pleasing; she rather hoped to lure Andy away from Mahala, and she crisply intended to win Zed Wintergeist. And to Bethel's innocent astonishment, that hard-minded image breaker was easily beguiled by Iris's faint wise smile. Whenever Zed had denounced Andy for producing merely another pretty-pretty version of *Romeo,* he looked in relief to Iris's cool magic and invited her out for a drink.

But on Andy, Iris's designs were idiotic. Mahala had claimed him again. She paraded him, in chains of taffy, be-

fore all the new audience—Satori and Schnable and Zed
and Mrs Boyle—as her very own. So far as Bethel could
tell, Andy was never so incautious as to mutter anything to
Mahala about the gallows march to the altar. He merely
said to Mahala that she was a greater actress than Rejane,
more beautiful than Diana Manners, and that it was a shame
for her to spoil such incomparably beautiful slim hands
with crimson nails like lobster claws. But Mahala incessantly
patted him, took his arm, smiled at him apropos of his observation that the weather was colder today, hummed at
him, looked up at him, looked up at him——

Bethel sighed, "That female floorwalker will capture
Andy, and Iris will seduce Zed—not such a complicated
campaign, I'm beginning to think—and even if Mrs Boyle
falls dead—I hope it won't be serious, but I hope it will be
soon—and I play Juliet, I'll still be left with only Tudor
Blackwall and Doc Keezer for beaux. Oh, this is going
to be a crusade of mud and glory."

She watched the end of the casting. The last stroke was
an error. Andy was so sick of rejecting applicants, of con-
demning them to starvation again, that when Mr Wyndham
Nooks proved, in reading the three parts of Apothecary,
Sampson and First Watchman, that at least he could pronounce the English language, Andy sighed, ignored Adrian
Satori's wildly frowning disapproval and blurted, "All right,
Mr Nooks, you can have the part, if you'll take fifty a
week. Okay? Go in and see my secretary, Miss Carpet,
about your contract."

Before midnight, well berated by Satori, he was groaning,
"Oh, I know it. I was tired. My foot slipped. I've gone and
wished a real ham onto the company. Well, that may be a
good thing—the rest of us saved souls will have somebody
besides Mrs Boyle to hate."

Mr Wyndham Nooks was portly, basso, slow and sentimental, and he quoted poetry—preferably Milton and Eddie
Guest—in answer to a request for a match. As a stripling, in

Tennessee, he had been a Fundamentalist Baptist preacher. There were two schools of thought as to why he had suddenly left this high calling.

He claimed to be sixty; he had acted, or enacted acting, for thirty-five years. He had been in medicine shows, in Tom shows, in pick-up companies playing Shakespeare and Dumas through the Southwest; he had been drunk with some of the richest cowmen in Oklahoma and in their homes had recited "Gunga Din." He had starved after his first venture to New York, but then had fallen into a good line of business doing congressmen and pompous clergymen—though he never did quite understand why audiences laughed so much when he delivered sentiments which he felt to be elegant and noble.

There was a whole gallery of people new to Bethel, and now very important to her, in the *Romeo* cast:

Young Douglas Fry, from the University of Pennsylvania; slim, colorless, capable. He was assistant stage manager and played Abraham, Friar John and the Second Watchman; he wanted eventually to be a director.

Lyle Johnson, who was to play Balthasar in a chauffeur's uniform, and any number of Torch-bearers and Citizens of Verona in between. He was a good actor, he was a drunken rowdy after eleven-thirty P.M., he looked like a loose farmhand off-stage, but on-stage looked like precisely whatever character he was ordered to portray. He would end in jail or in Hollywood.

Hugh Challis, that stately, kindly old Lambs' Club Englishman who dealt generously in charm. He was Capulet, a role which he had first played in the Nottingham at the age of twenty-two.

The Nurse was that sweetly sighing, tenderly patting and poisonously gossiping old character woman, Miss Mabel Staghorn.

Lady Montague was Charlotte Levison, who was Jewish and a Communist, and who resembled all young eighteenth-century English duchesses depicted against oaks in the deer park. Charlotte had inherited Communism from her family, as she might have inherited Catholicism or Quakerism, and she combined with her vague Marxianism a pious fondness for furs and ruby bracelets and guinea hen under glass.

Tybalt was Henry W. Purvis, Ph.D. in English of the University of Chicago. Harry Purvis was the hedge scholar, the Friar Tuck, whom even card-catalogue universities cannot kill out of the eternal human comedy. For a year (he was thirty now) he had been master in that select academy for young gentlemen, Hotchkiss. He was an excellent actor, fresh and vigorous and flexible; and on holidays and after hours, he was a much worse drunk, more sodden and suicidal, than Lyle Johnson. His real initials were H. W. L., but he was trying to lose the L.

Benvolio was the Canadian actor, Geoffrey Hoy—he was mostly clothes and smile. Escalus, Prince of Verona, was Victor Swenson, who, though he was broad-shouldered and Viking-maned, had followed the too-common American transition from wheat farm to decadence in one generation. Peter was Antonio Murphy, a dolorous comedian surly about taking direction.

There were two youngsters: Vera Cross, who understudied Lady Capulet, and Tom Wherry, who understudied all the younger men principals; and both of whom appeared as Citizens of Verona, along with almost everybody in the cast. There was so much doubling that Doc Keezer (Montague-Laurence) said (and frequently) "when you came offstage, you met yourself just leaving your dressing room. Still, that's nothing. Why, when I was playing with Lincoln J. Carter, I did six different characters and an off-stage pistol shot."

Of the permanent crew of three heads of mechanical departments, carried with the company to direct local crews of stagehands—carpenter, electrician and props—Bethel did not know or think for weeks yet, but she was to come to know them as a company of uncles, protective and wise. But

Tertius Tully, the company manager, who was as thin and salty and Yankee as a dried codfish, was to be her Chief Uncle.

This was her family, her tribe, her temple, her vagrant home. In it she still loved but almost forgot her earlier homes: her parents, Charley Hatch, Alva Prindle, college and Fletcher Hewitt . . . that innkeeper. She was a nun now, a probationer nun, and she was well content.

This was good enough!

21

THEIR FIRST REHEARSAL, when they read through their parts aloud, was at the historic Gotham Theater, but it was not on the stage, which still shone from the presences of Mrs Fiske and Maude Adams and John Drew and Nat Goodwin. The bones of a recent brief theatrical misfortune were being carted away from the stage; in the lounge, the management was trying to make old red-plush chairs into new red-plush chairs; and the lobby was being painted. And so the auspicious first rehearsal of *Romeo and Juliet* was held in the Ladies' Room.

It was quite a nice Ladies' Room, with a dressing table, a wide mirror edged with designs in frosted glass, six refined pink washbowls and a dozen gilt chairs, which were taken by the older troupers. Mrs Boyle pre-empted two of them, one for her fur, while the others sat on the floor.

As Mercutio's page and as understudy to Juliet, Bethel had nothing to read, in among the organ notes of Romeo and Lord Capulet and the Prince; but as Prologue, she had a whole sonnet, at the beginning of the first act, and she sang it out in the fresh voice of an eager young girl who loved "the traffic of our stage with the pair of star-crossed lovers."

She thought that Adrian Satori, directing, nodded a blessing. But afterwards it seemed to her that everyone else had read so much more richly: Andy the soul of youthful love, Zed Wintergeist so boldly gay a Mercutio, Harry Purvis a swift blade as Tybalt, Hugh Challis sputtering pomp as Capulet, and Mrs Boyle not forty-four but an eternal twenty.

(Bethel was quarreling with Shakespeare and the Nurse for their lie that Juliet was fourteen. Why, she herself was twenty-two, and it looked as though that enterprising young sprout Juliet had been around at least as much as she.)

When the reading was done, Mr Wyndham Nooks encompassed Bethel like a fog blowing from a distillery and boomed, "It's a shame to think of a lovely child like you having to open the play with the prologue. It will be beyond your powers. You'll blow, sure as hell! Of course I have almost more than I can carry already, with three bits, but I'll inform our good friend Deacon that for the good of the show, I can take on Prologue too."

"You'll get those lines over my dead body!" snarled the young actress who once had been our gentle little Bethel.

The rehearsals wandered from the Ladies' Room up to the stage of the Gotham, then to a hall where Romeo, supposed to be gazing down the long tessellated ballroom at the distant beloved, was actually looking into Satori's yawns, three feet away. But they settled down for two weeks on the stage of that competent new theater, the Prince Regent, not occupied just now by a play. Bethel felt happily that she had lived here all her days.

No first night, with chandeliers and Jerome Kern overture and furs and white shirt fronts and sparkling applause, could be more enchanting than the undressed stage, illuminated only by a work-light on a standard, with shadowy hints of the tall brick back wall, the bars of steam pipes, dusty stacks of old flats leaning against the wall, the electric switchboard and, mysterious above all, the upward-reaching darknesses of the fly loft. Against this quiet obscurity the actors, in shirt sleeves or old sweaters or too jaunty tweeds, moved back and forth, stammering their lines, repeating them, stopping to read not-quite-learned lines from the typed parts which they held up to their faces with one hand while the other hand made vague wild blind motions of wielding a club—or a girl.

Satori lounged over a kitchen table, making minute delicate notes on his script, and Nathan Eldred, the stage manager, in another chair discreetly drawn two feet farther back, prompted from his own script. . . . No audience, but darkness and strangeness, and in the midst of it, the worklight, and the moving actors beginning, gesture by gesture and word by beautiful word, to evoke the passion in Verona.

That was the stage for Bethel Merriday.

Only a few times did Satori run through with her the prologue to the first act—the second-act prologue was cut out; and as Mercutio's page, she was on but a few minutes. Her real task, as understudy for Juliet, was to sit down in the auditorium, unmoving, like a solemn little owl, concentrated on everything that Mrs Boyle did—every pronunciation of a musical line, every slightest movement of intense eyes, tender lips, eagerly graceful arms.

If she wanted to be up there with the others on the stage, she comforted herself with the assurance that soon she would be. In her next show *she* would have an understudy of her own—yes, and she'd treat her in a lot friendlier way than she was treated by Mrs Boyle, whose most ardent attention was to look at her as though she had got in here by mistake and mutter "Oh!"

Bethel understood better now the improbable stories of understudies who prayed that their principals would fall through a trap door.

It was a strain, sitting paralyzed and ignored from ten to

one and from two till six, particularly when the hour of
six meant, to Mr Satori, in scorn of Equity rules, seven-
thirty or nine-thirty or eleven. Yet she rejoiced in this long,
precise, four-week rehearsal as against the panic sketchiness
of five-day rehearsals in summer stock.

And she was very cross with Iris Pentire—it didn't take
much to make her cross with Iris—for sneaking away from
her observation post as understudy to both the Nurse and
Lady Capulet for a smoke in the lobby, or backstage to whisper glisteningly to Zed Wintergeist.

Zed was mutinous and critical from the first. Bethel was
a little surprised when, after the five-day probation period
before contracts were made permanent, Andy and Satori
still kept him in the cast.

He wanted to make the articulation of the lines as prosaic
and contemporary as the costumes; he wanted, he said, to
exchange the gilt decorations of a fairy tale for the beauty
of human emotions. Andy read Romeo, he said, like an
elocutionist at Chautauqua.

In one of the hysterical blow-ups at rehearsal which are a
proof that the play is progressing healthily, Zed denounced
Andy and Andy denounced Satori, and in a compromise Zed
was allowed to deliver his lines as though a laughing, aching
human being were talking, while Andy went on winging
the empyrean. . . . Even young Bethel could see that the
contrast was shocking, but Satori was dictator, as apparently
a director must be.

After rehearsal hours, Andrew Deacon was the producer,
with all the privilege of coaxing his friends to put money into
the venture, and the imperial right to decide whether they
should presently be playing three nights in Bonanza City, or
one night each in Coyote Crossing, Cathay and Carlsbad.
But during rehearsals, Satori told Andy and Zed—and Mrs
Boyle and Bethel—indiscriminately that they were stinking,
and Andy took it more gratefully than anybody else in the
company.

If there were skirmishes and barricades, there were no feuds or cliques in the company—yet. Everybody said that they were going to have a "hit." These modern clothes were making the play not an antique but a love story almost as good as one out of Hollywood. The married men of the cast, Hugh Challis, Geoffrey Hoy, Antonio Murphy, Wyndham Nooks, Nathan Eldred, the stage manager, and Tertius Tully, the company manager, muttered to one another that, after the past lean year, they would now be able to "send home enough for the little woman and the dear little ones to go out and get soused every Saturday night, like gentlemen."

Zed's nobly expanding grouch extended to Mr Schnable's scenery as much as to the speech.

Like Bethel, he did not see why a contemporary Romeo should be played in a mock Lombard palace. With Douglas Fry, the small industrious assistant stage manager, Zed sketched a permanent set suggesting modern Italy; a huddle of yellow plaster walls with red-tiled roofs and a mediaeval tower, the terrace of Lord Capulet's modern villa, strung with colored electric bulbs for dancing, with the door of Laurence's cell below the terrace, and behind all, the skeleton of a wireless tower.

They brought in their sketches—two enthusiastic young men who loved the stage so much they were willing to be damned for their impudence—and Mr Schnable, the designer, a middle-aged man who didn't love anything in particular, promptly damned them. Andy said mildly, Yes, well, it certainly was an interesting sketch, but afraid he'd spent all the money on scenery he could afford to . . .

Zed returned this benignity with a glare.

That newly fledged trouper, Bethel, was surprised that Mahala took direction almost as humbly as Andy. She began to respect Mahala as purely as she disliked her.

Mahala seemed mobilized now to capture Andy complete. The border-incident came from Joan Hinterwald, and it was Bethel who answered the call when Joan rang up.

Bethel summoned Andy to the telephone, and she couldn't help overhearing him—well, she *didn't* help it. He sputtered, "No, honestly, Joan, it's impossible. I can't leave. We're rehearsing. . . . What? . . . Serious? Of course it's serious! What do you think I'm doing? Playing at playing? . . . All right; *be* sure then."

Bethel saw him stalk back on the stage and ten minutes later sit down with Mahala. He must have murmured to her something of his troubles, for Mahala patted his arm sympathetically. Bethel sighed.

After that day Mahala was cockier than ever. She tore through the Lady Capulet role like a racing driver, and she had the cheek to say to Mrs Boyle (twenty-six being lofty to forty-four), "I wonder if any of the audiences will get the humor of my playing your mother?"

"Perhaps it isn't humorous, my dear," purred Mrs Boyle.

The two pages, Bethel and Iris, were not to wear tights and ruffles, but dreary military-school-cadet uniforms. Bethel was simultaneously glad that she would not have to be so immodest as to show her pretty legs in public, and sorry that she was not going to be more attractive. As to the conduct of their two minute parts, Iris and she fell out.

Iris intended to be as dainty and flirtatious in gray trousers as in chiffon.

"Of course! You don't want to miss being feminine, not with Zed and Douglas and Lyle and Tom Wherry around!" Bethel was guilty of remarking.

"And you an Equity member less than two weeks," sighed Iris.

"I don't see what that's got to do with it!" But this preposterous attack confused Bethel, and she ended, without much conviction: "I'm going to be as sturdy a young scrapper as I can."

"All right, dearie; don't tell me about it; tell Satori," mused Iris.

Never had Bethel been so put in the wrong, never had she so inexcusably put herself in the wrong. It didn't comfort her much to have Iris and Zed go off to lunch arm in arm. She was privately deciding that since Andy was apparently lost forever in the warm ardors of Mahala, like a bumble-bee enveloped in the vegetable horrors of the Venus flytrap, she would better think seriously about Zed.

Then was horrified to discover that she could take Zed very seriously indeed. She could admire his noisy courage; she could be tickled by his ever-changing monkey face.

But this was treachery! she accused herself, and her spirit sat down again before the kindly shrine of Andy.

Of the constant line changes compelled by the modern setting, none produced a better battle than Romeo's order to Balthasar: "And hire post-horses; I will hence tonight." Andy was all for rendering it, "Fill up the car with gas; I'll leave tonight." Zed (whom no one had consulted) agreed profanely. Satori insisted that this was a trifle too post-Elizabethan. "You don't absolutely *have* to have the apothecary sell Romeo a drum of carbon monoxide to kill himself with, you know. Let's make the speech, 'Have the car ready; I will hence tonight.' That's good enough—or bad enough."

It was Bethel who most profited by all the violences done to Shakespeare's words.

Iris had boasted though it might be Bethel who understudied Juliet, she had no lines on the stage except the "regular little college-girl speech" of the prologue, while Iris, as Paris's page, had four whole lines and a whistle.

But Satori and Andy condensed the end of the play. In the new version, after Juliet's death, in a light that rose to earliest dawn, cloaked figures that might have been ghosts moved slowly on stage, and the curtain came down after a speech combined from the last lines of Capulet, Montague and the Prince:

> Capulet! Montague!
> See what a scourge is laid upon your hate!
> But I will raise her statue in pure gold,
> That whiles Verona by that name is known,
> There shall no figure at such rate be set
> As that of true and faithful Juliet,
> And rich shall Romeo's by his lady's lie,
> Poor sacrifices of this enmity.
> A glooming peace this morning with it brings;
> The sun for sorrow will not show his head.
> Some shall be pardon'd, and some punished:
> For never was a story of more woe
> Than this of Juliet and her Romeo.

This speech, Victor Swenson, as Prince Escalus, assumed would be his own, while old Nooks pointed out that it would go very nicely indeed with the role of First Watchman. But Andy and Satori, to universal astonishment and considerably less than universal rejoicing, gave it to Bethel, as newly created Epilogue.

And she was to have a lovely new white silk robe and a gold laurel-crown, a combination of Elizabethan and Contemporary, in which to say both prologue and epilogue, and Iris was stunned and despairing, until Zed remarked that the costume looked like Memorial Day Services at the James A. Garfield High School.

She had to cue Mabel Staghorn, as the Nurse. She had to cue Mahala. Much worse, she had to get Iris to cue her, as Juliet. She had her role comma perfect before Mahala had learned half of hers. But that wasn't enough. Maggie Sample had told her that you don't really know a role until it's so deep in your unconscious that you aren't aware of saying the lines at all. So she chased Iris from auditorium to hidden dressing rooms to the prop room and cornered her, and thrust the part at her, and demanded, "Here, I want to be cued. You know I'm all ready to cue you, whenever you say the word."

"Oh, what's the hurry? We're only understudies. Wait till I get a real role," sighed Iris.

Satori had a theory that present-day audiences find Shakespeare dull because the productions are paced like a funeral. He yielded to Andy and kept Romeo's high poetic lines in a highfalutin elocution, but he drove the other actors to such speed that they went off into the wings and wept. There must not be a tenth of a second between cue and response; no gazing up to the wings with an archiepiscopal reverence. Yet he was precise about every detail of action.

Every cross, every slight lifting of the hand, must be fitted to every other movement like a micrometer gauge, and as to the exact meanings of lines Satori and Andy were always diving into the Variorum Shakespeare and coming up, philologically dripping, with "Look! Look! In the quartos there's no dash before the 'no.' This is Ritsen's punctuation."

"I see they got some nice Irish variorum on the menu today. Try some?" said Doc Keezer to Bethel at lunch. He had taken her to Sardi's, where all the debutantes try to look like actresses, and all the actresses try to look like—actresses. Normally the cast's communal lunch, between spasms of rehearsal, was a waxed-paper container of coffee and a ham sandwich from the drugstore, but occasionally Doc Keezer rebelled, and demanded time for real food.

"All that Shakespearean research stuff is the bunk," he said. "It's by no means proven that the best way to play Shakespeare isn't to do a Marmaduke Montmorency de Booth, with all the dog you can put on, tights and velvet hats and a lot of rapiers, and chew the scenery and yell and give everybody a good time—and you can get all the fittings second-hand then, and pick out the most rheumatic old ham at Billy McMoriarty's saloon for director. However, Beth, this is a theatrical engagement. We might have to go to work if we didn't have it. How about some cheese for dessert? When we get out on the road, you'll learn to take cheese instead of all this ice cream. It keeps your belly filled, and that's the chief purpose of a trouper, and not no purple ecstasies, or big notices by the police reporter in Cedar Rapids, Iowa."

"I'm going to love trouping," said Bethel.

"You are, eh? Wait till you have to catch a seven-A.M. train in Minnesota in January, with the thermometer eighteen below, and that old northwest wind scooting down the platform and the train an hour and a half late, and then it comes in with ice on it like armor, and the heating apparatus gone on the blink."

"I'll love it, Doc."

"Yes, you probably will, child. That 'll be the one thing that 'll finally tear it—to have you chattering like a canary bird at breakfast, when the rest of us have hang-overs and don't want to be suddenly jarred. You're a nice kid. I couldn't interest you in a goat farm in Vermont, could I? No? Okay, let's go back and see how much more of a beating the Bard will take."

She was still alone every evening—her companions of the day vanished into nonexistence after rehearsals—but she was not lonely. She curled on the bed in her room, repeating the Juliet part aloud; she washed her hair; she went by herself to a movie, humming such classic epodes as "Tea for Two," gliding in a warm, lilac-colored mist that shut out the November drizzle and cement pavements and iron gratings. For the first time in her life she was completely happy.

And once Andy invited her to an evening party at the Picardy, of which she recalled little except Mahala, in a black evening frock with a panel of silver from bosom to hem, being maddeningly gracious and proprietarial, and insisting on pouring out drinks for large strong men like Harry Purvis and Tony Murphy and Victor Swenson.

And once Andy took her to dinner at the Twenty-One

Club, at which he appeared at least twice a week for the purpose of explaining to a circle of professional wits that he never went to Twenty-One because there were too many professional wits there.

"Here's the picture you and I have to get, as apprentice actors, both of us. It's an allegory that Dorothy Gish told me," said Andy. "There was an old vaudeville couple; they'd been on the stage, mostly in the four-a-day, for thirty years, and they'd never made over sixty dollars a week between them. They'd done the same act—patter with a little Indian-club juggling, and then go into their dance—for fifteen years.

"Well, vaudeville is out, for the time being. They're living in a furnished housekeeping room, and Pop has been working in a clothes-pressing shop, evenings, to keep going. But they've had three days in a movie house in Altoona, and they land back in New York twenty-five dollars to the good. Tonight they'll have chicken, and Pop will be able to buy a new pair of pants for three-fifty, and that will keep the old coat going another year.

"It's evening and it's raining, and they carry their own suitcases from the ferryhouse, but they're cheerful until a Rolls-Royce limousine comes flying by, near the curb, and splashes mud all over them. In the limousine is a handsome, husky young couple—furs and top hat, staring straight ahead, ignoring everybody.

"Pop pulls out his old handkerchief, and wipes the mud off his wife's skirt, and he points after the expensive couple in the car and crows, *'But they can't act!'* There's our gospel, Beth."

And once, rather rudely, Zed invited her to dinner at an Italian restaurant in the East Forties, so far over that it was practically in Italy, and filled her with fetuccini, and lectured her as eloquently as Andy.

"This last week, the rehearsals will get pretty hysterical. Satori will work us all night. Nobody will know his lines.

Everybody will blow up. But that kind of strain you get over," said Zed. "The thing you've got to have the character to stand—good, old-fashioned, Scotch-Yankee-Montana word, 'character'; I like it—is after the show closes, and you go plumb loco, because month after month you can't get a job—you're in swell shape, all ready to go, and they won't let you up on any stage."

"I know. I've just had a month and a half of it."

"You've got to be prepared for a year and a half of it —ten years. Sitting by a telephone all day, waiting for a manager to call you."

"Do you?"

"No, but then I've got a special method. I insult people, and so they notice me. That takes too much pains and energy for most people. And then, too, it gets around that I'm a really good actor, and they need me."

"Upon my word! What about——"

"How do you know whether you're a good actress yet or not? How does anybody know? Don't be a lady. Don't look for insults."

"Uh—well—yes——"

"The actor and the portrait painter are the only artists that have to have people out in front. Writers are lucky! A writer can write even if he's fallen out of an aeroplane on the Sahara Desert."

"Write on what?"

"On the sand!"

"That wouldn't last very permanently, would it?"

"What writing does? Even Homer's only lasted three thousand years, and the human race's been going on for at least two hundred thousand."

"Zed! Do you think I'll be able to act?"

"My pet!" "Pet" was Zed's standard word of endearment, as "darling" and "kitten" were Andy's and "child" was Doc Keezer's. He would do wonderful, histrionic things with "pet"; he could make it insulting, belligerent, comforting or amorous.

"But *do* you think so?" insisted Bethel.

"I don't know yet. You're certainly not a dumb faker like Iris———"

"Then why do you go around with her so much?"

"Because she does what I tell her to, petty! You're not dumb like her, or phony and pretentious like Mahala, or sweet and pixie and dull like Mabel Staghorn. You belong more with Charlotte Levison—she's a tract-passing evangelical Fundamentalist Marxian, but a tricky actress. Or maybe you even belong with the big bad Boyle. Or you will, if you ever learn anything.

"At present you can't even walk across the stage as though you were really going somewhere and not being dangled on a string by the director. But—yes, you have a kind of—a touch of strangeness. God knows where you got it! A B.A. from a female college! But maybe you'll be able to do some conjuring yet, if you can ever learn to keep your hands from getting tangled up with your feet when you're pulling the rabbit out of your silver snood. *Bethel!*"

"Yes?"

"*Pet!*"

"Well?"

"This show will flop, of course. It won't last ten weeks on the road."

"Oh! No! Zed! It will succeed! It's got to! I'll make it! We'll all make it go. It's the world and all to Andy."

"But unfortunately Andy isn't anything to the world and all. He's a nice guy—and that's a lot of praise from me, because mostly I don't like these kindhearted, open-faced, upstanding young men from Yale and Princeton and Dale Carnegie's classes in oratory. But we haven't got anything. Modern dress? Hell, pants don't make a show—even the lack of 'em doesn't.

"It's the emotion, the philosophy, the *Stimmung*, and the *Stimmung* of our production is as old-fashioned as Joe Jefferson.

"Romeo is biology, that's what he is, not moonshine, and

Shakespeare knew it, the old devil—having been, like myself, educated under a hedgerow. Romeo is a decent young snob who's raving, fighting crazy about a girl who's the first one he's ever been really in love with. But to Andy and even to Mrs Boyle our presentation is merely a prankish pageant to be played in the glade, under the auspices of the Siddons Society of Sweet Briar College, and it's all the more prankish to wear herringbone tweed instead of velvet, so long as all the thoughts are in velvet. So what have we got? Just another semiprofessional road company of 'Abie's Italian Rose.' No, pet, I'm sorry; I like to eat, too, within reason; but we've got a flop on our hands."

Bethel was desolate; she was full of eager, loyal, imbecile plans for converting Andy to something which she didn't in the least understand. She loved Andy for his pathetic plans of an eager child; she hated Zed for his cynicism; she hated Andy for his amateurishness; she loved Zed for his integrity; and in excitement and bewilderment she lapped up spumoni like a cat lapping cream.

"So," Zed went on, "if I'm right, you and I will be back here in New York by about the end of February. We'll be just a couple of kids, with no job. Let's get acquainted on this tour. Really acquainted."

"You seem to be sufficiently really-acquainted with Iris."

"Yuh. Too well!"

"You're one of the gweat big men that all of the poor weak women follow!"

"Pet! Would you mind stopping talking like a fool—like a suburban wife flirting with the dentist? Let's get back to work."

She was angry and a little curious; not so much as to what his intentions might be as to whether this bumptious young stroller took enough trouble with women to have any intentions toward them at all.

It was a relief to ask cool, pleasant young Douglas Fry his opinion of their fate.

"Of course the show will succeed!" asserted Douglas. "Isn't *Romeo and Juliet* the greatest love story going? Aren't Americans the most sentimental people in the world? And isn't this the first time *Romeo* has been done so people today will identify themselves with it? Why, of course! It 'll be a wow!"

"Oh yes, I'm sure it will be a wow," exulted Bethel.

22

THERE WERE EXCURSIONS that made Bethel feel gratifyingly professional: the election of the company's Equity
deputy, when for a quarter-hour they ceased being artists
and vigorously became labor-union members who had jobs
and wages to protect. Wyndham Nooks diaconally offered
to serve and to guard them all like little lambs; so Doc
Keezer was elected. As a junior member of Equity, Bethel
had no vote. She just prayed for Doc's election.

And the first professional photographs: individual ones
to be exhibited in the frames in the theater lobbies. They
were photographed in a rapid-fire theatrical studio in a shaky
old building over an orangeade stand on that shockingly
decayed Rialto, Broadway.

The photographer, a black-haired young Pole who wore
a beret and a checked business suit, glared at Bethel, announced, "You've got a nice, sensitive face for Hollywood,
young lady, when you can get out of this damn-fool stage
business," and before she could protest that she was an
Artist, he was yelling at her, "Look up! Look down! Now

look up here where I'd be saying 'Look at the canary,' if you were about two years younger. Swell! Scram! Next!"

She was rather unausterely pleased when the proofs of her photographs made her seem alive and exciting, all living dark eyes, while the pictures of the lovely lily Iris revealed her as a little washed-out and plebeian. She told herself that she oughtn't to think things like that . . . she *told* herself.

The last ten days out of the four weeks of rehearsals accelerated like a car without brakes running down a mountain road.

For days it did not seem probable that there ever would be a performance. Half the time the old troupers like Doc Keezer and Hugh Challis and Mabel Staghorn saved their voices and dismayed Bethel by stingily talking only to themselves. Sometimes she was impressed by the dignity and noble pity of the prosaic Doc Keezer as Friar Laurence.

His whole face seemed larger; his forehead wider; his tranquil gestures more priestly. Then he would shrink again into peddling his gestures dully across a counter. Andy was always awake and romantic. Mrs Boyle was for an accidental moment, now and then, transformed into the passionate girl. Her voice was living music, and an inner glow seemed to make her whole body rosy as in divine tenderness she cried:

> "Be but sworn my love,
> And I'll no longer be a Capulet."

And five minutes later Mrs Boyle would be breaking the spell, and infuriating Romeo, by sweetly crooning, "Oh, Mr Deacon, I am *so* sorry to interrupt but, Mr Satori, did you say you thought I ought to lay my hand on the nurse's shoulder just before I say 'O, what a beast was I to chide at him,' or just afterwards?"

And when even the rock-bound Satori blew up with, "Oh, for God's sake, Aurelia, do it just the way you've been

doing it ever since you played it with Charles Kean in 1855!"
then Mrs Boyle smiled demurely.

Zed Wintergeist referred to Mrs Boyle as the "six-
minute egg."

By sheer torture Satori got old Wyndham Nooks not to
say his line as Sampson, "I strike quickly, being moved," as
though he were about to be sick. Most of the time most of
the cast floundered and forgot their lines and spoke them
like sulky schoolboys and forgot fifty times over just when
they were to turn and when to walk; and to the anxious
Bethel, the whole thing was a straw pile.

It was on Tuesday afternoon, in the last week of rehearsals, that the miracle happened, and suddenly they were
playing—they were not school children doing exercises but
trained actors playing, and then not actors at all, but real
people, suffering, loving, fighting. She cried a little, and she
saw Satori breathe deep, as line came smoothly after line
like water flowing.

Incredibly, the rehearsal time was almost over, and they
were preparing for their journey that would take them out
to Iowa, Kansas, perhaps to Colorado and California, that
might last a year and might end up in New York or Australia
—or in Palooka Junction.

They were all buying wardrobes and baggage, and all talking about it. Mahala was going to have a new evening frock
of silver lamé—she would be going to elegant parties with
Andy, she sniffed. Iris, at the celebrated "little dressmaker
on a side street, so cheap, and just as good as Bergdorf,"
was having made an evening frock that had a jet-black
front and tight long sleeves but, economically, no back at
all.

Bethel's father, always so amazingly understanding of
things that he couldn't possibly have understood or imagined,
had sent her a hundred dollars, with a note ending, "I
guess I can get along without this for a while and you will
want to buy trunk & etc. & be as well dressed as all the

other girls in Show, guess to do that would cost three four hundred, afraid can't quite afford that but hope enclosed will help a little."

She tenderly sent back ten dollars, and spent the rest on underclothes and a sweater and a trunk. She was suddenly sharply impatient with the swank of Mahala and Iris. If she bought anything, it would be out of her savings along the road after she had paid Sol Gadto for his lessons —and if the others sniffed at her shabbiness, why, she'd just have to get along with being as badly dressed, off-stage, as Mrs Lumley Boyle!

But she excitedly shopped for a second-hand trunk. She calmly drove a number of Third Avenue Jewish dealers in such baggage, dealers esteemed in the profession for their shrewdness and persistence, to frothing madness by picking at the corners of wardrobe-trunk drawers and counting the number of clotheshangers and refusing to be moved by broken-hinged coffers with lovely flowery chintz lining.

No newly made knight had more satisfaction than did Bethel when the new old trunk arrived in her room— necessitating her standing on the bed when she was dressing—and she beamed at its lordly inscription:

B. M.

N. Y. C.

_____ **THEATER**

She read timetables. She looked at maps in the library. She mugged up on such exotic knowledge as the origin of the names Des Moines and Milwaukee. And she was somewhat terrified all the while, because the longest journey she had ever made had been from Sladesbury to Bar Harbor, by motorcar, and she had never spent a night on a Pullman car in her life—to her generation, aeroplanes were more familiar than trains. And she was sure, up to the moment when their train left for Belluca, Indiana, that this grown-up company of real actors would never actually pay her train fare and take her along.

Andy Deacon had a rich cousin, one Romer Ingalls, in the plumbing-supply-manufacture and Sons of the American Revolution line in Belluca, and no professional play had opened there for years. With these two advantages, they were bound to succeed, and to all of the company, even Doc Keezer and Mrs Boyle, Belluca suddenly took on the aspect of Bethlehem.

Rather numbly, as on the morning before execution, Bethel realized that at seven P.M., this very Saturday, November 26, 1938, she would be starting with the company for Belluca. She packed her trunk and three bags, made sure that her purple lining pencil and mascara were in her make-up box, paid her final hotel bill, sent down her baggage, and sat on her bed in the vacated, horribly empty, horribly quiet and utterly strange room, in a panic.

Volitionless, dream-walking, she coaxed herself downstairs and into a taxicab to the Pennsylvania Station.

With a feeling that the flow of passengers would stop and rush up to her, begging for her autograph, if they knew who she really was—i.e., a woman explorer starting for Greenland—she gave her suitcase to an unimpressed redcap.

The whole company were surging in circles or standing patiently at the train gate. She did not know them, for they wore not the familiar, rather back-attic clothes in which they had rehearsed, but their best winter overcoats. How familiar she would become with those overcoats in the next months!—Andy's dark gray herringbone, Zed's loose and cloaklike camel's-hair with the high collar, Iris's vain lilac garment, with two huge purple buttons on the back of the waist (and one tiny grease spot, later to spread by parthenogenesis, on the front hem), Doc Keezer's gloomy, heavy gray worsted which (he told you) he had bought in

Wheeling, West Virginia, for thirty-two dollars three years ago.

As she recognized them, her timidity was gone in the joy of this, her family. They were so welcoming, so gay. Everyone's smile said that they loved her and that they were going forth to conquer.

But Andy was edging away by himself, walking up and down the shed, head bent, his hands behind him. Doubtfully she followed him and begged, "Anything the matter?"

He held her by both arms and burst out, "Kitten, I suddenly feel so responsible, taking all of you out on this gamble, and a lot of you with dependents—kids and mothers. Real actors, not semi-amateurs like me, trusting their whole lives to an enterprise like this. It scares me! Darling, I want you to kneel in your berth tonight and pray, 'God make me a good actress and help me to help Andy put this crazy adventure over'!"

For the first time, she was not shy with him. As he held her shoulders, she put her light hands affectionately about his waist and cried, "You've been an angel to all of us. And we do appreciate it, though I guess we've all been too stupid to thank you. And we will succeed. We will!"

"Thanks, Beth." He looked at her with a curious, bright sensitiveness, unlike his complacent bulk, patted her shoulders and hurried away to buy mounds of magazines.

The train gate was open. The company were a ship's complement, shouting farewell to land, anchors aweigh for Ultima Thule, where summer and winter the golden globes shine on the trees and in the street lie pieces of eight. Antonio Murphy, the solemnly comic Peter, was kissing a surprisingly pretty young wife good-by; so was Geoffrey Hoy, the Benvolio; Mabel Staghorn was crying on the shoulder of a thin, painfully reasonable little man; and Wyndham Nooks kissing the hand of a faded and aging wife, faded yellow hair and faded pink cheeks and faded pink summery hat, who had been his companion in rackety medicine-show days and who looked at her lion-maned Henry Irving so adoringly, with such loneliness, that Bethel pinched herself for having ever made fun of Nooks.

And they all stamped down the stairs and onto the Pullmans.

They had one and a half Pullmans reserved for them. In the half-car, the Adults' Car, to which were assigned such nobles as Hugh Challis and Mabel Staghorn, Mrs Boyle had the drawing room, which is the sign and privilege of a star; in the other, the frivolous Young People's Caravan, the drawing room was Andy's, but tonight it was shared by Director Satori, who was going out to Belluca to stay with the show the first week. And on the whole journey it was jammed less with Andy than with blown newspapers, the girls of the company, bridge games, Wyndham Nooks rumbling, portable radios yawping, and everybody's excess luggage, rubbers and troubles. It was as private and honorific as the vestibule.

Before the train started, Andy summoned everybody into the Young People's Car for an announcement. Beth long remembered those twenty-eight people, plus Sally Carpet, come down to the train with the final telegrams for Andy, standing thick in the car aisle, their faces, carven in high planes and shadows by the car lights, uplifted to Andy as he stood up on a pile of suitcases and shouted:

"Ladies and gentlemen of the company! We are about to assault and capture the West. West where the West begins. Where the handclasps are a little warmer and we hope the box offices are a little busier."

Bethel sharply remembered that, however Andy might joke, she, who had never been more than ten miles west of the Hudson, really was Going West: California sands and yellow rivers and desert and the peaks of Colorado; covered wagons, and John Brown riding, and young men singing on ranches with the moon enormous across the plains. She was almost dancing as he went on:

"So to start us off on our mission—of making a fairly honest living—I want to tell you that I have just received a wire from Belluca that we shall go clean on Monday night, opening night, and that there is a very good chance of our being sold out for all the rest of the week. We're a hit already, boys and girls. Skip, Sally; the train's going."

Everybody cheered. Miss Carpet darted off, to the tune of that twilight wail "All-ll-ll abo-oo-ooard!" from the platform, and the train was moving.

The car was littered with baggage like the debris of a hurricane. Bethel was to know the company's belongings as well as she knew the owners: Doc Keezer's portable radio, canvas-covered with a band of red and yellow, which he played very softly in his berth on the long, train-shaking nights when he couldn't sleep; Mahala's extravagant four bags, in blue morocco so expensive and so easily scratched that she kept them protected by a variety of little dog blankets, so that you never could see the fine leather at all; the two-volume set of Karl Marx which Charlotte Levison always had with her, in train seat and hotel and dressing room, and which she was never seen to read for more than five minutes at a time; the whole series of plays and books on stage design which Zed Wintergeist and Douglas Fry did read and trade back and forth; Henry W. Purvis's private flask, and Henry W. Purvis's folding pocket chessboard, which he shared with Douglas, Hugh Challis and Mabel Staghorn; and, most conspicuous, most horrible of all the impedimenta, Mrs Lumley Boyle's hell-born and heaven-hated Pekingese dog, named Pluto.

These objects Bethel came to know better than any piece of furniture in the house in Sladesbury—even the ancient folding card table on which she had done her homework and had drawn hearts and flowers. At home things did get put away in closets now and then, while here you stumbled over Mahala's imperial blue bags, and cracked your shins on them, on the train, in hotel corridors and in front of her dressing room, all day long.

It was a traveling circus; it was an army with paper banners. There seemed to be no end to the people Bethel met as her new family. On the train she first really talked with the company manager and wet nurse, the Yankee Tertius Tully, and first saw the master carpenter, the electrician and the property man, who would manage local theater crews: Gene Doric, Wilson Kinloch, and Phil Schoenberg. They were all middle-aged, all hopelessly married, all given to black sateen shirts. Gene and Phil became her amiable and loyal friends; Bethel felt more at home with them than ever with Victor Swenson or Tudor Blackwall.

But Wilson Kinloch proved that a man may be a member of a labor union, in good standing, and still be rather less than a saint. Kinloch hated, roughly in this order: Andy's wealth, Andy's acting, Gene Doric's not altogether guileless habit of dropping hammers on his (Wilson's) toes, William Green, president of the American Federation of Labor, J. Pierpont Morgan, Zed Wintergeist's jeering, Iris Pentire's softness, and Pluto, the dog of Boyle. And he hated them so heartily and industriously that, before the tour was over, he became rather of a sympathetic character to a Bethel getting fed up with balconies, moonlight effects and genius.

She now met first the final members of the excursion: Hilda Donnersberg, Mrs Boyle's maid, a wild strained Austrian who was convinced that everybody but Mrs Boyle was a fool; and Ernie Smith, the boy who came along to sell the illustrated programs in the lobbies and who loved nothing so much as giving Iris and Bethel his opinion of the acting of Francine Larrimore and Katharine Hepburn and Pauline Lord. It seems that all of these ladies had frequently called him to their dressing rooms for technical advice, and had benefited gratifyingly. Miss Larrimore had said to him—asserted Ernie—"I consider you the smartest critic of acting in New York. You got it all over George Jean Nathan, Ernie. It's an injustice, Ernie, that you aren't up here on the stage yourself, instead of out in that lobby wasting your voice selling programs."

"I see!" said Bethel.

They would be much quieter later, but perhaps the company were a little loud, this first evening in the diner. Lyle Johnson and Charlotte Levison sang "Frankie and Johnnie." Zed and Douglas Fry rehearsed *Waiting for Lefty*. Iris rather loudly told Victor Swenson her theories of make-up. When they settled down in the sleeper again, it was already beginning to be home.

Three bridge games started, with suitcases, supported on knees, for tables. Miss Staghorn was knitting. Charlotte returned to not reading some more Marx. Hugh Challis, who belonged in the bleak correctitude of the other car, was telling Gene Doric, the master carpenter, about the trick Larry Lewis, the music-hall comedian, had played on Billy Bush, the expert on playing Mayfair butlers, at the golf club in Little Pimple, Surrey, at or about three in the afternoon on September 16th, though it may have been the 17th, 1903.

In the drawing room, their legs rather cramped with suitcases, Andy and Satori and Tertius Tully and Eldred, the stage manager, were wearily scribbling on papers—papers—papers. If Andy was a Romeo belated, he had also heard about the need of bookkeeping.

Only Zed and Douglas and Bethel were reading, and she was too restless to keep her attention even on Noel Coward's *Present Indicative*. She raised the blind, pressed her forehead against the cold glass, stared out on the dark farm lands that passed her. Oh, she was going to see and grasp every state in the vast Union!

In each lone light that raced past her, she saw a farmhouse, saw the family—the father, the old aunt, the ambitious son with his manual of automotive engineering, the wild, dangerous daughter listening. She wanted to know them; she wanted by playing them to give them to the world.

She had never been so content.

And that night, unsleeping but happily drowsy in her berth, she listened to the train whistle—that familiar magic summons to be up and wandering—from the engine on her very own train.

23

Belluca, Indiana, pop. 277,000; on the Wabusha River; site state aviation sch.; Belluca Univ., Littlefield Art Museum cont. a Fra Angelico, an El Greco; mfrs. plumbing supplies, sewer pipe, machine tools, watches, gloves, glass.

As THEY ALL PEERED out of the car windows, in Belluca, at eleven in the morning, everything was as it should be: reporters on the platform, photographers with flashlights, and Andy's great rich cousin, Mr Romer Ingalls, escorted by cousinlets and a uniformed chauffeur.

Whether it was because of Mr Ingalls's patronage, or because no Eastern professional play had opened in Belluca for twenty years, or because, in ten years now, no play except WPA productions had been announced for more than a three-night run, or because of a pure love of the Bard and Mrs Lumley Boyle, the whole city of Belluca—that is, the section of it that considered the drama as important as ice-cream sodas—was prepared to take the Deacon Romeo & Juliet Production to its friendly Midwestern heart.

Each of the three newspapers had sent at least two reporters—the drama editor and a society chronicler. Behind them and the light-flashing photographers were a medley of horrible little girls with autograph albums; little girls who would delightedly have interrupted Romeo just as he was climbing the balcony but who would much rather have had the sacred totem of the gangster in the film *Stick 'Em Up*. But they made a very pretty crush to excite Bethel and Iris.

All but one of the reporters packed in about Mrs Boyle. That one was a baby-faced, eager-faced young man, who grabbed the arms of the two girls, crowing, "You Iris Pentire and Beth Merriday? I'm Carl Frazee of the *News*. Look at the sacred white journalistic cows mooing at the Boyle woman—and see her smile at them. Not very strong on smiling privately, is she?"

Bethel giggled. Iris said indignantly, "She never smiles, in rehearsal, except when she thinks it 'll make somebody mad."

"Lookit, kids. I'll be in and buy you a drink, soon as you get settled in your hotel. I suppose you'll go to the Buckingham-Bradley."

With dignity, an actress listening to the nobler call, Bethel stated, "I'm sorry but we have to Be In The Theater all day. We're Rehearsing All Afternoon, and Dress Rehearsal This Evening. Mr Satori decided to hold it here instead of New York. But perhaps we'll see you sometime this week. You are a reporter?"

"No. He's a college boy!" sniffed Iris. "Aren't you now, Carl?"

"Ye-es. Well. I was. University of Michigan B.A. Oxford M.A. Licentiate of the Sorbonne. And I'll do the review of your show for the *News* tomorrow night."

But of the two girls, one did have sense enough to know how much she had been put in her place, and, from twenty-nine cheerful words, to learn a great deal about Indiana, about the Middle West, about the whole sprawling United States.

"See you soon, kids. Don't take any wooden money," said Carl Frazee.

They heard Andy's cousin, Romer Ingalls—a thick man with a cigar and an improbable Legion of Honor ribbon— shouting, "Course you're going to stay with us, Andy, but do you think Mrs Boyle would like to come, too?"

Andy looked horrified. "No! I'm going to stay with My Company!"

And, loving him, Bethel knew that Andrew Deacon was as young as she, and as armorless against a cynical world.

Reluctantly, but agreeing because it would save money, Bethel had promised to share hotel rooms with Iris on the tour, and they drove off together in a taxicab.

Iris (before she had seen any of the city) sneered that Belluca was a "miserable little dump," compared with New York, which was her native city only by very recent absorption, the vital statistics accrediting her to a side street in Wheeling, West Virginia. To Bethel this new city seemed huge and surprising. She looked through the rear window of the taxi at the white limestone façade of the Union Station, with its white tower five hundred feet high; she looked around at the station plaza, with its fountains and sycamore alleys; and she felt that she had come, with her fellow adventurers in cap and bells, on festivity to Rome.

The taxi sped out of the plaza, round a corner, and she saw their first playbills:

MRS LUMLEY BOYLE
(*in person*)
in
The world's first production of
the world's greatest love story
ROMEO AND JULIET
in MODERN clothes
with Andrew Deacon and an all-star
Broadway cast
World Premiere in Belluca
AMERICAN THEATER
Nov. 28 – Dec. 3

Before they drove up to the Hotel Buckingham-Bradley (1,000 rooms, 1,000 baths, your home-town newspaper at your door in the morning), Iris and the squealing Bethel had seen nine more posters. The girls were innocent. They did not know the benevolent deception of what is known as "depot billing," whereby the company's advance man and the local theater manager make sure that whether the local citizens ever learn that the show is coming or not, at least the producer, arriving in town in a state of exaltation, doubt and suspicion, will have plenty to gladden him on the way to the hotel section.

Their room in the Buckingham-Bradley seemed to Bethel ten times as large as her den in New York and—she had known so few towns: Sladesbury, Point Royal, Grampion, New York—it looked out over enchantingly different streets: a very fine structure in the way of a granite jail, and a circular park with a statue of General Nelson A. Miles.

But Iris was wallowing in the local Sunday newspapers, the *News,* the *American* and the *Daily Republican,* bought on the way up.

"Look! Look! Beth, look! Here's both our pictures, and stories about us."

Bethel squatted on the floor with Iris and stared at a group picture of herself, Iris, Charlotte and Vera Cross (Lady Capulet's understudy), all adoringly surrounding Mrs Boyle. The advance man had done honor to his profession as press agent. In the *News* Bethel read a spirited account of herself (some inches below the rhetorical splendors devoted to Mrs Boyle) and learned that—

in college, at a certain famous old institution for women on the banks of the historic Hudson River, she was president of the dramatic club, star in many elaborate college productions. After college her ability was immediately recognized, and she has had such an extensive training in stock as falls to the lot of but few young actresses.

Bethel moaned, "But they might have put in my studies in the Alva Prindle School of Garage Acting."

Radio Station WXXW, owned by the Belluca *Daily Republican* and the most influential fount of wisdom and of jazz in all that section of Indiana, was turning over a whole half-hour of time—magic like to Jehovah's, that can own and turn over Time!—to an interview with the Romeo Company by no less a local prophet than the Indiana Walter Winchell, Mr Ted Gronitz, mention in whose daily column "Hot on the Spot" was more sought by Belluca debutantes, prize fighters and pulpit orators than was sleep or raiment. Andy, Mahala and Mrs Boyle were to broadcast, of course. But at lunchtime—a dozen of the youngsters of the company at three tables down in the Buckingham-Bradley Coffee Shop, being very professional and stagy over Ham and Eggs, Country Style—Bethel was summoned by a bellboy to report at Andy's suite, to be ready to broadcast.

"Me . . . broadcast?" squeaked Bethel.

"Sure. I done it once. I'm a swell crooner," said the bellboy.

In Andy's suite—a Louis Seize apartment with the useful additions of a Dinette, and a purple-and-black-tiled Kitchenette with an electric refrigerator—Bethel found Mr Ted Gronitz, their broadcaster, pacing and shrieking. He was a squat, bristly haired little man who had been a featherweight boxer, a county-fair spieler and a financial reporter. He was a dream in brown—brown suit, brown handkerchief at his breast, autumn-leaf-brown tie, cigar-brown shirt and cigar-brown cigar. He yelled amiably at her:

"Bethel? Listen, kid. I got nidea. Of course I'm going to interview these stuffed shirts here—Andy and Mahally and the Boyle—but how about getting the impressions of an understudy? How do you like having to sit back and listen to the old champ play Juliet when you know you could wipe her out? Ever want to bump her off?"

Mrs Boyle, listening, looked pained.

Not waiting for Bethel's answer, Ted Gronitz exulted, "That 'll be fine. That 'll give the old girls sitting home by the radio something to talk about. One in ten thousand

might even go to your show. Now, Andy, I want you to
keep off dramatic subjects—you're not so hot on those—
and talk about High Sassiety in Newport. Didn't your Old
Lady entertain an English Lord there last year? Swell!
That's the stuff."

In panic Bethel had fled to the sheltering side of Andy
and was whispering, "Oh, do I have to do this? I've never
talked on a mike. And he seems so—crude."

"No, kitten, of course you don't have to. But it would
help me a lot. We've got to put the show over in this one
town, anyway. Can you stand it?"

"Oh, of course, Andy!" she glowed. . . . To be able
to "help a lot," to help Andy Deacon! For that had she been
born!

The *Daily Republican* building was an aged pile of pasty-
faced yellow brick, and the corridors were inky and lathy,
but as the delegation of five from the Romeo Company,
headed by Ted Gronitz and Tertius Tully, stepped from
the elevator into the top story, devoted to Station WXXW,
they were in a set from the Follies. The vestibule, lined with
faun-colored leather, was filled with "modernistic" chairs
with scarlet-and-yellow leather seats and nickel arms and
legs and had, at the end, a tall desk, beneath which stood
the chorus: slim girls in uniforms as military as Bethel's on
stage, with cocky pillbox caps.

"Peg, go in and tell the old man the Shakespeare and
Barnum and Bailey Circus has arrived," yelled Gronitz,
and one seraph darted away. She returned with Andy's
cousin, Ingalls, and six eyeglassed men, as portly and
solemn as canons. Bethel never did find out just who they
all were, but they all looked like observers at an execution
as, in terror, seizing Andy's arm, she marched down the
cork-floored gallows walk to Studio No. 3.

The broadcasting room itself was cheery enough, and a
little on the littered side: a long room managing to contain
two grand pianos, a row of nickel-and-ebony folding chairs

—immediately occupied by the observers—a harp, a bust of Beethoven, a plaster Tudor fireplace with electric logs, and a directors' table. But in the center was a thin standard on which was a double-faced microphone, like a double-ended wedge. From the side it resembled the stiffly upreared head of a boa constrictor; from the front, an electric toaster.

Bethel quaked with the thought of the millions about to listen to her, in city homes and automobiles and those farm-houses always designated in radio accounts as "far-flung." Far-flung farmhouses with gimlet-eyed, terrier-eared, far-flung farm wives listening to Bethel Merriday!

In a coop shut off from the studio by a glass-window wall was an engineer at a gigantic control board. Would he, maybe, cut her off the air if she wasn't at once very reverent and very witty? He was such a dry, stern, green-eyeshaded engineer, not likely to be tender to dewy young actresses.

She was trembling.

Of course there was no proof whatever that millions were going to listen to her, or ever did listen to her. In fact with the two or three broadcasts every week which she was going to do on the rest of the tour, she had no proof that anybody ever did hear her. Perhaps no one did.

Mr Ted Gronitz was capering with not the slightest awe. As the red second hand on the clock on the wall reached the exact half-hour, Ted pulled the microphone stand toward him as though it were a lively sweetheart and chuckled, softly, rapidly:

"Hot spots on the air! Ted Gronitz speaking from the Belluca *Daily Republican* offices. I've got a real hot cul-turureal hot spot for you this afternoon, boys and girls, but I can't get going before I whet my whistle with a bottle of Corn-Cola, the NEW thirst quencher and taste tickler. Yum, yum, yum, maybe that wasn't good."

He didn't really have a bottle of Corn-Cola there, you know. He was pretending. And Bethel was moaning in-

wardly, "What has all this got to do with playing Shakespeare?"

"YesSIR, folks, that goes right to the spot. Don't forget:
at your druggist's or grocer's, five cents the throw, CORN-
COLA, and you'll thank me for the tip.

"Now who do you think we've got with us this afternoon,
folks? None other than Romeo and Juliet themselves, the
most famous lovers in history, and you'd better look sharp,
all you young folks, and get onto how the professionals do
their love-making. YesSIR, for the first time in a quarter
of a century, Belluca is being honored by the world pre-
meer . . ."

He said that Mrs Lumley Boyle was too great an actress
and too good a sport to mind a little kidding, and so would
Mrs Boyle tell them how many English counts and lords
and kings and barons and all those she had kissed?

A number, it seemed, by her modest account.

And now would Andrew Deacon—once known as Ole
Andy Deacon, the Pride of the Yale Gridiron—tell the
boys and girls how he would win a Juliet if he met her off-
stage?

Bethel saw his Adam's apple bobbing and his eyes turning inside out with fear as Andy tried to be witty and then,
earnestly, boyishly (sweetly, she thought, and pretty badly)
switched into an account of what he was trying to do: pour
into the immortal body of Shakespeare the life blood of today.

Suddenly Andy had drooped away from the microphone
and had sunk in one of the line of folding chairs, mopping
his head, while she wanted to run over and kiss him and tell
him how good he was. It was presumably Mahala's turn
to be pixie. But, horribly, it was at herself that Ted was
grinning, while he chatted to his audience:

"Now we'll get away from the big guns of the stage and
turn the mike over to a darling kid, Bethel Merriday, Mrs

Boyle's understudy, who if you could see her, as I do now, all you youngsters would rush in and try to date her up for the next ten years. Here you are, Beth. Attagirl!"

Certainly by no volition of her own she had got from her chair to the other side of the standard from Ted and was facing that mocking small grid, her knees and stomach failing her, as Ted piped, "Now tell us, baby, what's your chief ambition?" And by no will of her own, Bethel was answering —instantly, briskly, "To be as good an actress as Mrs Boyle someday."

She smiled over at the star, who beamed back, eyes like black glass. Bethel never had any trouble with Mrs Boyle after that day—no violent trouble.

"Why do you want to go on the stage, Beth, pretty kid like you?"

"Because I believe that if an actress can do it—*if* she can —she'll be something bigger than her own self, when she's playing great roles."

Bethel realized that she could snap back answers instantly; that Andy and Tertius Tully were nodding to each other, as who should say that she was good.

"The great tradition, eh? That's the stuff. But wouldn't you rather marry a handsome young fellow with lots of money?"

"I would not!"

"What's your advice to the girls that would like to get on the stage?"

"Work and wait, I guess."

As she went on—on—on—four prodigious minutes, Bethel hated everything she was saying more and more. She was being banal. She was being smirkingly good-natured. It wasn't good enough!

And still she went on, while Ted smiled gratitude for her quickness. What choked and stopped her at last was not disgust with her own glibness but a panicky feeling that the blank microphone before her was not connected. It never applauded. It never changed. She was talking into a cold hole in the air, and that contemptuous coldness defeated her.

At the end she heard them all praising her. Andy cried, "Darling, you're going to be one of our biggest roper-inners."

Then she saw Zed Wintergeist—heaven knows when or why he had got into the room—standing by the door, smiling bitterly, and she was very sick.

And was Ted Gronitz, in the derisive secret refuges of his heart, as vulgar and half literate as he seemed? He had used Hugh Challis's favorite war cry, "The great tradition." She was frightened.

But in the dress rehearsal she forgot all that.

They had held two scenery rehearsals in New York, but this, their first complete dress rehearsal, began at five o'clock Sunday afternoon and staggered to something like an ending at five o'clock next morning.

As they walked from their hotel for the rehearsal, Iris insisted that they enter by way of the theater lobby, to see the frames with their photographs. "Nosir!" Bethel said stoutly. "I'm going back to the stage entrance. That's where an actor belongs, and only an actor has any real right to enter there. Lobby? Frames? The laity can have those. Huh! The carriage trade!"

(But it is true, however, that she had already seen a frame, in the hotel lobby!)

Like a priestess, alone privileged to enter the sanctuary by the low sacred door, Bethel skipped along a cobble-paved alley, between the side of a steam laundry and the back of the old American Theater of Belluca. She chattered to Iris, but she chattered to keep from crying, for she was remembering the Crystal Theater of Sladesbury, and Caryl McDermid and frail Elsie Krall, and the first time she had dared go back to watch their glory-trailing appearance at the stage door. The rough, dark red brick side wall of the alley seemed to her beautiful; something out of Dickens, or an enchantment that belonged to Garrick and Mrs Siddons and Eleonora Duse.

Except for Grampion, and the temporary refuges for re-hearsals in New York, this was her first theater; it really was hers; it belonged to her, and she served it. Looking down from the ivory, cloud-hung thrones of the seraphim, she listened to the doorman—satisfactorily old and mus-tached and wrinkled—when he snapped, "You girls in the cast?" They smiled at him, entered his narrow coop, and, having left New York a whole twenty-two hours ago, both Iris and she looked carefully through the letters in the box below the callboard.

Bethel stole away from Iris, to be alone in her first moment of coming out on a professional stage.

Andy and Satori were yelling; Zed Wintergeist was yell-ing in his dressing room and simultaneously playing an un-explained violin; the company stagehands were yelling at the local stage crew; Douglas Fry was going quietly about with a floor plan in front of his nose; pillars of plywood and stone walls of canvas were leaning over threateningly as they were moved into place. But the curtain was up, and as Bethel slipped through an entrance and stood down on the apron of the stage, looking into the enormous unpeopled auditorium, this, her cathedral, was quiet as midnight, awe-some as the still tombs in the cathedral crypt.

The American Theater of Belluca, which remembered the chariot race in *Ben Hur,* was a handsome, portly old house, with three balconies, terminating in the perilous mountain shelf of the old-fashioned "nigger heaven." The ceiling, in dark wooden panels divided by smoke-darkened ridges of gold, was painted with the twisted Richard III, with Lear raving to the breakers, with soft-sighing Rosalind. The boxes were gilded sea shells. The seats were in faded red plush upholstery; the sharply raked aisles carpeted in maroon. It was in dolorous taste, but it was a real theater, not a movie shop with neat walls of tan-tinted celotex.

All of the sixteen hundred seats that she could see climb-ing up in front of her looked like flat-chested people, quiet, polite-faced, waiting for her to begin to act. And she was not afraid of them as she had been of the silent cynicism on the porous face of the microphone. She wanted to begin.

She was to share a dressing room with Charlotte Levison, Vera Cross and Mabel Staghorn, the character woman who belabored the part of the Nurse on stage and belabored sweetness off. As they dressed for this final rehearsal—Charlotte a Rue-de-la-Paix Lady Montague—Bethel was envious of their make-ups. Charlotte, that handsome countess of Communism, with touches of blue-gray along the sides of her nose, became high-well-born, and Miss Staghorn, in her own person a mirror of the Ladies' Foreign Missionary Society of Augusta, Maine, became red-nosed and ribald and toothless.

Proudly they took themselves out on the damp cement basement floor, bordering which were the coops of their dressing rooms. All the company, so long familiar, were exclaiming over one another's metamorphoses. Only Andy, in the tweed jacket and gray bags which he intended to wear as a gay and easygoing Romeo, seemed the same kind self.

Zed, Henry Purvis, Geoffrey Hoy and Tudor Blackwall —Mercutio, Tybalt, Benvolio and Paris—they were in the uniforms of Italian officers. No, worse than that: they were suddenly professional actors, and our Bethel felt herself entirely out of it, wanted to blow her little amateur nose and run home crying.

It was Zed who most overwhelmed her. That tousled young rebel, with the frayed ties and the wrinkled soft shirt collars, was an incredibly elegant young nobleman now, a fencer and polo player and aviator, with his oiled hair, his tall peaked uniform cap cockily tilted, his wide shoulders, his thin knees in riding breeches, his scornfully shining boots. Bethel would have told you, earnestly and honestly, that she loathed war and hated Fascism, but when Captain Zed Mercutio-Montague stalked toward her with the gay hard grin of the warrior, when he shouted, "Well, pet, how do you like your totalitarian hero?" when he squeezed

her shoulder—superior, reckless, probably cruel—she was
faint, and from no democratic ideology.

When Charlotte saw the uniforms, she clasped her hands
like Modjeska and wailed, "But I hate everything Fascist!
I can't stay on in this show!" Harry Purvis (Ph.D., but
sober now), flaunted, "So do I hate it. But don't tie the party
line around the end of your nose, my comrade and my particular darling. Who's ever going to connect Tybalt with
the Duce? Let's go argue about it." Charlotte went.

Then the curtain was down, and in front of it Bethel was
quavering her prologue. As she came off, Satori grunted at
her, "Okay. Just remember three things: keep your head up,
so the gallery can see and hear you. Enunciate—let's hear
your *r*'s and *t*'s and *m*'s. And if your foot slips in a line,
don't ever go back and correct it. Okay. *Take her up!*"

They took her up—her being the curtain—and the theory
was that, on its rising, Sampson Nooks and Peter Antonio
Murphy would gaily be clumping out, ready for a street
row. They weren't. They had, that second, appallingly
found that one of them had gold buttons on his livery coat
and the other silver.

That meant a conference of Satori, Andy, Nooks, Murphy
and Mrs Golly, the wardrobe mistress, who finally relieved
them all by the inspired suggestion of keeping the buttons
as they were—the audience would think it was intentional.
Once, under canvas, Mrs Golly had played moonshiners'
beautiful daughters, then moonshiners' loyal wives, and
finally moonshiners' comic grandmothers; and she had played
Juliet for two nights in Cheyenne, Wyoming, in 1906.

For twelve blasphemous hours, when everybody slumped
on chairs and looked glassy-eyed above limp cigarettes, they
carried on what Satori afterward called a fine, satisfactory
dress rehearsal.

Over Act I, Scene V—Romeo's first glimpse of Juliet, at
Capulet's party—there was an hour of shrieking conference.
None of the walk-ons, which included all the young people

in the company, agreed with any other on just which cue they were to come gamboling in as maskers. Half the batteries in their electric torches would not work. There was a loud ideological and commercial argument with the union musician who was running the phonograph producing guaranteed genuine old Italian dance music, off-stage, and at this moment of painful class struggle Zed pleased everybody by piping up with what nobody had thought of till now: they ought, with modern clothes, to have modern tango music.

"Oh, shut up!" said Andy to Zed.

"Okay," said Zed.

There was battle over the ad libs of the entering Bacchantes at the Capulet party. Iris, in character, kept saying, "Oh, isn't this a lovely party, I think it's just dandy" and Lyle Johnson (as a Cinquecento Veronese) kept growling, "What's the idea we can't smoke in this show; it would be twice as natural; modern costume—nuts!" And first they were too loud, then Satori couldn't hear them at all, then they were too loud again.

And a completely serious debate as to whether Tybalt-Purvis ought to carry brass knuckles (benevolently replacing the wicked ancient rapier) in the pocket of his white evening waistcoat. . . .

And a half-hour's wait while Satori, Andy, Stage Manager Eldred and Kinloch, the electrician, turned lights off and on, and apparently got none of the effects they wanted, and apparently didn't care much. Hoy and Lyle and Harry Purvis sat on the floor meantime, lighting cigarettes and smearily crushing out the butts, and yawned, "What the hell's holding us up now? Why the hell don't they get on with it? How the hell do they expect us to give a show tomorrow night? Who the hell is running this amateur benefit? The hell!"

But Zed was surprisingly patient. Given a rehearsal, he seemed to have none of the nerves and muscles and stomach that in all the others were quivering with shaky weariness. This was his sport. He only grinned when, listening to

Andy's fervent, "Oh, she doth teach the torches to burn bright . . . beauty too rich for use, for earth too dear!" Tony Murphy snarled, "Zed, I don't know how long I can stand here and listen to that student emote!"

All of Bethel's curiosity and her eagerness chilled as she heard this. She did not know whether it was more for love of Andy or her own pride as a judge of acting. . . . She had been moved again by Andy's warmth and richness and clear nobility. . . . Was she perhaps wrong—was he perhaps bad? . . .

Whatever went wrong—even Lyle Johnson's insertions of a filling-station "Yuh!" in emendation of the Bard, and the failure of the stage manager's off-stage revolver, with which he had to give voice to Romeo's and Tybalt's pistols, to make any sound but a flat click—the immediate criminal invariably said, "Oh, that 'll be all right tomorrow," and that seemed to repair everything. It was all magic and madness.

Every two hours Andy had coffee and sandwiches brought in. The rehearsal halted, and the comparative silence of homicidal arguments about direction gave way to a crash of joyous babbling, and they all, except perhaps Tony Murphy, loved one another. Hugh Challis murmured, "In forty-five years on the stage, Bethel, I've occasionally known producers who served coffee once during a dress rehearsal. And I've occasionally known producers who borrowed the money from the actors to go out and get coffee for themselves. But I've none too often heard of one who thought that actors could take to eating as a regular accomplishment. This Andy is a very sweet lad. You're fond of him, I take it."

"W-why—y-yes—— Yes, I am! Very!"

"Splendid. And I rather think, my good girl, that one of these days he'll have time to take a look at our Mahala and see what a tuppenny-ha'penny young woman she is, and turn to you."

"Me? I don't think there is much of a Me yet, Mr Challis."

"No? Perhaps not. Perhaps not. There will be, I fancy, when our company is a great success. Oh yes, we shall be. Can't afford not to be."

"No!"

Toward three A.M., when even Satori and Zed and Andy were worn down and Mrs Boyle began to vanish backstage and to smell, though faintly, of whisky, then that old Player King, that Vincent Crummles of the purple sage, Wyndham Nooks, rose to his own.

By the time they had reached the chief of Mr Nooks's three roles, that of the Apothecary, no one else cared what he did with it. But Mr Nooks cared. He was convinced that he could "steal the show" with his enactment of the meager and inhibited bootlegger, and now he gave his all. In New York he had read the Apothecary's line, "My poverty, but not my will, consents," inoffensively. But he chose the dress rehearsal to pause after "my poverty," to raise his chin, look up at God, hold it for three agonizing seconds, then hurl "but NOT my WILL" into the teeth of destiny.

Satori, watching from the tenth row of the orchestra, held up his hand. "Mr Nooks! What are you doing?"

"I don't understand, Mr Director."

"You are giving rather an exaggerated characterization to the unfortunate Apothecary."

"I've always thought he is a real cameo of a character picture, and nobody has ever done enough with him. I'm trying to show how the Apothecary is the victim of awful bad luck, and poor fellow, he has to do this awful thing——"

"Quite, Mr Nooks. Yes. A cameo. But I don't want it to be such a big cameo and get dropped on Romeo's head. I think I'd just play it down."

Nooks breathed with the joy of being, for the first time, the center of a Kulturkampf. Ignoring Satori's impatient fingers on the orchestra seat in front of him, Nooks droned, "Well now, I'll tell you, Mr Director, I acted it that way when I was with Otto Knippler's company, and Otto said it was real good; he said it was different. And while we're discussing it, Mr Director, if you don't mind a suggestion from an old actor, I think when Romeo enters, in this scene, and sees me—you know he says, 'I see that thou art poor'—he ought to pause and look me over more carefully. I know you're trying to get tempo and all that modern stuff, but when I was with Theodate Thuriber, in 1907, she said——"

"Mr Nooks!" Satori's voice was rather high. "This is the dress rehearsal! We'll dispense with all ancient history—all of it!"

"But Mr Director——"

"You heard what I said!"

Bethel was hurt by the drop of Nooks's seamed old jaw and the glaze in his eyes.

But, an hour later, Nooks was trying to tell a testy Victor Swenson, Prince of Verona, how to return the curtsy of his awed subjects, and she perceived that not time nor tide nor fate's unkindest slam can dull the smiling smugness of the ham.

The last skirmish across the barricades, at a quarter to five on that icy November morning, was the schedule of curtain calls.

Mrs Boyle suggested, brightly, "Wouldn't this save a lot of time, Mr Satori? Not bring the minor members of the cast on at all? I'm sure they'll all be very competent some-day—if they ever learn to act. But just now, I don't really see why the Public should be interested in them. I think it would be an interesting and quite original way to have me take my calls, first with Romeo, then with Mercutio, then with the two Capulets, then with the Nurse, then with Tybalt, then with Friar Laurence, then with Paris, and just forget the others."

Now Bethel knew why Satori was a good director. Debo-nair, blithe—at 4:47 A.M. and 37° above—he trilled, "I think it would be original and sensible. But what can you and I do against the selfishness and conceit of actors, Mrs Boyle? I'm afraid we'll have to let them be seen."

And at the end he said to Andy, to the peppery-eyed Bethel's admiration and dumbfounding, "Let's go out and find a drink. It's been a first-rate dress rehearsal—very easy and satisfactory. Worked like a clock, didn't it."

Monday through
Saturday

BELLUCA

Nov. 28—Dec. 3
1938

Andrew Deacon presents

MRS LUMLEY BOYLE

in

ROMEO AND JULIET
IN MODERN CLOTHES AND SPIRIT

Staged by Adrian Satori   *Settings by* William Schnable

IN TWO ACTS

Dramatis Personae

JULIET.............	Played by....	Mrs Lumley Boyle
ROMEO............. "	"	......Andrew Deacon
CAPULET............ "	"	.........Hugh Challis
LADY CAPULET...... "	"	....Miss Mahala Vale
MONTAGUE......... "	"	.......George Keezer
LADY MONTAGUE... "	"	Miss Charlotte Levison
NURSE TO JULIET... "	"	..Miss Mabel Staghorn
MERCUTIO........... "	"	......Zed Wintergeist
TYBALT............. "	"	.....Henry W. Purvis
BENVOLIO.......... "	"	.........Geoffrey Hoy
PARIS.............. "	"	.....Tudor Blackwall
PRINCE ESCALUS.... "	"	......Victor Swenson
FRIAR LAURENCE... "	"	.......George Keezer
BALTHASAR......... "	"	.........Lyle Johnson
PETER.............. "	"	......Antonio Murphy
FRIAR JOHN		
ABRAHAM .... "	"	.........Douglas Fry
SECOND WATCHMAN		
APOTHECARY		
SAMPSON........... "	"	.....Wyndham Nooks
FIRST WATCHMAN		
PAGE TO MERCUTIO. "	"	..Miss Bethel Merriday
PAGE TO PARIS...... "	"	......Miss Iris Pentire

SERVANTS TO CAPULET, CITIZENS IN THE STREETS OF VERONA, MASKERS, TORCH–BEARERS, DANCERS, MUSICIANS, etc.: Iris Pentire, Bethel Merriday, Nathan Eldred, Wyndham Nooks, Zed Wintergeist, Victor Swenson, Tudor Blackwall, Douglas Fry, Lyle Johnson, Henry W. Purvis, Geoffrey Hoy, Charlotte Levison, Antonio Murphy, Vera Cross, Tom Wherry.

The Prologue and Epilogue are said by Miss Bethel Merriday. The character of "Gregory" is replaced by that of "Peter."

------------------◆------------------

STAFF

Stage Manager	Nathan Eldred
Assistant Stage Manager	Douglas Fry
Press Representative and Advance Agent	Don Rumball
Company Manager	Tertius Tully
In Charge of Setting	Gene Doric
In Charge of Lighting	Wilson Kinloch
In Charge of Properties	Philip Schoenberg
Wardrobe Mistress	Mrs Albert Golly

------------------◆------------------

All inquiries regarding future bookings of the company should be addressed to Mr Andrew Deacon's secretary, Miss Sally Carpet, Romenterprises Corporation, Capuchin Bldg., Park Avenue, New York City.

THEATER STAFF

Manager	Vincent Dvorak St John
Treasurer	Benjamin Stubbs
Assistant Treasurer	Cosley Eltinger

*****The Management is not responsible for the apparel or the personal property of patrons unless checked with the theater attendant.

Cooling drinks may be obtained during intermissions in the Tibetan Pheasant Room, adjoining the Grand Lobby.

24

IN HER ENERGETIC small life, Bethel had rarely loafed and lolled and languished; and never, till this morning between dress rehearsal and first night, had she reveled in it. But today she slept till noon, and lay afterward on the bed, gossiping yawningly with Iris, reading the newspapers down to the real-estate transfers, and feeling like an actress in society novels. But in her new plain camel's-hair dressing gown and her pale blue cotton pajamas, she looked like a counselor in a girls' camp; while Iris's pale delicacy was set off by plum-colored silk pajamas piped with white, and a dressing gown of green taffeta with a batik scarf for sash. On her milky feet were mules of gilded alligator hide.

"Isn't that outfit all new?" said Bethel. Maybe just on the sniffy side.

"And how!"

"Where 'd you ever raise the money?"

Iris smiled, tender as a young cobra. "A gentleman friend, he asked me if I had anything to wear cold mornings on the tour, and I said no——"

"But you have! You had a swell dressing gown in Grampion."

"Oh. That? I—lost it. And I said no, and he just *dragged* me into Bonwit Teller's and bought this layout—honestly, I had no *idea* he meant it for *me,* I thought he just wanted my advice about colors, I thought prob'ly he meant it for his sister or somebody, and then when he shoved the parcels into my arms and said, 'It's all yours, baby,' I was so surprised, and I said, 'For *me?* Oh, I can't take presents from a man,' and he said if I didn't take 'em, he'd throw 'em down the subway, and I made it clear he couldn't buy my affections, not with anything, and he said yes, sure, he understood that. So what could I do?'"

The epithet "gold digger" dazzled Bethel's mind as crimson spheres dazzle the lidded eyes when you close them in bed, but she managed to keep still, as she made several notes about rooming by herself before the tour was over. She recalled now Iris's new silver bracelet, her new silver brush and comb; she remembered Iris coming out of a luggage shop, in New York, with Zed Wintergeist—and Iris had a new hatbox with that shop's label.

But she didn't want to be a prig. She did think the bumptious Zed ought to have enough wit to protect himself. Perhaps, on that page in Saint Peter's folio devoted to Bethel, there stands a small gold star because she shut up.

With innocent outrageousness, young gentlemen also in dressing gowns—Andy, Douglas Fry, Lyle Johnson, Antonio Murphy—banged at the door and came in and sat on the beds and talked about the only subjects that could be of interest to the world—how the dress rehearsal had gone, how Miss Staghorn had blown, and the prospects for to-night. By evening there were cigarette butts in every receptacle in the room except Bethel's slippers. And in a growing, edgy tension, ten of them, boiling with chatter, ate at a round table in the Coffee Shop.

"Gosh, we've got to be good!" agonized Henry Purvis. "I hear the house is sold out."

"And there's a reviewer come from *Chicago!*" quaked Charlotte.

Mahala leered at Bethel, "And the audience aren't good neighbors here, like a summer theater, that are pulling for you to succeed. These are wolves. They want their two dollars and eighty cents' worth."

And so they shakily set out to walk to the theater and the opening.

When, in her Goddess of Liberty gown for the role of Prologue, Bethel stood way down right in the wings, listening to the orchestra's slow murder of Tchaikovsky and waiting for the signal to go on, when it was too late to do anything about it, she knew that her first nights in *A Doll's House* and *Stage Door* hadn't helped her in the least, and that if she played for thirty years and endured fifty first nights, she would be just as terrified and just as watery in the knees.

Terrified of what? she demanded.

Of making a fool of herself before that mob—friendly, gay and cruel. Of forgetting her lines. Of standing out there a bedlam fool.

Then Nathan Eldred, gently pushing her, was muttering, "On you go, dear. Good luck!" and she was edging between the tormentor and the backing flats, in front of the curtain, holding her small hands out to the sudden-silenced audience and appealing: "Two households, both alike in dignity, in fair Verona, where we lay our scene . . ."

Her voice was warm and young and so earnest. She was begging them so to love the pair of star-crossed lovers.

As the voice went on, without her having much to do with it, she found that she could, through the haze of beams from the spotlights, make out, not individual faces, but the circling front of the top balcony. She must have unknown friends up there, among the students; all the young girls and boys who wanted to go on the stage. They were with her—and all her terror was gone.

Her voice came sure and urgent at the end of the prologue:

"If you with patient ears attend, what here shall miss, our
toil shall strive to mend."

"Swell!" whispered Eldred, as she pushed back into the
wings again, and the pompous curtain set sail upward.

As much as she could, she watched from the wings.

Andy maintained through the play the easy serenity he
had shown at dress rehearsal, but Zed Wintergeist ceased
to be himself; he was Mercutio, completely. His Mab speech
was half drunk with young fantasy; in his duel with Tybalt
he was the young nobleman, fierce, swift, haughty, one who
could revel in every sin save cowardice.

Doc Keezer—in frock coat and reversed collar, as Friar
Laurence—stood beside Bethel, his arm lightly through hers,
as they watched Zed's last scene: Mercutio blazingly angry
with Death, but not afraid.

Doc sighed: "I certainly don't like that young Wintergeist. He thinks he knows it all . . . and he whistles in his
dressing room. I'm not superstitious, but everybody knows
that's bad luck. And he's the kind that 'd treat women like
cattle. But just the same, *he* ought to be playing Romeo!"

"And what ought Andy to be playing?"

"My two parts, chick. He'd be a fine sun-ripened Montague and a holy friar. And me, I ought to be playing animal
noises on the radio. Or playing checkers back in Vermont.
I'll lure you up there yet."

It seemed to roll. Andy was voluminously in love; Mrs
Boyle sighed her softest sighs; Hugh Challis-Capulet was
undiluted acid of domestic petulance; and Mabel Staghorn
the most lewdly winking beldam that ever set a gallery
giggling.

In the one long intermission the actors hugged one another, not quite sure just whom they were hugging, and

shook the powder off their make-up aprons, and screamed,
"Oh, they're loving it—they're eating it up—we've got a
Success!"

And when, a little reluctant to end the sweet last chords,
Bethel appealed to them with her epilogue—"Go hence, to
have more talk of these sad things"—the applause was
like the roof falling.

There were sixteen curtain calls. And on one of them
Andy led out Bethel and Iris, and it seemed to Bethel that
the pounding hands were louder than for Mrs Boyle and
Mahala. At the end of it all, Andy made a curtain speech,
while Bethel stood in the wings and worshiped. He was boyish and grateful and endearingly awkward:

. . . They were all so grateful to this, the first audience
to greet their humble efforts, and if the audience had had
half the pleasure that the company had felt . . .

Zed, beside Bethel, was grunting, "What a lousy
Mother's Day speech *that* is!"

Bethel actually swung about, her hand up like a cat's
paw, to slap him, and if she stayed her hand, it was because of Zed's expectant leering and not for the sake of
manners befitting a little lady. Later she heard Iris con-
fiding to Zed, "Let's go out and dance after the show; I've
heard about a place with a hot orchestra," and Zed agreeing. But it was over, and they were all too tired to be anything but hysterically happy.

She had seven opening-night telegrams. (Andy had
sixty-three, Mrs Boyle had four, Hugh Challis had one
hundred and sixteen, and Zed had seventeen.) In one wire
Fletcher Hewitt coaxed her:

THIS NIGHT DO ENVY YOU HOWEVER WE GOING HAVE
HOUSEFUL GUESTS CHRISTMAS HOLIDAYS WISH WERE THERE
TONIGHT TO GIVE EARNEST WISHES IN PERSON DON'T FOR-
GET FLETCHER.

But most astounding was the wire from Professor Miss Bickling:

IN YOUR GREAT TRIUMPH DO NOT FORGET OLD FRIENDS WHO WERE HAPPY EARLY TO PREDICT YOUR FUTURE SUCCESS.

Bethel laid that yellow telegram down in a mess of tan powder and burnt-out paper matches and lining pencils and sat quiet, almost weeping. She had forgotten Miss Bickling and Point Royal College. They were antique and dated and a little absurd and achingly kind.

It was six months and nine days since she had played Nora.

The Belluca stage doorman had pretty liberal ideas about admitting visitors without bothering himself by taking in their cards.

Into their dressing room—Charlotte's, Vera Cross's, Miss Staghorn's and Bethel's—after the play, the visitors moved like doubtful elephants blundering down to a new waterhole. Charlotte had two Belluca residents who apparently knew and detested each other: a tall woman, very diamond and sable and positive, and a thin, shy, olive-colored young man who was certainly either a Communist or so guilty about not being one that he was going to a psychoanalyst. There was no one for Vera—who was at least as lost an orphan, as Bethel—and for Miss Staghorn only an overstuffed woman who sighed between phrases and smiled as though it hurt her. She had apparently given up the stage for matrimony, and didn't think it had been much of an idea.

Then, with horror, Bethel saw oozing into the door a trial of her own: a classmate in Point Royal whom she had always disliked. She was, in fact, the kind of a girl who wasn't any kind of a girl but solely a classmate. Bethel was yet to learn that there is a separate breed, roughly to be classed among human beings, called College Classmates. You can recognize the species on the street ten buildings away, but never place any of its individuals. "That looks like a classmate," you say, and shudder.

This particular one had had the habit of leaning over Bethel's shoulder at a table in the college library and smacking gum, slowly and firmly, in her ear. She entered now remarking: "And you never even let me know you were coming! Getting the big head already!"

"Why, Mary, I didn't know you lived here in Belluca!" gurgled Bethel.

Of course she didn't know it! If she had, that would have been the one secret, haunting horror in this otherwise benign and imperial city.

"Oh yes, I'm married now!"

Already? Impossible! Bethel felt herself still a baby.

"Well, isn't that dandy," said Bethel.

"Oh yes, I'm very happy. But my, who ever thought you'd be an actress. You were so cranky to everybody about acting in college, and talking about discipline and what have you, that I thought you really hated it!"

Oh, a darling, just a Belluca darling.

The classmate was followed by a woman, stringy and chronically indignant and to Bethel perfectly strange, who shrieked, "Well, Beth, guess you don't remember me."

"Oh, I'm sorry——"

"Well, 's matter of fact, I don't know how you could, because you never saw me, not really, but I'm your cousin Lizzie."

"Oh-uh."

"Well, your second cousin, I guess it is, really. Lizzie Porch—you know—Mrs Reginald Porch. My husband is in gents' outfitting, but he hasn't been so well lately. I'm your mother's sister's husband's first wife's daughter, and I don't know just what that makes us, but after all, relatives are relatives, aren't they, and they can't very well be strangers."

"Yes, that's dandy!" said Bethel. Detestable word "dandy" with which she had not befouled her virginal tongue since she had left Sladesbury but that she had used now—so corrupting and hideous are unwanted visitors to dressing rooms—twice in five minutes. "That's dandy. And did you enjoy our show?"

"That's what I came to see you about. Reggie and I can't afford to buy theater tickets, now that we're paying for the new car and the new electric garbage disposer and Junior's tennis lessons, but of course as you're my cousin, I did think it would be nice to honor you while you're here by giving you a supper party, with a theater party beforehand, and I'd be delighted to arrange it any time you say, any evening at all, except Wednesday or Thursday, and if you'll choose the time that's most convenient to you, and if you could get me eight tickets—they needn't be in a box; the orchestra would be all right—I'll go right ahead and arrange it."

There had been times when Bethel's feeling for Mabel Staghorn had been somewhat less than adoration. Mabel asked questions about her feeling for Andy; Mabel looked at the notes on Bethel's little pad; Mabel had a hot and puffy hand. But now did Mabel arise and become a comrade at arms.

"Excuse my intruding, Mrs Porch, but Beth is so shy she'd never tell you—but you know she's cuing all of us every evening—gracious, almost till dawn, sometimes—and of course you know that she'd have to BUY the tickets, and eight times two-eighty—what *does* that make?—I never *was* any good at figures, but it'd set her back somewhere around twenty-five bucks, wouldn't it, and nobody asked me, but it strikes me that's a whole lot to ask of a cousin you never seen before!"

"Oh, if you feel *that* way about it, but I must say, it strikes me as a pretty poor return for all my efforts to introduce Bethel to some of the most influential people in town!" said Mrs Porch to Mabel, and to Bethel, "But of course if you prefer casual people you just met on the stage to your own flesh and blood, well, all I can say is——"

"Good night," suggested Charlotte.

And Mrs Porch was stamping out, and Bethel was very

happy and a professional and a success beyond dreams . . . for ten minutes more.

She had assumed that the lot of them would go some-where to celebrate, that night. Andy would take care of it—trust old Andy.

She came out into the waste of cement floor about the dressing rooms, to see Zed going off with Iris, Charlotte with her two friends and with Henry Purvis, Vera Cross with young Douglas Fry, and then a whole cavalcade. Andy's rich cousin and his wife were leading it, and after them, laughing, shouting, misquoting Shakespeare, came Andy, Mahala, Mrs Boyle and Hugh Challis, and they were all in evening clothes.

It was the first time that Bethel had ever seen Andy in the unapproachable magnificence of tails, white tie, top hat and ebony stick. Mahala was in an ivory frock, and Andy's cousin was Raleighesquely hanging her cape about her.

They all went past Bethel, at her dressing-room door, with not one look.

She felt not so much poor and dull-tongued and un-beautiful as immature and brattish. How had she ever dared to think that she could be really friendly with smiling, sure-footed, older gods like Andy?

She saw herself walking alone back to the hotel, into the littered double room to which Iris would not return till dawn. The glory of being Epilogue in a silk dress was gone. And the small of her back hurt with weariness. She turned toward the stairs up from the basement.

Then there was Andy, flying down to her, his Inverness cape (so silly to her, and so darling!) agitated with his speed, crying to her, "Beth, it just occurred to me that some of you kids won't be having a party tonight. How about you and Iris and Vera?"

"They're—uh—going dancing."

"You're alone?"

"It doesn't matter. I'd rather be. I'm so tired."

"Darling! Poor sweet darling! Now you *do* look like a half-drowned kitten—back all ruffled and paws all wet—shaking 'em so ruefully! I'll tell you what. Come along with us."

"I couldn't."

"You'd save my life! My cousin is *the* worst stuffed shirt in a family renowned for stuffiness and shirtiness."

From the stairs, the voice of Romer Ingalls, the cousin: "Andy? Where are you? Come on! We're waiting."

Andy urged her, "Oh, come on. It 'll be a favor to me. I'll have somebody to talk to."

"Huh! You'll have your Mahala."

"Our Mahala is talented, but—well, she's too fond of being coyly rebuking. No, honestly, I wouldn't go to the party at all—champagne and the rhumba and Corona-Coronas—except to work up some carriage trade for the show."

"I'm merely an understudy, Mr Deacon!"

"Please don't be haughty."

"But Andy, honestly, I haven't an evening dress. I will have, as soon as I save up, and then——"

"Look, kitten, I'll take you out and buy you a frock to-morrow. Shall we?"

"No, I'm afraid not."

"I'd like to!"

"I couldn't wear anything I didn't earn. I'd feel——" She didn't quite end up the sentence "like an Iris."

"I know, darling. And if this show goes over—as it will!—maybe you'll have a big enough raise in salary to earn twenty dresses, all gold and emeralds. Good night. I'll miss you!" And he was gone with a kiss that—she wasn't quite sure but that it had almost meant something.

She had a warm small happiness curled inside her then, and she turned to find Doc Keezer looking on, friendly, only a little sardonic. He said nothing about Andy's kiss; he merely yawned, "Come on to the Yorkshire Grill and I'll buy you a bevy of chops."

It was consoling to walk the winter streets to the Grill with Doc Keezer. He did not prance like Andy or Zed or Douglas Fry, did not pour out plans to vanquish fairyland. He walked steadily, held her arm steadily, knew exactly where he was going, waited for the red light at street corners, and told her that on stage she "gargled her *l*'s too much," which was the most useful thing anyone had said since Sol Gadto.

The Yorkshire Grill was an imitation of all the New York Chop Houses that imitate Ye Olde Cheshire Cheese, of London, which imitates itself. Bethel was ashamed of her Lone Cinderella role back at the theater when she saw that there were plenty of other members of the company who were not festive on first night.

At the Grill, Tudor Blackwall and Victor Swenson were sedately eating Irish stew—"Oh, Bethel, *darling,* you were too, too lovely tonight!" they chorused. Old Wyndham Nooks (steak, rare) was telling Mrs Golly, the wardrobe mistress (deviled beef bone) of his early triumphs—early or not at all. Bethel heard from him a trailing, "So I said to Dave Belasco, 'Dave, I've got an idea that 'll make a fortune for you,' and Dave said to me, 'Wyndy, let's have it.'" Douglas was demonstrating to Vera Cross a ground plan for a new setting for *Macbeth.*

She was at home again, and comforted, and Doc Keezer ordered chops, with bitter ale in pewter mugs, which, for the sake of her well-loved Dickens and J. B. Priestley, she tried to enjoy, and which for her own sake she thought was nasty.

"Get a wire from Fletch Hewitt tonight, Beth?" said Doc Keezer.

"Yes. A nice one."

"You're the kind of young woman, chick, neither too maternal nor too grasping, with a career but not willing to step on everybody to get it, that 'll always have good, steady, dull dogs like Hewitt and Charley Hatch hanging around you, claiming they want to support you, but really wanting to be supported mentally."

"How did you ever know anything about Charley Hatch?"

"I watched him when he came to visit you at Grampion. An old unmarried trouper like me—oh, I was married for about a year one time, when I was a hoofer, but she liked Italian orchestra leaders with mustaches—most of us get to be great hermits, and as tightwad as a Yankee character actor—walk twenty blocks out of the way to find a hotel room that smells more of old carpets and costs fifty cents less a night. And we sit off one side backstage and nurse our arms, and prob'ly we only know our own parts, and never find out whether Juliet marries the apothecary or Prince Escalus at the end of the play.

"But we do get a kind of compensation: we study the people around us, all the time, and get to know 'em. I know you better than Andy does, or young Wintergeist or any of 'em. They think you're a lively kid, pretty naïve yet, but sweet. I know you're a serious student—maybe you'll never be a great actress, but you'll be a dependable one, if the luck runs with you. Ergal, you ought to count a lot more on me than on those young flibbertigibbets—who I also know them better than you do. Andy is better 'n ninety-five per cent. of Rich Young Men. But if he doesn't make a ten strike at play producing quick, it 'll be a wonder if he doesn't go back to his gardener and his butler. Wintergeist has ability. *If* he stays clear of booze and gold diggers. He's the kind that's born drunk, and born in love, and just one extra drink or one more girl will send him haywire."

"But Doc, if you're disposing of 'em, what about the boys I really like—Douglas Fry and Harry Purvis?"

"Two light-waisted, both of 'em. And too self-satisfied. But there is a lot bigger threat."

"Eh?"

"What you have to watch out for is your own friendly heart, and it makes you feel responsible to the Steady Old

Dogs—the home-town boys—Fletcher and Hatch . . . and me."

"Oh!"

"Yes. Haven't you sort of noticed that in my methodical aged way, I've been falling in love with you, Bethel?"

"Oh no. Oh, Doc——"

"I know, dear. I know all the lines. I've played 'em in Clyde Fitch and Charles Klein: You just felt that we were good friends. That you could depend on me. Can't it remain like that? . . . And it can, dear. I hope it will. I'm too old and too lazy to go and get lyric on you. I won't write you one single triolet—that's its name, ain't it? I'll always be here—holding the gloves and buying you hot dogs, and sending you home to bed early—and alone. But if you ever should get sick of these galloping young men, you might someday get interested in an old ham that's gone through about all the rough weather there is, and come out pretty cheerful, and even reasonably kind and honest—which is all the flowers I'm ever going to hand myself. Posi*tively*! And a fellow pro that would nurse your career and guide you and cue you—and of course the only reason any sensible actress ever gets married is to have somebody cue her.

"And as to what you would do for me—well, it would give me a youth I never really had."

"How old are you, Doc? Please forgive me——"

"Sure. I'm fifty, last month. And you're twenty-two. I know all the arguments about May versus December—the poor kid sitting at home when she wants to go dancing, because Pop loves his pipe and slippers—though nowadays, seems like it's just the opposite: Pop wants to be out doing the rhumba with the cuties, the old fool, and his girl wants to stay home and study her admiralty law. But when a couple are together, in the same art, like acting, or the same profession, then maybe age don't matter as much. You don't get along with Wintergeist just because he's only a year or a couple years older, but because you're playing his page. And that's all on the subject. Have a brandy? . . . No? I think

I will, if you don't mind. Say, did you hear old Nooks squawking tonight? The steam pipes in his dressing room were leaking . . ."

She looked over at Vera Cross and Douglas Fry, young and credulous. Youth seemed to her not a quality, but an objective thing, not rosy-cheeked, as they said, and robust, but fragile and ardently to be protected and preserved.

And then the young Carl Frazee, of the *Evening News,* came charging up.

"There you are, Beth—I've been looking in every joint in town for you."

And then she was young, too; a child escaped from the house on Sunday afternoon when Aunty Bess and Gramma have come visiting, and blessedly invited to a good, wholesome, violent game of cops and robbers.

"Did you give us a good review?" begged Bethel.

"Not ethics to ask, young Juliet. But I don't think you'll kick much, when you see it tomorrow."

Carl had, instantly, Douglas, Vera, Tudor, Swenson about him, as well as Bethel and Doc Keezer. He effervescently told them that they were all (he included himself, and Tudor, who was thirty-five) young and brave and missionaries of culture. (As Carl shouted, Bethel was very pleased about it, and would have gone on touring in Shakespeare if she had had to walk.) They were more important than all the college presidents and bishops and gross newspaper owners—God what a stinker *his* boss was!—in the world. And Lord but did it save his (Carl's) life, when a real theatrical troupe came to this jungle, where you were expected to report the speeches of bathtub barons and the Da Vincis of insulated piping.

Yawning, Doc Keezer arose.

"Well, I'll leave you infants to build a chain of theaters. Just let me have a job. Will you see the baby here gets home safe, Carl?"

When Doc was gone, Bethel said defensively, "He's really sweet. He's my Friar Laurence."

"Look—look—something I want to ask you—c'm'ere," yelled Carl, and dragged her out to the vestibule. He was only a little crazy. "Don't you make any mistake about Doc Keezer!"

"I don't. He's safe as houses."

"You're telling me! He prob'ly thinks the whole gang of us are a bunch of chicks who want to tell the old hens what a swell place a barnyard is, and he's prob'ly right. He's a professional. He'll put on a good show the night you play Arroyo City in a blizzard, yes, and old Ma Boyle will, too, when your Andy blows higher than a kite, and Mahala won't leave the hotel, and you, my precious, are too scared to speak. My guess, from the way you look at Andy, is that you're in love with him—or will be. But I'll bet that before this tour is over—and it 'll last at least two years, no doubt of that——"

"You honestly think so?"

"I know it! You'll play clear out to L.A., and then prob'ly Australia."

"That would be glorious."

"Yuh, and before it's over, you'll marry Doc Keezer— I've seen *him* look at *you.* You two will have an abandoned farm house in Connecticut, you and Doc, and I'll come stay with you, and Doc and I will write a play together—he'll supply all stagecrafts—exits are the *damnedest* things, in my experience!—and you'll star in it. But what a time I'm going to have keeping myself from taking you away from him, when the play is finished. What a wow the play's going to be—and you too, I mean. Come on, come on, urchin, we can't keep those people waiting all night, you know, and I want to tell Doug about how to stage a Carlo van Loo comedy!"

And by this strident egotism of Youth, it is regretfully to be reported that Bethel was not shocked at all.

When Carl escorted her home—talking—he insisted on peeping into the Pocahontas Room of the Buckingham-

Bradley, an affair of black-and-gold tiled walls, and lights that shifted from rose to saffron to green, and the smart young things of Belluca moving smoothly and slowly in what they thought to be a dance. And instantly she saw Iris moving so with Zed; they were cheek to cheek, and Iris's head was tilted back, her eyes closed, her eyelids like little mounds of pale blue silk.

The worldly wise Carl Frazee followed her look, and pontificated, "And thank God, in marrying you Doc will keep you from ever falling for that guy Wintergeist there, who's too bumptious to live. Modesty is *so* important, don't you think?"

"Oh *yes!*" said the young Bethel.

25

Iɴ ᴛʜᴇ ᴇɴᴛᴇʀᴘʀɪsɪɴɢ ᴄɪᴛʏ of Belluca, the "morning" papers appeared at ten-thirty the night before, the "evening" papers at ten in the morning. The company had an informal invitation to be in Andy's suite in the Buckingham at ten on the morning after the opening, to see the reviews by Carl Frazee and Ted Gronitz in the *Evening News* and *Daily Republican*, and Tertius Tully had promised to wangle an advance proof from the *Morning Herald*, which would be of supreme importance (Tertius explained) because it would be by Professor Stanley Thrush, of the English Department of the University of Belluca.

Though of course (explained Tertius, to whom any company that he was managing, whether it was Sally Rand or the Lunts, was more important than the conquest of Europe and almost as important as the circuses that were his real boyhood love), each of the others was also of international importance, because Carl Frazee was a young genius, and Ted Gronitz, with his radio audience, remarkably like the President.

As she dressed, sleepily and by no means with a Slades-bury neatness, Bethel cried to the dozing Iris, "Come on; we're due in Andy's apartment, to hear the death sentence."

"E-uu-uu-uu-uu! I'm so sleepy. You skip along. I'm going to Zed's room, to read the reviews with him and Jeff Hoy and Tony Murphy," yawned Iris.

In her voice there was to Bethel the sound of conspiracy.

Since when had Iris become so intimate with Geoffrey Hoy—Benvolio—that glass-haired, courteous, competent incognito-minded actor? With Antonio Murphy, that surly comedian?

Bethel felt troubled and incompetent as she trailed up to Andy's rooms, and to a litter of dressing gowns, coffee, Mrs Boyle, brocade mules, shaving lather, marmalade, proofs of advertisements, Wyndham Nooks talking about himself, Charlotte Levison insisting on lending the latest copy of the *New Masses* to Hugh Challis, sweaters and orange juice. Andy was, rather astonishingly, already dressed, fresh-looking in gray flannel; he beamed at her like one who rode the world, and began reading from the papers that a bellboy was bringing in as she arrived.

Mr Carl Frazee in the Belluca *Evening News:*

Will Shakespeare, who is, I understand, a country boy from Strat-ford, is the most promising young playwright in the theater today. More plays by him are being seen on Broadway and out here, where the tall corn grows, than by Clifford Odets or Sidney Kingsley. And to the most important of Will's recent successes, to the Gielgud and Evans Hamlets, Orson Welles' Julius Caesar, and the little Globe Theater at the Chicago World's Fair, and if you missed that you missed something good, must now be distinctly added the highly meritorious Andrew Deacon version of *Romeo and Juliet* in modern clothes, starring Mrs Lumley Boyle, which honored Belluca and honored the renascent theater in America, last evening, by holding its world premiere here, at our historic American Theater, which in past days has seen so much of beauty and eloquence.

Belluca may well be proud of this recognition of its position as a first-class theater town, and we welcome Mr Deacon and Mrs Boyle not only because of the favor to our home town but because they are putting out beyond any question an absolutely first-class show and stirring entertainment.

. . . magic of Mrs Boyle who must certainly be only sixteen no matter what the reference books say . . . Deacon a charming and romantic Romeo bringing the sad old tale to an exciting rebirth and showing himself a fine actor . . . comedy well stressed in the characters of Peter and the Nurse by . . . first moment of shock you were glad to have them in recognizable latter-day clothes instead of the conventional tights, and as for the excellent scenery it is enough to say . . . in two girls, Bethel Merriday and Iris Pentire, found real treasures from whom much will be heard in the future. Miss Merriday gave the prologue and epilogue in such a fresh, winning young voice . . .

"That young man writes with a hoe," said Mrs Boyle.

"Ye-es, but he does like us," said Andy.

"Means money in the box office," said Tertius Tully, who had come in with the advance proof from the *Herald*.

Mr Ted Gronitz, in the *Daily Republican:*

RIALTO RIPPLES

Rating:
No stars.

Mr Shakespeare may not have turned over in his cement coffin yestdy eveng, but he certainly didn't feel so hot.

We're supposed to be all hot & bothered by gt honor bestowed on our poor hick bible-belt bivouac by having sure-nuff Bwy show open here, but your column reports we better still count on our watch-export & baseball record for Belluca's rep.

The bard's *Romeo & Juliet* was pulled off in soup & fish last night, at the American Theater. Results: no hits, no runs, plenty errors.

Hokum in ice-cream pants looks just like hokum in the pink union suits that's the ham's idea of what they used to wear back in Queen Liz's England.

Mrs Boyle, from dear ole Lunnon—quit now, I didn't say anything about her having known Queen Liz personally—is a pretty good Model T Juliet. Deacon, though this column will report that personally and at the bar he is a good guy, reads Romeo like he did back in freshman year in Yale.

The other boys and girls will be happier when they get back to the shoestore and the tea shoppe.

Except for a new Thesp named Zed Wintergeist, who is a wiz, and plays Mercutio like Hellzapoppin instead of like a Vassar daisy chain.

"Aurelia, with what sort of implement did you say the other young gentleman wrote?" said Hugh Challis to Mrs Boyle.

"Shut up," said Mrs Boyle.

"That hurt—that hurt plenty," said Andy.

Charlotte looked as though she were crying inside her eyes. Bethel was unable to be so restrained. Mahala and Lyle Johnson simultaneously said, "The son—of—a——"

"But here! This one is swell," said Tertius Tully, as he handed the proof sheet to Andy.

Professor Stanley Thrush (B.A., St Stephen's College, Ph.D., University of Michigan), in the *Morning Herald:*

With an apprehension due less, perhaps, to conservatism in belles-lettres than to past observations of a too frequent confusion of artistic innovation with technical slovenliness, the more literate acolytes of the drama edged into the American Theater, last evening, stoutly prepared for catastrophe in the spectacle of a presentation—announced as the first ever beheld—of *Romeo and Juliet* in contemporary costume. Their delight was, perhaps, the keener when they encountered a sound and beautiful production of the great romance. . . . Mr Deacon played Romeo not only as a gifted mime but as a gentleman . . . Boyle a lovely Juliet in the tradition of Julia Marlowe . . . studied naïveté of Miss Merriday, our Prologue, with her eagerness and charm, gave a promise of an evening of youth and sentiment which was generously fulfilled. The only player to be gently castigated is a Mr Zed Wintergeist, who doubtless means well but who depends less on subtlety than on brawling and blather and who made it grossly evident that he felt superior to the manly, graceful and sincere bearing of Mr Andrew Deacon. In a word, we shall certainly go to this show again this week while we have the chance.

Andy kissed Mrs Boyle, Mahala and Bethel.

Lyle Johnson kissed Charlotte and Vera Cross.

Doc Keezer kissed Bethel.

Bethel said, "Shan't I phone down and order some waffles?" and everybody, amazed, cried, "Oh yes, that would be a wonderful idea."

Andy said, "I hope Zed never sees Thrush's slam," and Bethel loved him for his generosity. But he exploded then: "No, I hope he does see it—plenty. It'll be good for that young man!" And so Bethel loved him for his attacks of humanness.

The house was nearly sold out every night that week, at both matinées there were "standees," and the company felt virtuous and powerful. They stayed for half an hour after the play on Wednesday evening, sitting on prop trunks and segments of stairways and on the floor, while Adrian Satori, who for two days had been giving to all of them little copper-plate last notes of criticism, said good-by:

"Ladies and gentlemen, I feel that my job as director is done; I feel pretty well satisfied; I'm off for New York to-night; and I turn you over to Andy—and to yourselves. You're most of you pretty good—though there isn't one of you who can't improve if he, and especially she, will just sit down and try to think what the characters that you are play-ing are feeling and thinking. That's all, boys and girls. You go forth into the great world, standing with reluctant feet where the brook and river meet, and God keep you from the critics and the room clerks and the autograph fiends!"

Andy took over with a hearty and optimistic address to the company.

It was, felt Bethel, a real Yale pep talk. It smelled of the football-squad quarters, of sweat and childishness. He was so very sweet about it, and so affectionate, and she was em-barrassed to the point of itching.

"Fellow troupers, I've really got nothing to say," he ex-plained, and went ahead and said it for ten minutes . . .

while Bethel irritably watched Zed leer sidewise at Tony Murphy. "Our prospects for a smash-hit tour are better than good. My advices from the next towns on our route, Treverton and Paddock and Milwaukee and Madison, look swell, especially in party bookings. Now all I want to say is that I'm here to help any of you any way I can, twenty-four hours a day.

"I know you're all of you right on your toes, rarin' to go, and while I won't say anything about what I think of the artistic merits of our production—I guess you can guess how I feel about that—I do want to say that I'm proud there's one company where the manager isn't going off to Europe but is going to stay right with the job and with you, and where we're all working together, cards on the table, and there isn't one single feud or clique . . ."

And all the while Zed was maliciously smiling.

On Thursday morning, with Nathan Eldred, the stage manager, directing, there was held in the lobby the first understudy rehearsal. Bethel for the first time was Juliet; Iris was alternately the Nurse and Lady Montague; Vera Cross was Lady Capulet; Eldred himself was the older men, and Tom Wherry demonstrated that he was equally unsure of his lines as Romeo, Mercutio, Tybalt, Benvolio and Balthasar. It was, indeed, a fairly complete mess, and Bethel thudded abruptly from pride in herself as Prologue to terror about herself as Juliet.

She had been placidly sure that she knew every word, and perhaps she did, but when Wherry-Romeo threw a line at her (after agitatedly finding the right place in his typed part, and coughing, and scraping his right foot, and beginning with "Uh-hh-hh"), she didn't know a word in answer.

There was nothing in her skull but a dun-colored chaos. She discovered that learning lines and keeping them learned have no especial relationship. A long speech, like "Thou know'st the mask of night is on my face"—oh, she started it ever so brightly, but the rest of the passage was blank.

"Else—else——" Oh, what *did* come after that? She sat hunched and agonized till Eldred, a little bored, gave her the line, grunting, "Else would a maiden." She rushed triumphantly on with "blush bepaint my cheek"—and all she knew of the rest was a large dazzling nothing.

But when they had gone through the first act, it had all come back to her.

"You kids know this stuff all right, if you'd just let yourself. You're scared of being scared. Now relax," mumbled Eldred.

They, the juveniles, the future hopes of the stage, had come into the lobby for the rehearsal high-stepping and babbling, ready to show up poor old Mrs Boyle and Challis and Hoy. Now they hunched over on silly little gilt chairs and suffered.

It was all fine.

"Good first understudy rehearsal. Some of you know some of the lines. Call for next Thursday, same hour— that 'll be in Paddock, Illinois."

On Tuesday evening, as Bethel and she walked to the theater, Iris stopped at a jeweler's window and pointed to an elaborate mechanism to be carried by ladies for the repair of an evening's ravages. It was in enamel, orange with streaks of black, and it combined a vanity case, a cigarette case, a lighter and a miniature clock, of which latter two it was improbable that they would work.

"Isn't that cute?" moaned Iris. "Gee, I wish I had it."

"You've already got all that junk—three compacts and two cigarette cases," said the prosaic, provincial Bethel.

"But this is the newest thing there is."

"Hm. Like Charlotte's newest thing in the Communist party line. I'm just getting surrounded by novelties."

"I don't know what you mean. But this combination com-pact——" Iris chilled her elegant little nose against the shop window. "Lookit! They call it the 'Demoiselle's D-e-l-i-t-e'—'delight,' I guess that must be. Oh, that's a cunning name, isn't it! So amusing. I bet it comes right straight from Paris. Think of finding it out here in the sticks!" marveled the daughter of Wheeling. "Oh, travel and learn, I always say. I just got to have this. It's so sweet and original. I noticed it yesterday afternoon, and I dreamed about it last night. When we were dancing last night, after the opening, oh, we had a swell time, I told Zed Wintergeist about it——"

Bethel winced.

"——but he didn't seem interested. I don't know what I'm going to do. And it only costs twenty-five dollars."

"Well, buy it then, if you want it so much."

"Me? I haven't a cent. And I've got to pay up *some* of my debts back in New York—people do get so mean about things like that. Oh dear. Well, come *on!* Do you want us to be late?"

Wednesday, walking to the matinée, Bethel saw Iris and Zed stop at that jewelry window, and as she passed them, heard Iris say indignantly to Zed, "You know I've *told* you, I don't allow *any* gentlemen to give me presents, not even innocent ones like this—isn't it just too *darling!*"

After the matinée, Bethel saw Andy, after certain whisperings, hand over to Zed two bank notes.

That evening, when Iris and Bethel were dressing to go out to dinner—cross and touchy after the between-performances nap—a bellboy delivered a package for Iris. Anything wrapped in tissue paper excited Iris. Squealing, she scrabbled with the wrappings and took out the black-and-orange compact.

She hugged it to her breast, crooning, as though it were a baby. She took out the card, read its inscription, blushed, and looked at Bethel with sly triumph that changed—an excellent performance before an audience of only one—into indignant innocence.

And Bethel did not dare to speak.

Iris and Zed left the theater together that evening, following Satori's farewell, and Iris did not come home till after three. Bethel awoke to cock an eye at her and, as Iris was obviously waiting for a scene, she had a small solid pleasure in not giving it to her. At breakfast, which Iris had tempted her into the wasteful luxury of having in their room, Bethel was inspired to attack.

"Iris!"

"Eh?"

"Why did you coax Zed into giving you that compact?"

"Who said he gave it to me?"

"Why did you coax him—tease him—gold-dig him, if you like it that way!"

"Why, I never heard of such an outrageous accusation in all my life! Me coax him? Me tease him? Me gold-dig anybody? Let me tell you, Beth Merriday, I've had rich men, oh, very rich, beg for the chance to give me—uh—jewels and French perfume and hatboxes and everything, and I always said, certainly not, no one can buy my favors, and they said, why no, of course not, they just wanted to show their appreciation of me, but even so, no, I told them, a beautiful girl in my position where you haven't got a father or a brother or anybody to defend you, you've just got to be beyond criticism, I told them, and my reputation was just as dear to me as it was to Helen Hayes or a banker or anybody——"

"Why did you make Zed buy that junk for you? You didn't need it!"

Iris was suddenly snarling. "And why shouldn't he? He's the damnedest tightwad in the company! Oh, he wants everything he can get, all right, and when it's convenient to *him*, but you have to throw a fit to even get him to buy you a champagne cocktail!"

"Iris! Stop it! He hasn't much more money than we have. He isn't much older than we are. He's a baby. He seems grown up because he knows so much and is so conceited, but he's a mere baby. You might save your wiles——"

"My what?"

"Your wiles."

"What do you mean, *wiles?*"

"I'll admit it's a bad word. It's rafained. Like you! Call it your gutter tricks, then."

"I never in my life——"

"It's none of my business. I hardly know whether I hate Zed or love him. He's the measles. But he's good active measles, anyway. He really loves the theater. He'll do something with it. And it makes me sick to see you hanging onto him——"

"I am not, and you know it!"

"—and to think that because I room with you, maybe Zed 'll think—and Andy 'll think and Hugh Challis——"

"Why don't you bring in your doddering boy friend Doc Keezer, too, while you're about it!"

"I do! I certainly do! Doc is the squarest, kindest man in the whole company, except maybe Andy! And I don't want him, or any of 'em, to think that I'm a sponge like you, just because I have to be with you a lot."

"You don't have to, you know."

"Yes, that was the idea I was working around to myself!"

She walked alone, that Thursday morning, to the understudy rehearsal which has already been recorded, and it was no comfort to her that Iris, trained in stock, should know her understudy lines. That afternoon she moved to a single room at the Buckingham. It was exhilarating to have her own clear, uncluttered place in which she could breathe, and after she had duly puzzled over whether she had been priggish with Iris, and brawled like a market woman, she asserted, "I don't care," and felt lonely and happy.

She wanted to tell Zed of Iris's depths of calculated depravity—and expensiveness—but she was no informer, and she felt that that brash young man deserved what he got . . . and she suspected that he wouldn't listen to her. She said nothing about Iris when Zed and she were sent out to the Belluca University Theater, on Friday afternoon.

Andy Deacon, backed by his weighty local cousin, was doing in Belluca all the brisk, desperate, publicity-cadging tricks which, in the Age of Rotogravure, were supposed to lure disciples to the sweets of the drama. Andy gave interviews, was photographed holding a pipe, holding a copy of Shakespeare, holding Mrs Boyle; he talked daily on the radio—trying craftily to insinuate into a discourse on the Globe Theater the fact that we may be seen right here in town tonight at the American Theater, top two-eighty.

He was manly and athletic at luncheons of the Rotary Club and the Belluca Athletic Club; he was manly and boyish and romantic at the Women's Drama League tea and, with Bethel, Mahala and Charlotte supporting him, did not blench till the very end of a receiving line of one hundred and seventy-six women with whom he shook hands as they maternally murmured to him, "I'm so glad you're Doing Shakespeare. My husband and I do hope we'll have time to run in and see you this week, though of course we're awfully busy and there's a bridge tournament on."

Hugh Challis entertained the Drama League, the Tomawattis Club Monthly Literary Luncheon and the English-Speaking Union with anecdotes of Henry Irving, Disraeli's favorite horse and the Duke of Windsor. Lyle Johnson rushed over to the City Auditorium during a scene in which he did not appear and presented a silver cup to the winner of the Boy Scout Hurdle Contest—a stunt which Andy had approved, though Tertius Tully, the procurer of the other personal appearances, had fretted that the Boy Scouts and their doggone hurdling were nothing but Competition for the Show.

Henry Purvis resumed his Ph.D. and addressed the Geographic Club of St Aloysius College on "The History and Significance of the Oberammergau Passion Play," Jeff Hoy and Tony Murphy sang duets at a smoker of the Bathtub Executives' Club, Tudor Blackwall dedicated the new Swiss Knitwork Department in Burpling & Blum's Department Store, and Wyndham Nooks, entirely without Tertius

Tully's sanction, was found to have given (gratis) a program of "Great Moments from Shakespeare" at a six-o'clock Get Together Supper of the Wisconsin Association—it was reported that, with a beard handy in his pocket, he turned himself from a Prince in the Tower to King Lear in ten seconds.

But Mrs Boyle refused to go out soliciting at all. Between shows she slept, and wrote letters home to England, and encouraged Hilda Donnersberg, her maid, to tell her how bad Andy and Mahala and Charlotte and Mabel Staghorn were.

As part of this campaign, Tertius Tully sent the reluctant Zed and Bethel to represent Shakespeare at tea at the Belluca University Theater, at five on Friday.

As they rode out on the East Philadelphia Avenue & University Heights bus, they were annoyed.

"It makes me tired, having to go out and be arty with a bunch of college actors that don't know a ground cloth from a grommet. I wanted to go to the St Louis Symphony concert this afternoon and see the Chinese stuff in the Art Museum," complained Zed, a tireless explorer of new towns. "It 'll be awful. They'll all ask us—they don't get a chance at real professional actors very often, and they'll ask us how they can get on the stage on Broadway, and Do we do our own make-up, and Don't we meet such interesting people in our dressing rooms! The theater will be a hall over the horse-doctoring laboratory, and we'll be expected to admire an eighteen-foot stage with a hand roll drop. To ask actors to do a thing like this! Artistic slumming! Andy Deacon is a traveling salesman for the drama."

"He is not—but it will be dreadful," said Bethel. "I remember my own college plays. But maybe we'll meet some wide-awake young professors. I hear these Middle Western colleges are so progressive."

"You think so, do you! You read our review in the *Herald*, didn't you, by Professor Stanley Thrush, of the university, the old songbird? There ought to be a law."

"How old are you really, Zed?"

"Twenty-three. What's that got to do with it?"

"Baby!"

"I was more perceptive at six than old Thrush and the whole gang of Belluca profs are at sixty-six, which is probably their average age. Well, here we are at the business college. We'll probably be greeted by twenty-one rah-rah-rah's and the chief artistic nucleus of the university—the glee club, singing 'Down on the Bingo Farm.' And Thrush will be swanking around, looking benevolently amused. I hope I won't be rude to him—I don't really *like* to be so rude to stuffed shirts—not *too* rude."

She had never made a quantitative analysis of the relationship of ivy to education, but from observation of Point Royal and Yale, she had concluded that it was direct. The Point Royal buildings were, perhaps, pretty ugly: of bumpy brown sandstone, and given to arched windows with clotted glass, but they dripped with ivy, and so that must be necessary. The Belluca University buildings, ivyless and of a correct and uninspired ⚹32A Tudor, seemed to her like factories, and the trees were anemic, the turf was scraggly.

Before they had time to ask for the way to the theater, they came to a pillared, white-limestone structure with the inscription "McCoggins Memorial Theater" on the pediment. (A Mr McCoggins, third-generation manufacturer of machinery, who had loved Maude Adams and William Gillette more than cream separators, had left to the new university a million dollars.)

"Have they got a whole building to themselves?" said Zed, uneasily.

In the formal, black-and-white marble lobby they asked for Professor Mattocks, the Director of Productions. They were shown into a too luxurious office, with tapestry chairs and a table of magazines with diagrams and colored photographs.

"Professor Mattocks. Sounds like a funeral. Worse than

Stanley Thrush," grumbled Zed, turning his sodden brown felt hat.

In on them charged a man not over thirty, a man of Zed's own rough, driving, intellectual type, with the same pretentious simplicity, as exhibited in flannel shirt and wrinkled trousers, paint-spattered. He was a flaming sun of welcome. "Miss Merriday? Mr Wintergeist? We were terribly pleased when Mr Tully said you might come. Tickled to death! I'm Bill Mattocks."

"Fine!" Zed swiftly looked him over, then grinned and demanded, confidentially, as one alley pup to another, "When do we meet Prof Thrush?"

"Cheer up. You don't. They keep him on ice, over in the English Department. His only connection with our theater is to lecture to all the women's clubs in the state about how crude and subversive we are. We're all apologetic as hell to you for his review of Romeo. We thought you were a brilliant Mercutio, something fabulous, and we liked your prologue, Miss Merriday—we'll be waiting for you when you get a real part. Don't for God's sake blame Thrush on me! I've played and directed summer and winter stock, and I toured with Miss Cornell in *Romeo* and Miss Hayes in *Victoria*. We're theater workers, not academic phonographs."

They had coffee and cakes with a dozen university actors and directors and scene designers, in the greenroom, which was actually green, beneath the stage. Three of them were teachers, the rest students, but they could not easily be told apart.

The whole group seemed to Bethel to have one sharp, common characteristic: they were all akin to Zed and to Bill Mattocks (who were already first-naming each other as though they had been intimates for years) in being revolutionary and youthful.

Some of them, she thought, worked at their revolution a little too hard and a little too obviously. They felt it a duty to have their trousers and their khaki shirts very wrinkled and very spotty, their ties either greasy or orange-colored, and one even displayed a horrid little canvas hat with autographs of his fellow souls penned on it. In hatred of the staleness of their homes, some of these children would jump into the hysterical, pseudo-artistic half-world. But that had always been the chromo-colored fault of every Quartier Latin, and these experimentalists, she felt, unlike some of the quack doctors of dramaturgy whom she had met in left-wing theatrical circles in New York, had enough gaiety and salutary cynicism to inoculate them against cults.

And then they got beyond her entirely.

The proud professional Bethel, who had heard Sol Gadto talk about Stanislavski, and Adrian Satori tell how Lunt and Fontanne rehearsed, was stunned now by a babble about Meyerhold's productions in Moscow, and Nimerovitch-Danchenko's, about Louis Jouvet's pioneering in Paris, about the Gaston Baty version of *Crime and Punishment* at the Théâtre Montparnasse, about Piscator in the dead great days in Berlin.

It was an almost respectful young Mr Wintergeist who, with Bethel, followed Mattocks on a tour of the theater: huge stage, auditorium and lounge with murals by Grant Wood and Tom Benton, dressing rooms with full-length mirrors surrounded with electric globes in every color that stage lights could give, workshop with a paint frame, so that the scenic artist could stand up, instead of, like Bethel at Grampion, sitting on the floor, sitting on the canvas flat, or lying on it, while trying to do feather strokes with a ponderous paintbrush.

They sat, Zed and Bethel, on a bench on the campus.

Zed spoke with a curious meekness: "Beth, do you realize that that university theater is probably better equipped than any on Broadway? That it has a thirty-eight-foot revolving stage, and a plaster horizont that's actually portable, and a

Pre-Selective Remote Control Board, the very latest Von Kleybourg model? You saw that?"

"Oh yes," said Bethel, who hadn't.

"I tell you, those boys give me a new faith in the theater. I do believe in Broadway. I don't believe the endowed stage is as real as one that has to fight for its life. But let me tell you that if Broadway closed up entirely, if the Fabulous Invalid finally kicks the bucket, there'll be a new theater coming out of these universities. That's exciting. Universities actually creating something, and not just teaching boys to write advertising and sell bonds and hold patients' hands. But why not? That's what Oxford and Cambridge did, when the monks kept civilization alive. Oh, I've never been so hopeful of the living theater, never been so proud of my profession and so glad I picked it out and stuck to it. Now I'm dead sure that not even Hollywood and the radio and an education formed by the comic strips can kill the drama—which is as old as religion. But——"

He took her hand, he held it tight, almost as though he were seeking protection, and he spoke humbly:

"But I certainly got mine. Beth. Pet. Do you mind kicking me, tonight, after the show, when we'll have plenty of time for it? I went in there feeling so superior. I thought those collitch boys would just be another bunch of rah-rah Andys or, at best, learned sots like Harry Purvis. But these kids really study. Isn't that something—to find learning in an institution of learning! Maybe America really is growing up. . . . But it was hard on me! I've read a lot about Piscator, but I didn't know much about Baty and Jouvet. Not a thing. Was my face red!"

"I didn't know anything about 'em, either."

"Yes, but you've never gone around being a bright new genius of the theater, like Comrade Wintergeist, pet! Forgive me. No. There's no use. I'll be just as bumptious tomorrow."

"You're never bumptious . . . really. You're just eager."

"Am I? Well, maybe. Anyway, you were the perfect companion to see that stuff with today. Now you take Iris——"

Bethel flinched. She did not want to take Iris, particularly not just now.

"Don't jump so, darling," he said. "I know you think Iris is dumb. She isn't really. She doesn't know anything, not with her brains. But she has magic."

"Has she?"

"Yes. She'd be ridiculous, with a bunch like that over there. She'd probably tell Bill Mattocks that she went to swimming classes with Jouvet, and taught Piscator how to play polo, and showed Mordecai Gorelik how to paint light."

"And that Meyerhold insisted on giving her that new vanity case, because he admired her mastery of Russian!"

"Wait! Whoa! Let's look at you!" Zed dropped her hand, seized her shoulders, swung her halfway around, so that he could pierce her look. "Iris was telling me you went and got pure on her, and even moved out on her, because I insisted on giving her a little token of affection."

"Insisted?"

"Well—practically. Look here, pet. When I first met you, I told you I could get interested in you."

She was adequately angry. "Not really? Not the great Maestro Wintergeist? In a poor apprentice?"

"Yes, and maybe he *is* the great Maestro, too! I'll admit those university sharks know more than I do about the new European technic. And a fifty-foot plaster horizont is something handy to carry in your pocket. But I can act on a checkroom counter, and play my own mouthorgan for incidental music."

"You certainly can play your own——"

"That's not worthy of you! Listen, Beth. I know I'm conceited. I used to be ashamed of it. But I guess I always will be. Won't you try and stand it? It's too bad you let me get sidetracked onto Iris. Because I'll admit, to *you,* that that young ten-cent-store siren has got me. Magic, that's what she had—black magic. But yours is white. Come on, pet. There's our bus."

26

It seemed to bethel that *Romeo and Juliet* was not merely a collection of amusing anachronisms, whereby "modern" very sensibly meant "commonplace," but also a vehemently human report of vehement human love. She had heard Andy and Satori argue as to what "skains-mates" meant, and whether Quarto 4 with "swashing" or Quarto 2 with "washing" was correct, but she couldn't be much interested. She was too absorbed in seeing Juliet as a laughing, shattered girl of 1938—of 2038.

Let's see. She lived in a marble palace, with a prim garden edged with stone pines, and the murmur of gay, quarrelsome Verona was filtered through jasmine showering down before her window. Oh yes. Down the corridor, paved with marble in squares of soft old red and yellow, was an oriel window and beneath it an oak chest, carved with passion flowers and crescents interlaced, that her ancestor, the sailor-doge of Venice, had brought home from raids of Tartary (where *was* Tartary?). And here her father, testy old Lord Capulet, who could be so sweet to his little daughter when no one was here to watch him, would come with stories of boar hunting in the Apennines, come down the corridor, his scarlet-braided robe of silver damask swinging, and his old rapier hilt, crowned with polished agate——

Oh no! She was Juliet in modern dress!

No! It was not Verona and marble arches that she lived in, but—oh, let's see, let's see—maybe Hartford, Connecticut, and an old brick mansion out on Asylum Street. Her father was old Governor Capulet, rather like that grand old executive, Governor Wilbur Cross, who had become head of Connecticut after being dean of the Yale Graduate School. Only her father was not sweet-tempered like Dr Cross.

Let's see. Yes, he'd have to be a Catholic—oh, maybe a very High Church Episcopalian—who had sent her to a strict church school, so that the only handsome young man she had ever known well was her cousin, Tybalt Capulet— he'd played polo in Yale and been chairman of the Prom. Her childhood intimates (since her mother was a social busy-body, much concerned with the D.A.R. and the lecture committee of the Charter Oak Study Club) had been a comic small kitten, and her nurse—uh—uh—Mrs O'Leary, widow of a bartender, a woman given to winking and to placid bawdiness, so that Juliet knew much more about the sound vulgarities than any of the Sisters in her school. And the Sisters had innocently let the girls read the Bible—apple-cheeked maidens beneath the apple trees, all in gingham aprons and black hair ribbons and disgusting cotton stockings, softly reading the Song of Solomon aloud, and giggling.

The best heroine of Juliet-Bethel was Ruth. Yes, she would gladly follow her lover and live with him amid the alien corn, if he was true to her and young and strong . . . and ambitious . . . and always true.

The girls in the school were often taken on long walks over the hills west of Hartford. On the hilltop, under the great sky, she had sat dreaming of a winged hero who

. . . bestrides the lazy-pacing clouds
And sails upon the bosom of the air.

Her little window, high up in the whitewashed wall of Capulet Dormitory—her grandfather, the munitions maker, partner of old Jeremiah Deacon, had given it to the school —looked out on stars above and a valley filled with moving stars below, and once she had thought of an imaginary lover that, when he should die, the gods would

> Take him and cut him out in little stars,
> And he would make the face of heaven so fine
> That all the world would be in love with night,
> And pay no worship to the garish sun.

And she knew that even on her most finicking, fantastical days, the young Juliet loved to scrape the crystallized orange sugar from the inside of a marmalade jar, and lick the spoon.

She was studying the Juliet part all over again, for the second understudy rehearsal. But she would not let Iris cue her, nor did Iris ask to be cued.

She went over her part, marking her every error till the typed pages of the "sides" looked like bird tracks. How Doc Keezer knew, she did not learn, but between acts on Friday evening he snorted, "Studying Juliet hard? Want to come out and have a hamburger tonight? And I'll cue you."

So he did, patiently, demandingly, not letting her off on one wrong "a" or "the." They sat in a lunchroom, with hash and catsup and coffee and sides mixed up together on the wide arms of their chairs. Bethel, stooped and solemn, was staring down at a paper napkin, while Doc persisted, "No. You hesitated on that. Do it again, dear," and, to the mild horror of a refrigerator salesman in the row of chairs facing them, Bethel lifted her head, glared at him, blank-eyed, and yelled, "Blister'd be thy tongue for such a wish! He was not born to shame." The salesman grabbed his neat gray felt hat, picked up his check, dropped it, picked it up and fled.

Bethel did not see him. But she did hear, from behind

them, in Iris's light jeering voice, "Look, Zed. There's the happy young couple, billing and cuing."

The ghost walked between the matinée and evening, on Saturday—Bethel's first ghost. Smiling like her father, patting her shoulder, Tertius Tully laid on the shelf of her dressing table a fat little envelope with the first money she had ever earned in the theater.

It was the first money she had ever earned anywhere, except for the supposititious pay for Saturday afternoons in her father's store, and a few awe-bringing quarters earned by digging dandelions for Mrs Frank Ziffer, two doors down the block. She slit the envelope with a nail file and reverently took out the soiled bills and the silver.

It was a quaint sum—thirty-nine dollars and sixty cents— her weekly forty minus one per cent. Government social security. She held it to her bosom. It was not money at all. It was a new car for her mother and father. It was a journey to Europe for herself, and the theater in London and Paris and Moscow. It was Chekhov and Shaw and Molnar and Somerset Maugham. . . . And it was a dressing gown like Iris's.

Andy gave them another pep talk, just before that evening performance; it was a brief pep talk, but—well, it was a pep talk, and Tony Murphy snickered.

. . . The ladies and gentlemen of the company would be glad to know that they had put it over, this first week in Belluca. The reviews had been corking, and they had made money! Yes! Not very much money. Not what they were bound to make on one-night stands. But they had more than cleared expenses, and next week they would un-*ques*-tionably begin to pay back production expenses and be in the black— yes*sir*, in the black—and pretty soon he would be able to think about raising everybody's salary . . .

Everybody, thereupon, cheered. Including Hoy and Tony Murphy and Zed Wintergeist.

At two in the morning, after the Saturday night performance, they took Pullman for their three-night-stand in Treverton, Illinois (pop. 195,000; brewing and silos). There was no homeward-looking now, but gaiety and expectation and accustomed friendliness, as they pattered down the long cement platform, in the bowels of the Belluca station (celebrated murals of Lewis & Clark; portrait of James Whitcomb Riley in Italian mosaic) to their car.

Bethel felt important when the redcap, carrying her bags, asked, "Do you belong to the Troupe?" and she came, in the lofty train shed, in a glare of arclights on steel and cement, to their own cars, with the sign:

Mrs Lumley Boyle
ROMEO & JULIET IN MODERN DRESS

She was again aware of the importance of Zed's loose camel's-hair coat, of Doc Keezer's portable radio—from which he evoked the far-off incantations of a jazz orchestra in Cincinnati as soon as he had set it in his berth—of Mahala's snooty blue suitcases, and Mrs Boyle's damned dog.

The family loyalty of Andy's rich cousin was not strong enough to bring him to the station at two A.M., but the faithful Carl Frazee saw them off—and Carl alone. To Bethel and Doc Keezer he mourned, "Gee, I'm going to miss you people. The only fun I get is when a troupe like you come to town and let me tag along. Don't forget that even if the papers should pan you sometimes, you are sure-enough missionaries to lonely cranks like me. I love you both! And you *will* be married! Don't forget to send me a bid to your wedding, you two." And Carl hesitated, sighed and bolted.

The train was off, to a chorus of "My Heart Belongs to Daddy" in young voices, and one of "Oh, shut up and go to bed" in older ones, but Bethel, still dressed, sat in her berth, hands clasping knees, rocking unhappily to the roll of the train. She would miss Carl Frazee. She would probably forget him, after a dozen other towns, a dozen other Carls, but she had never had such pure and kindly affection, nor been so encouraged to believe in her own career.

Could he be right? Was she anything but another girl to the busy Andy, to Zed, to the Douglas Fry who had stage diagrams for veins? She had so often been lonely; she could be lonely again in this traveling village; only Doc Keezer was always there—her Gibraltar.

The singing stopped, and through the train's bumbling she was conscious of Zed and Iris talking, not very discreetly, sitting on the edge of Iris's berth just across the aisle.

"You were leering at him." (That was Zed.)

"I was not leering at him."

"I didn't mind even that so much, Iris. Lyle Johnson reaches for a girl the way I do for a Camel. A girl like you, that's simply all one fever of vanity——"

"I am not!"

"—*would* leer at him. But what I minded was your fatuousness. So proud that you could win Lyle's attentions—which is just about as difficult as winning the influenza. I don't know 's I'm much interested any longer, but I hate to see even you acting like a comic strip."

"You can't talk to me like that!"

"I am talking to you like that, ain't I?"

And silence, and Bethel peeped between the weighty green curtains to see Iris alone, framed by the curtains, slowly weeping. Bethel loved her then, and was her sister, and hated Zed for his contempt of foolish, soft girls whom simpering men had begged, all these years, to be feminine and foolish and soft.

She bounced out from her berth like a small, earnest schoolma'am going after the local bully, and came on Zed, standing alone, stoop-shouldered and unhappy, in the vestibule of the fast train, with the thick canvas of the bellows pulsing, and the gray steel plates, arching over to make a passageway from car to car, lifting and dropping and clanking . . . a place of grime and steel and snow-streaked glass and ceaseless clamor . . . after midnight, pounding through the snow-smeared darkness of the unknown prairie.

He glared at her and said, "Women!"

"Yes?"

"I've always thought the most naïve thing you could do was to make generalizations about women, but it's true. Women are all alike."

"Zed! I've been listening to you and Iris——"

"Just couldn't help overhearing it, eh!"

"Certainly I could. I didn't want to. And you were beastly to that poor, pretentious little guttersnipe."

"You see? One girl praising another. 'Guttersnipe.' "

"You listen to me! She's vain, but she's gay and sweet. And you talked to her like Lyle Johnson. Like a bartender. A cheap, smirking bartender in a cheap hotel. Beating a butterfly, to show how strong you are!"

"Oh, pet, I know it! She's a wild rose. I could kick myself. I got sore at her because she was flirting with Lyle a little. And here I'd gone and built up a real understanding with her. Poor kid, she's got a tough nut of a brother that's in trouble, and she's desperate about raising some money to send him, and here she'd finally promised to let me lend her some——"

"How much?"

"Oh, fifty bucks or so."

"Have you got it—if you pay any of your debts out of this week's salary?"

"No, not exactly, but I can prob'ly get it from Andy."

"And you had to coax her to let you 'help' her?"

"How do you mean?"

"So that when she does take it, and plenty more after it, you won't feel she's under any obligation to you—it'll be she who's done the favor? I couldn't 've believed it. Honestly, I couldn't 've believed it. You're so intelligent about scripts and acting, so right, and then about girls, you're just another green young man. Emotionally, you're aged thirteen."

"Hey, what the——"

"Your Iris is a gold digger of the first water. You ought to know. She trapped you into buying her that mangy new fur."

"How did you know about—— Look! It wasn't mangy! It was a very nice fur. . . . It ought to be! How did you know I bought it?"

"I watched her leading you up to it. You child!"

"Imagine our little Beth trying to be superior!"

"I am. Though I didn't know it till now."

"Oh, I know all about it. You've been panning me to Iris. You told her I was crude. You said my acting technique was all ham. And you even said I didn't make up my nose right!"

"I never said anything of the kind. Don't you know that Iris is a congenital liar? Don't you? Don't you?"

"And you just defending her!"

"She never even talks honestly to herself. Don't you know it?"

"Yes, I suppose I do, if I think about her with my brain, instead of my heart. But why are you so keen about showing her up, all of a sudden?"

She stumbled in replying; she could not answer his "Why?"

"I'm not keen about it. I've kept myself from telling you anything about her for days now. I just hate to see anybody in this company getting hurt—oh, by his own generosity," she said.

"Well, I'm not going to be. I know Iris is a liar, all right—though I'm not such a small boy that I needed to have *you* tell me, pet! I'm going to cut her out. I'm going to cut out all the women in this company. You're all a bunch of spiritual grafters. You all want admiration. And you're the worst of the lot."

"Oh, Zed, please don't."

"Yes! You wouldn't take presents from me, but *you*

feel you're the only true devoted actor in the whole bunch! You're the savior of the stage! You're the only one that's always on time at rehearsals! You're the only one that's read clear through Gene O'Neill! You think you're as devoted as Francine Larrimore. But you're nothing but Andy Deacon's stooge!"

"I——"

"You're the Teacher's Pet in this company! The good little girl that scrubs her face and tattles to teacher!"

At this point she left him, with rapidity.

As she passed the open slanting door of Andy's drawing room, he called out to her, "Beth! Just who I was looking for! C'm in here!"

He was slouched on the green divan, tucked in among the impedimenta of the company—mostly, Mahala's blue bags. He was wearing a vile tan sweater and discouraged gray trousers and wrinkled Pullman slippers, like black gloves for his feet.

"What is it?" she worried.

"Here!" He absent-mindedly threw two of Mahala's bags out into the aisle. "Sit down. I just want to look at you. I'm all in."

"Oh, not after our grand week in Belluca!"

"It was swell, wasn't it! I knew we'd be a success. But there's been a lot of work—broadcasting and luncheon spiels, and you know, I don't act easily. I'm not a natural actor. I can't relax. I'm always afraid that I'll go up higher than a kite."

"Honestly? I never knew that." He had always seemed exasperatingly confident on the stage.

"Yep. I'm the eternal amateur, as your friend Zed would say."

"Oh—*him!*"

"So sometimes, to try and relax, I like to just sit down and look at someone who's cool and sweet and good, like you."

She hooted. "And I've just this minute been engaged in pulling hair."

"With *who?* I'll fire her—or him."

"Oh no. It's all over. It's just one of those silly self-deceptions, I guess."

"Kitten! You look tired, too. Skip to bed, then. Bless you!"

She was surprised. She had expected Zed to go childishly back to Iris, but he kept his word, which is a noteworthy phenomenon among young men who are professionally in love. He did, sharply, "cut out all the women in this company." He took dinner with none of them, nor supper after the show; and on the train he talked to none except Mrs Boyle, whom he admired and hated. His chief childishness was in being noticeably merry with cigar-stand girls whenever members of the company were in a hotel lobby to watch him.

He was always seen lunching with Jeff Hoy and Tony Murphy, the three of them leaning over the table to mutter secretly, looking about with supercilious brightness, and then stooping over the table again to mutter humor and conspiracy.

Iris was aflutter at Zed's inattention. The good girl had accepted his statement that he wasn't much interested in her any longer in what she supposed to be the spirit in which it was meant—that is, as meaning nothing at all. She hovered over him, bleating, "Ze-ed, aren't you going to take me out to supper tonight?" He answered, "I am not!" so bleakly, so emotionlessly, that Iris quivered, and Bethel hated the young man for his cruelty . . . and was afraid of him.

27

THREE NIGHTS EACH in Treverton, Paddock and Milwaukee; one-night stands in Madison and La Crosse and—
crossing the Mississippi, to the excitement of Bethel—in
Dubuque.

Six fluttering arrivals, with reporters on the station platform and photographers' flashlights blasting the gloom. Six
dashes to get taxis away from her beloved companions in
the company. Six anxious inquiries of marble-fronted-hotel
clerks about rates; and twice when she angrily made it
plain that she couldn't afford it, and quit the caravanserai
where Andy and Mahala and Mrs Boyle were to loll in
kitchenette-bedizened splendor and hunted up a smaller
hotel that looked like a private house with obesity.

Six broadcasts—in four of which Bethel had a part—and
six attempts on the radio to work in, among lively observations on the art of acting and the joy of being in the Middle
West, the facts that they would be visible at the Blank
Theater *that evening*—hurry, hurry, hurry—and that they

were a Real Troupe Just From Broadway, Appearing in
Person, and not a movie. Six interviews in which Andy
and Mrs Boyle and Hugh Challis, with Mahala and Bethel
and Iris and Charlotte sitting in an uncomfortable grinning
row on a hotel settee for extra decoration, caroled that
Shakespeare was a very fine article for the Middle West and
the Middle West was fine for Shakespeare.

Six new banging Coffee Shops in hotel basements, with six
new and ever fancier names for beef stew, and six and sixty
overworked waitresses who merely looked cross-eyed and
fled, if a Professional wailed, "Look, honey, could you
hustle my order? I got to get to the theater."

Six new after-theater restaurants with dancing: The
Jeunesse Dorée, with Billy Bagshot's Sunny South Saxo-
phonists; the Hot Spot, with Tommy Trexler's Cowpuncher
Chorus; the Covered Wagon, with Teddy Taormina's
Yankee Yodlers; the Shanghai Divan, Chinese & American
Specialties, with Sven Svenson and His Demon Accordion;
the Petit Prunier, with Abe Garfinkle's Dress Suit Boys;
and Gus's Lunch, with a radio.

And in every one of these Iris went dancing, with Lyle
Johnson or Jeff Hoy or Douglas Fry, while Bethel solemnly
sat at a table way back, with Doc Keezer and Tertius Tully,
and ate hash while they went pretty thoroughly into the topic
of comparative box-office receipts during the past sixteen
years.

Six new walks to the theater, each of them passing a
jewelry shop and a beauty shop, into whose windows Iris
looked passionately, and a brand-new Bank Building, full of
architecture, up at which Douglas looked critically. Six theaters, ranging from an ancient structure rather like a Sara-
toga trunk to the Treverton auditorium.

This was so very new and mammoth and civically conscious
an institution that it could hold six thousand people, and a
record audience of twelve hundred people felt lost and forlorn in its leatherette wastes. The actors could be heard, like
the horns of elfinland considerably out of tune, only through

a Public Address System, and the more intimate love passages between Romeo and Juliet were played as from the balcony of the Grand Central Terminal just after the arrival of the Twentieth Century. On that vast stage, with an apron thirty feet deep, their sets looked like toy houses of cardboard.

And six new dressing rooms in six different towns, and the speculation as to whether Bethel's next one would be a private suite, or a stall, without running water or ventilation but with a richness of steam pipes, which she would share with all the other women except Mrs Boyle. . . . Not that she speculated much, though. She was fairly sure which it would be.

And six first nights of terror in her stomach. But no matter what changed and what remained, once she saw the familiar sets, she was at home—they were her home.

For a while she could remember the shifting cities by the dressing rooms, by the hotel rooms—whether they looked out on an alley or on a Motor Oil Building that was a reproduction of the Palazzo Vecchio—by the criticisms, which, in the very same town, might be either "diverting, ingenious and brilliantly acted" or "this presumptuous but slipshod effort to improve Henry Irving and E. H. Sothern," and by Andy's assurances that though maybe tonight's receipts weren't quite all he'd been led to expect, they would build by the end of the week, and anyway, they couldn't fail to make a ten-strike in this next town—"why, say, *Kiss the Boys Goodbye* just played it, and took ten thousand bucks out of town, so if we can't do twelve, I'll shoot myself."

But presently she could remember the cities only by the banana royal that had made her sick, or by being charged twenty cents for coffee, or by the red rubber overshoes she had bought.

So went the second and third weeks of their gypsying, and Bethel became a trouper.

And to her the sensation of those weeks was the genteel murder of Wyndham Nooks.

In Belluca, with some awe of Adrian Satori still hanging about, Mr Nooks had merely overplayed—"hoked" is the technical word—the role of the Apothecary, which is a pretty easy role for anyone to hoke, if he has been born an earnest, congenital ham.

But in Treverton, the next town, Nooks began to brighten up the normally disregarded role of First Watchman, in the final act. When he bounced on stage, in a New York policeman's uniform not too well fitting at the neck, his speech was "Lead boy; which way?" But for Nooks, Shakespeare unadorned was not enough. He had to have a lot of Nooks in his Shakespeare. He stopped after the word "boy"; he peered about, long pale hand on the visor of his cap; his knees and elbows quivered; and he yelled out "which way?" as one would yell a fire alarm.

As this all happened just before the death of Juliet, Mrs Boyle was not pleased.

Andy spoke to Nooks about it every night after the show, in Treverton. But in the city of Paddock it was the resident manager of the theater who spoke about it—and to Andy.

This manager was named Sam Lee Regis, and he was quite a pleasant old thug and loafer. The Paddock theater was, in legal theory, owned by the estate of a defunct tin-can manufacturer, whose only chick, a spinster, lived in Vicenza and wasn't very bright about investments, or anything else except Italian primitives.

Mr Regis's salary continued just the same, whether that handsome old black-walnut-and-crimson-velvet theater, the Sherman Square, provided a new play every week or was dark the whole year through. The local Carl Frazee jabbered to Andy that Mr Regis preferred the latter—it gave him less to do. He particularly disliked any unusual attraction, like Romeo in gray bags, that required attentive publicity, but his favorite phrase about almost every star was, "He don't mean a dime in the box office."

Thus, this season, Sir Cedric Hardwicke in *Shadow and Substance,* Cornelia Otis Skinner in *Candida,* Frank Craven in *Our Town,* they none of them to Sam Lee Regis meant "a dime in the box office." That gave the serene old gentleman—who had a large mustache, and yet chewed gum during the moments when he was not slumbering in his old leather chair in the theater office—an excuse for spending almost nothing on advertising, a topic which Andy was discussing with him, warmly.

This expense the company and the theater were supposed to share equally, but as Mr Regis looked at it, it wasn't an expense at all, but just a bad idea.

Mr Regis droned, "Boyle don't mean a cent in the box office, and that old ham you got playing the Watchman and Apothecary, say, when he wriggled his nose—it's made of rubber, ain't it?—I had the first good laugh I've had since George Cohan was in town. Now there's a show that *is* something—singin' and dancin'. Why don't you get a show like that, Mr Deacon? *Shakespeare!"*

The less Andy thought of Sam Lee Regis, the more he was irritated that Nooks should give Mr Regis such an opening. But nothing happened in Paddock; nothing till Dubuque.

There Bethel was called to Andy's dressing room before the evening performance.

Andy looked massive in his loose green silk dressing gown (slightly spotty with brown face powder and cold cream), but he sounded feeble.

"Kitten, I need some advice bad. I've never been so scared. I've got to fire old Nooks——"

"Oh, you can't!"

"I'll have to, Beth."

"But it 'll kill him! He's so proud of his technic. He told me you were thinking of him for Capulet, if Challis ever quit. And he's showed me twice now the line in the Milwaukee *Sentinel* that said he was 'a stalwart actor of the old school.' And he's been sending money home—his wife has been paying the rent for the first time in a year, he told

me, and he wants to start a rep theater . . . and he bought
me an ice-cream soda!"

"Don't I know it, kitten! It's murder. He's probably five
years older than he claims to be. Maybe he'll never get another job. But if I don't do it, he'll murder the whole company, and our tour, and throw twenty-eight people out of
work. Because he's getting worse, and he just won't change.
But I don't know how to tell the poor gaffer. I wouldn't
mind facing Lyle and Tony, but this—— Nooks is like an
old man crazy in love with a young girl."

Then she knew.

Andy was inconceivably hoping that she would do his
slaughtering for him. Between contempt for his weakness
and pride in his sensitiveness and happiness in his turning to
her not as the star to a baby understudy but as one trusty
friend to another, she was dizzy.

She spoke anxiously. "Can't you pension him off or something? Maybe money will help to heal the pride."

"My Beth that's growing up so! You'll be doing Juliet
and Boyle understudying you, before we hit Broadway,
but—— No, I can't even pension Nooks. Sweet, I'm going
to tell you something that nobody knows except Tertius
Tully and me. I'm nearly broke. If our business don't get
better, we'll have to close in three-four more weeks."

It was like telling a dancing passenger that the ship was
afire and sinking. "Oh *no!*" was all she could do.

"Don't tell anybody—and I mean that. Ever since our
summer in Grampion, I've always sort of felt that you and I
were confidants, even if we have had a whole mess of
Mahalas and Zeds keeping us apart. And now—it's a comfort to confess to you. I spent a lot on the sets and costumes in the first place, and ever since we opened, I've spent
more on advertising than usual, and I'm paying big salaries
—most of the company are getting more than they ever did
in their lives.

"About six thousand a week is the very least we can get

along on, with railroad fares, and trucking the scenery, and what the union truck drivers and loaders charge us. Well, our first week, in Belluca, we did make expenses—with exactly ten cents over, which I sent to my mother, who's had it mounted in diamonds. But these last two weeks we've been losing. I thought that, with the one-night stands, we'd catch up. Everybody told me that all the farmers for sixty miles around would leap in their Fords and drive through blizzards to see Romeo Meets Juliet. Well, either they got sand in their carburetors or they preferred to stay home and listen to the radio, and maybe they're right. I can stand it a little while yet, but—— And one thing you can help me with, darling. If we do pull through, I've got to have the most unwavering loyalty from every member of the company. Nobody can let down, on stage or off. I say this to you, kitten, because I know you're always loyal, and maybe you can influence the ones that aren't."

And he looked at her. And she looked at him. And both waited. And at last she got out, "Andy, would you like me to fire Nooks for you?"

"I don't think I could let you do that. . . . I won't pretend it wouldn't be a big relief. Could you really stand doing it, chick?"

"Maybe it would be easier for me than for you, Andy. I'm not so much involved."

"Maybe it would. I certainly 'd appreciate it. Take him out and buy him a drink, before we go to the train tonight, and spring it gently—but I know you would. And tell him that besides his regular two weeks' notice, I'll give him two weeks' extra pay. And agree with him that I'm a bum and don't appreciate good acting when I see it."

The prologue was rather shaky that night, and the epilogue a sob. She had invited Nooks out "for a little supper"; he had accepted with such grandiloquent gratitude that she felt like a woman spy tempting a benign admiral.

With a hope that Andy would regard it as business expense and repay the fabulous cost, she took Mr Nooks to the Kungsholm Swedish-American Restaurant, in Dubuque, which has colored tablecloths, smörgåsbord, and waitresses in that colorful peasant costume which is apparently the same in Sweden, Hungary, Albania and Iceland. They had glasses of piercing aquavit and plates of sausage, and just as Bethel was trying to bring out the noose tactfully, Wyndham beamed and cried happily:

"I'm sorry that I've been too busy helping Andy get the company launched into a sound interpretation of Shakespeare to see much of you, my dear. I have noticed how pleasant you are to everybody, even to pompous old hams like Challis and Miss Staghorn, and I do hope that after this little fling at play-acting, you'll be able to settle down with a nice husband.

"It's a hard life, the drayma, and now that it's in the hands of the vicious commercial managers on the one hand, and on the other, upstarts like the Group Theater and Cheryl Crawford and Antoinette Perry and Margaret Webster——women directing and managing——! I've known periods of despondency when I didn't think I would ever be appreciated again, and in a way I'm very grateful to our young friend Andy Deacon——no actor, poor lad, and a terrible interpreter of the wings of poetry, but he means so well, and I'm delighted to help him out.

"And I won't pretend to you, with your fresh young face looking at me, and I can't tell you how touched and gratified I am to have you blow me to supper this way and to find there are still a few young people who revere the technic and integrity of a Professional, and I won't deny that I've been very glad of this opportunity, however small, though perhaps it would have been better for the show if they had cast *me* as Capulet, instead of that Englishman, Challis, with his old-fashioned delivery, and so——

"But what has been especially gratifying—— It doesn't matter about me. I'm a trouper. I can take it. I can put up with malodorous bedrooms and chop sooey and the dreadful embarrassment, to a man of my scholarly rearing, of having to consort with subway conductors instead of taking taxis. But my wife, Mrs Nooks, is a woman of the utmost talent and delicacy. She's not as young as she was, but that little woman's ambitions recognize no bounds, as does her affection for my poor self.

"She has for years been longing to study French, but she has lacked both the means and, when I have been in Gotham, the time, since her chief preoccupation has been to give me the most incessant and tender care. But now at last I have been able to begin sending her enough, not only to begin paying up our debts, but for her to enter upon the study of the sparkling native tongue of the witty Gaels, or I suppose you would call them the Franks.

"She has found the most sympathetic teacher, a French lady, not so young any longer, but from a very high-placed aristocratic Parisian family, and Mrs Nooks has written me, on a postcard which just arrived this morning, that after only one lesson she can say, 'Send the head-waiter, I wish to order dinner in this restaurant.'

"So I hope that to a dear child like you I shall not seem ridiculous if I confide to you that a lifelong ambition of Mrs Nooks and myself has been to travel abroad and see with our own eyes the treasures of ancient culture. And now at last we shall be able to do so.

"Our Romeo tour and Broadway appearance are certain to continue for two years at a minimum—I hope so for Andy's sake as well as mine; he is an amateur at acting, but a very generous and loyal young friend—and I am sedulously saving my not overexcessive salary—which I trust that Andy will increase—and at the end of our run—think of it—our dream for years and years of boardinghouses and local trains—our dream that we've talked of till far into the night —Mimi and I will go to France!"

She tried.
She hinted that Andy had vulgar conceptions of the

classics; that he was in the clutches of Mahala Vale, who wanted to turn the play into her private bridge to Hollywood.

Nooks did not hear a word. He was talking about his Conception of the Role of the Apothecary. There was a light of bliss upon his tumbling soft white hair, his ever-changing thick red face, and he felt himself a priest and a servant of mankind.

They were at the point where Nooks was booming, "I know I'm too old to tackle Romeo, but I have some ideas that will surprise you about playing Macbeth," and Bethel was desperately wondering whether her purse and her sobriety would stand another Swedish punch, when she saw Andy fling into the restaurant, look about, look relieved, and shoulder toward them.

His eyes asked what had happened. She shook her head. His lips formed "I'll do it," silently, and then aloud, very noisily and collegiately aloud, Andy greeted them: "Well, I'll be darned! What're you two doing here? Buy you a drink? Do you mind if I sit down with you a minute?"

"My dear boy, it's a pleasure," said Nooks. "I think of you both as my children. I have just been telling little Bethel here that she mustn't let it worry her if the interpretation of Shakespeare is beyond her feminine powers. She is all the luckier to be born to blush unseen as some good man's wife. I was telling her . . ."

He did not stop for seven minutes.

Andy was able to convey to Bethel, "Felt like a dog for asking you. I'll do it." But he got no farther than, "I'm a little disappointed in the critics' reception, Mr Nooks. We may have to make some changes," when Nooks was off on the interesting theory that all critics are born of an especial brand of acrobats.

Bethel was less sorry now for him than for Andy, with twenty-eight people's livings to protect—the forlorn big Andy who looked beaten. She heard herself piping:

"Mr Nooks! Please! Please *listen* a moment! No—listen!

I think that you ought to know that Andy has been compelled to plan some changes. He may have to drop either Iris Pentire or myself—he hasn't decided which, and I hope it won't be me, but of course I'll submit without feeling a bit hurt, if it's necessary for the good of the show—which is what we're all after, *isn't* it?"

She got in a glance at Andy. He was astonished, he was grateful, he was almost adoring. (Well, he ought to be!)

"And in the same way—— I happen to know that he's not satisfied with Zed Wintergeist, and may replace him with an actor who has more suavity."

At this thundering lie poor Nooks looked delighted.

"And—you can blame it all on me—I'm afraid I've rather encouraged him to feel that just because you *do* so wonderfully represent one great classic school of acting, Mr Nooks, you scarcely fit in with the crazy experimental way in which Andy and Satori have done this show, and so——"

Nooks abruptly turned from her to Andy. His mouth, with its wide loose pale lips, opened deeply. Bethel expected a roar. But it was very quietly that he said, "Andy, do you want to give me my notice, sir?"

"Well—in a way—not exactly—but still——" said Andy.

Nooks slowly stood up, his great head back, his eyes closed for a moment, and his face was the face of a dead man. "All right." His eyes were wet. "I have been very lonely for my wife, anyway. She hasn't many friends in New York. She'll be glad of my return. I'll leave as soon as my successor is ready to take over, sir. Good night to you both, and the greatest of success."

He walked out of the restaurant slowly, his shoulders back and his head up.

Bethel and Andy sat silent. Silently he pulled out a bank note and left it on the table for the waiter. Silently he walked with her to her hotel. Only at the door he said, "I love you for what you've done for me. Good night."

28

Two weeks more of one-night stands.

Station platforms and cues and shirred eggs with little farm sausages and No. 17 purple lining salve and the 7:47 A.M. and the rhumba on a revolving floor under lights changing from green to fog to crocus and handkerchiefs washed in the bowl and plastered on the side of a bathtub and looking at the name of the newspaper to recall in which town you were and the line "See what a scourge is laid upon your hate" and a Van Gogh print on a hotel bedroom wall and brown powder that never quite got out of your ears and Doc's organ voice as Friar Laurence and chewing gum and the white mark your hand left on a dusty day-coach seat when you slapped it and telegraph poles scurrying back and borrowing Kleenex from Mabel and a world-long rim of pale scarlet along the horizon at dusk beyond cold December prairies and pots and pots of coffee and Zed's sad hazel eyes as he brooded over a volume of Rupert Brooke by a frosted car window and Exit UR and moonlight lamps staring down pale blue from the border lights and giggling at a film along with Vera and Charlotte and street crossings of packed snow in corduroy rows glistening under the lights between you and the theater and here it was almost the half-hour call already and across the way "Romeo and Juliet" exciting in electric lights on the theater marquee and bath towels long as yourself and acting beside Zed and small boxes of individual orders of corn flakes and the cross-word puzzle in the morning paper with which you tried to keep awake when your eyes looked red and felt red and your lungs were tickling with train dust and unexpectedly kindly applause and fried oyster sandwiches and Mrs Boyle heartbreaking in "It was the nightingale and not the lark."

Down and across the mighty prairies of the Mississippi Valley: Iowa and South Dakota and Nebraska where, through today's cornfields and cement roads, move the ghosts of Mormon pioneers.

The fourth and fifth weeks of the tour. Waterloo and Mason City and Sioux Falls and Sioux City and Des Moines, Cedar Rapids and Davenport and Burlington and two nights in Omaha, and on New Year's Eve, St Joseph, only it's really "St Joe," with its bright hills above the Missouri River that are shrines to Jesse James, who was the Hitler of his day, with gold watches for his Vienna and Prague and Warsaw.

When she reached Nebraska, the Bethel who had been coddled in Connecticut as in cotton batting was certain that she was already practically in California, and only a step more from Hawaii and China and Australia—yes, and perhaps really going there.

Andy was beginning to hint about their touring Australia. He whispered to Bethel that she need worry no more about the tour's closing; yes, he was still losing money, but not so much, and in the metropolises of Kansas City and St Louis, so justly proud of their auditoriums, their Little Theaters, their symphony orchestras, he would "make a pile—enough to carry them till the luck changed and they began to coin money."

So they went on, descendants of the Covered Wagon, with portable radios instead of the slim columns of signal smoke seen across the sun-drowsing plains. And so she discovered America.

The stretch of plains was so unpunctuated. All morning long, from the train window, the snow and sky had been confused in one slope of empty gray, and Bethel was weighed down by the sky's heaviness. She was homesick for the New England stone walls, lively with squirrels and thrushes that had invited her girlhood outings. But here the farmhouses, cruelly far from one another, crouched with their barns and grim cement silos in little nests of cottonwood trees, as alone and individual and strange as a shepherd's cot in the Highlands.

An hour before they came to their next stand, the sun was through, and the morning of creation was miraculously renewed. Suddenly the sky was tremendous, glorious with unsoiled blue; the snow was a silver mantle; and she saw how many of the houses, along with lean and gray-streaked prairie poverty, were new-painted bungalows, with solid, hip-roofed barns jauntily bearing bright galvanized-iron ventilating cowls. The silos were towers, now, brave as the old, sea-facing watchtowers she had seen in pictures of southern France.

Their city, when they came to it, was gay with sun, young and eager. The station had miles of leather-and-chromium chairs in the waiting room, and the attendants were like collegians, very friendly with young actresses. The hotel was new, and her room, all in maple, with a Navajo bedspread, was on the thirtieth floor. She looked out on the medley of Old West and New Pan-America that is characteristic of all that land: skyscrapers and a marble Art Institute and a luxurious-looking Georgian brick Town Hall Club among a Shanghai sprawling of tin-roofed one-story shacks plastered with signs advertising beer and candy bars.

Then her nap, curled snugly on that heavenly bed. (The

mattress was astonishingly named the Slumber Coaxie, and had, it seems, been Scientifically Constructed in accordance with the findings of a Conference of Forty Professors, Housewives and Social Leaders. But it really was a good mattress, once you got to sleep and forgot the lush poetry.)

She awoke to sunset.

She had not known such extravagant sunsets as these of the plains. In Connecticut sunsets were usually frail, tranquil, pretty affairs, that economically afforded you a couple of strips of pale crimson, and one of old gold, with a good effort in the way of an apple-green sky beneath. They were the crisp bacons of sunsets. But these displays in Iowa and Nebraska were Ninth Symphonies, battle pieces, insanities of flame and gold.

She discovered a curious rule: A truly great sunset will always be in this form: it portrays a seabound land of burning lava, through which winds a golden river to the bright bays and inlets of a glowing sea.

When they had crossed the Missouri River, she decided that she was no longer in the prosperous Middle West but in the real West that, with its myths and true memories of cowpunchers and John Brown and the Santa Fe Trail and the Gold Rush and Indian braves, of frontier saloons and railroad builders and two-gun sheriffs, of mountains and ranches and deserts, is one of the five or six romantic districts of the whole world.

She loved her tight New England as much as ever; she was not parrot enough to echo, "New York isn't America." But she had had a bath of greatness, and she came out of all this not a Yankee but an American.

And an American who, born in 1916, might live to see the fabulous Great Land of the year 2000.

All the time that she was thus tasting greatness, she was entirely surrounded by love, and none of it was hers, and she didn't like the idea at all.

The corporation of Mahala and Andy Deacon, an institution engaged in dancing together, expensively dining together, and squabbling together, went on like tired matrimony, with none of the advantages. Bethel suspected that Mahala would never give up Andy so long as she rather thought he was a good actor and decisively thought that he was a good athlete and very rich; and that Andy stuck only because he was expected to. Bethel was irritated by Andy's unimaginative humbleness. His good-night kisses of Mahala in hotel lobbies were like porridge without cream. And in the fifth week Mahala began writing many letters; began receiving, from New York, many letters, air-mailed, all in the same masculine script.

Bethel could tell exactly the day on which Mahala must have learned that Andy was (if possibly still quite as athletic) not so rich as he had been. It was on December 23d, in Des Moines. That evening she came gushing into Bethel's dressing room, which normally Mahala would as soon have thought of entering as she would a lecture room on foreign affairs. She was an angel in a voluminous white linen dressing gown with blue ribbons. She gurgled, "My, you've got such a sweet dressing room! An armchair! Well, you deserve it, Beth. I was just saying to Hugh Challis last night that you have the real, sure-enough Old Vic touch in your—what d' you call it?—prologue."

"Did you?"

"Oh yes! And he agreed with me. Uh—Beth! Have you heard rumors about Andy not being able to get any more backing, and being busted? I know we're not making any money but——"

"I don't know a thing about it," lied Bethel.

Afterward she wondered why, since she was going to lie anyway, she hadn't done a really good, crooked, malicious lie and told Mahala that Andy was sneaking off early mornings and pawning his silver-backed brushes and his silver brandy flask and his sapphire-studded (and rather pretentious) cigarette lighter. Then Mahala might have chucked him; then Andy might have stooped fondly down to her, the adoring peasant girl.

But would she have cared, now?

Oh yes! Andy was so much kindlier than Zed, so much younger than Doc Keezer, so much wilder and warmer than Doug Fry, so much more desirous of a shining future than Fletcher Hewitt and so much her own good tutelary god.

She saw Andy, now, taking Mahala to cheaper restaurants and buying sherry instead of champagne cocktails; she saw that Mahala was complaining; but seemingly it did not occur to Andy to complain of her complaining.

With all the fury that he gave to rehearsals, to learning a part, or to being rude to people he considered bogus, Zed had dived into books. He was as out of the arena of love as Bethel herself. He was reading—really reading, and not talking about it, like Challis or Mahala or Charlotte: marching through the novels of Hemingway, Dos Passos, Steinbeck, James Farrell.

And Iris had become intellectual—that is, for Iris. As there seemed to be no one more lucrative available, she had cleaved to Douglas Fry, and she listened to his talk about cycloramas and gelatins with a sweet, sedate vacuousness . . . and out of it she did at least have, as a pledge of Douglas's low-pressure ardor, a new trinket bracelet, on which she hung miniature elephants, locomotives, giant pandas, Charlie McCarthys and orchids.

But the torch of the caravan was the somewhat argumentative passion of Henry W. L. Purvis, Ph.D., and Charlotte Levison.

Harry Purvis could make dirty puns in Greek, Italian and Chaucerian English. Even when they were in Greek, which naturally you didn't understand as well as you did Chaucer, you knew they sounded dirty.

Harry was born in Gooversville, Georgia. Eight years ago he had graduated from William and Mary College, where he had majored in tennis and drinking and been the life of a small, rebellious dramatic society that put on plays ridiculing the Old South. He had taken his doctorate in English and Philosophy at Chicago, just barely *cum laude;* had gone to teaching in Hotchkiss School, and after six months of it, been enthusiastically fired.

Various reasons have been alleged: that he had been too obliging about lending Rabelais to students; that he had got drunk at Torrington with three students and, on the way home, not liking the diction of one of them, a young gentleman from Brooklyn, had chased him out of the car, removed his trousers, and left him beside the road; and that he knew more than all the rest of the faculty put together and mocked their learning. Being cheerful and handsome and completely penniless, he had been accepted by the Federal Theater, and had played a Rich Young Man so pleasantly that the audiences cheered every night when he was killed off by a sturdy striker.

He had been in the theater for four years now, and he was the most devoted trouper in the whole Romeo company. He even liked one-night stands, except that fourteen hours seemed to him too long to stay in any town that served highballs with the whisky in one glass and soda in another. He was never drunk before eleven-thirty P.M., and never sober between that hour and three A.M., and in all states of inebriety he quoted Ernest Dowson, Artemus Ward and Albert Jay Nock.

He looked like a young Velasquez cavalier.

At just what crisis he had been married, no one was certain, but his wife was tucked away on Morningside Heights. He did not speak of her often, but apparently she had been the youthful error of a lonely young man in a Chicago boardinghouse, and apparently she was named Amarette (with an *a*).

Rehearsals had not gone on four days, back in New York, before the Don from Gooversville and the Gainsborough Duchess from Grand Street, Charlotte Levison, had begun dining together, and before the company left Belluca, the relationship seemed almost legal. Purvis and Charlotte sat up till three A.M., drinking and talking about stopping drinking, and arguing about the folly of arguing about Communism.

No Bible-kiver-to-kiver Southern Fundamentalist Baptist could have taken her Gospel, her Party Line, more seriously and more credulously than Charlotte. Whenever the Moscow government was shocked to discover that the highly placed and trusted Admiral Asky group were traitors and saboteurs, and re-educated them with pistols in the backs of their necks, and replaced them with the long known and loyal set of General Bsky, and then, with naïve yelps, found that the Bsky scoundrels were even worse and had, without Stalin's noticing it, been sending notes to the English from his own back office when all the while he had thought they were sitting there playing solitaire, and he defended the rights of humanity by slaughtering them, too, and put in the incorruptible cohorts of Commissar Csky—who turned pale and hastily made their wills—then the kind Charlotte, who secretly loved *Peter Pan* better than she did Gorky and who wouldn't step on a backstage cockroach, not even a Trotzkyist cockroach, just smiled and carelessly explained to Purvis that it was all for purity.

Sitting in a grill with Purvis, she liked to tell of her father's escape from a burning Jewish village in Russia, after seeing his father disemboweled before him, and then add brightly that no immigrant to America and particularly no Jew has a chance in this wickedest of all capitalisms, and that 78 per cent of these immigrants are lying out under the Brooklyn Bridge and rapidly starving to death—and have been for years.

Purvis, equally loving her and exasperated by her bland dogmatism, always snarled back that if he were a Communist, he would be out of this in five minutes and go live in a factory tenement; certainly not use an airy Communism as a means of being fashionable, and sit beside a tiled swimming pool, like the famous and fashionable Hollywood fellow travelers, and condone slaughter over a mint julep. But it was the fate of this Tybalt to play whirligig through all his romance.

The moment he had done a passionate job of denouncing Charlotte, they would be joined by such reactionaries as Hugh Challis or Tertius Tully, and instantly, ranging up beside Charlotte, Purvis would be heard announcing that in Russia all actors are cared for by the government like pet rabbits and that any peasant just off the seat of a tractor can act with more disciplined technic than Noel Coward and design scenery more artfully than Oenslager or Bel Geddes.

Then, in Mason City, at a party given to the company by the citizens, Harry Purvis announced that Charlotte and he were going to be married.

The members of the company sat with dumb mouths. Purvis was already married! What about poor Amarette (with an *a*)? Had she gone to Reno?

In a pleased way he explained that there wasn't any Amarette. Ever a cautious drunk, Harry had invented her because otherwise he might never have known to whom he would find himself married some morning.

Charlotte was one of the people who were surprised and somewhat gratified by the announcements that Harry was unwed and that she was going to marry him. Oh well, said her ducal and matronly smile, you just never could tell what her bad boy would be up to next.

They were married after the show, in Sioux Falls, South Dakota, and the wedding party was held on the train. Andy had provided champagne and canned alligator pears. But a few of the merry rout drank nothing at all—Bethel, Vera Cross, Mabel Staghorn, Douglas Fry and Dr Henry W. L. Purvis.

In a long speech with footnotes Harry explained that he was now a teetotaler and a working Communist, and that as soon as the tour was ended, he was going to do something (vague but powerful) for the Cause.

His wife smiled on him sleepily and murmured, "That's swell. But let's see if we can't save up for a month in Ber-

muda first, Harry, and rent a cottage. I've always longed so
for a house of my own, where you can go up and downstairs."

"Well, okay then, dearie," said that scholarly, that fierily
crusading, that passionately romantic Tybalt, Comrade
Purvis.

But the catastrophe to Bethel was the desertion of her
heart's guardian, Doc Keezer. And it was actually to Mabel
Staghorn that she lost him, and all along of Miss Staghorn's new kitten, a soft but in no way remarkable kitten,
vilely named Pippy.

Miss Staghorn, who off stage was Mrs Wallace Tibby,
wife of the esteemed taxidermist, was the kindliest and the
friendliest person in the company, and much the worst
nuisance. Anyone who did not dodge quickly, she would
assault with loving greetings just at the edgy moment before
he made an entrance on stage. Not for her the quick pat on
the back and the cheery "Good luck!" of the ordinary
trouper. Just when Doc Keezer was trying to remember
whether his entrance line, as Friar Laurence, was "Romeo,
come forth; come forth, thou fearful man," or "Come
forth, thou fearful man, come, Romeo," or "Romeo, thou
fearful man, come forth, come forth," or what the devil it
was that came forth, Mabel Staghorn would maternally pat
him, and gurgle, "Now I just know you're not going to slip
again on that line." And so he would enter and slip.

On trains and at restaurants Mabel took the trouble to go
from seat to seat, conveying what she frequently called
"little bluebird greetings to keep everybody happy." She
always, on such occasions, cried cheerily to the men, "Now
don't stand up," and, if they didn't stand up, looked pained.

If the theories of scrambled time are correct, to this moment there stand all over the Middle West annoyed groups
of male actors, holding their napkins and watching their
minute steaks grow cold, while Miss Staghorn vocally
caresses them in liquids like a brook at eventide:

"Now don't let me disturb you—I just wanted to see if you were all comfortable—is there anything I can do for anybody?—oh, did you *notice* how slow Andy was on his cues tonight?—I'm sure he's worried—my, I do hope we're making money this week . . ."

Mabel believed in all the stage superstitions. Stronger even than her faith in a rabbit's foot for powder brush was her certainty that you mustn't whistle in the dressing room— perhaps she wouldn't have asserted that the San Francisco earthquake was due to some noodle's whistling in his dressing room, but she would have looked into it.

At a rehearsal you should never give the tag line—that finished off the show, didn't it? You mustn't open an umbrella on the stage (and this even after the cast had opened umbrellas all over the stage in *Our Town*), or put shoes on your dressing table or pass anyone on the stairs on the way to your dressing room, or have yellow in the room, or sing "Home, Sweet Home" on the stage; and in your hotel room, to lay a hat on the bed was to affront God himself.

Doc Keezer didn't exactly believe in any of these voodoos. He just didn't take a chance on them. He grunted, "Why the devil does Zed *have* to whistle in his dressing room? I'm not superstitious about it. But it makes such a row. Why can't he just sing?"

Mabel Staghorn had an infallible taste for banalities. Having been on the stage since she was eleven, and reared on Shakespeare, Molière, Sheridan and *Variety*—whose renowned headline, "Stix Nix Hix Pix," is but an example of its contribution to a living American Language—Mabel never said anything whatever that would have been unexpected in Mrs George F. Babbitt. When Jeff Hoy observed that Mabel turned Shakespeare's Nurse into a Red Cross nurse, Mabel sighed, "I never pay any attention to him; I just consider the source."

She thought it all over and said profoundly to Zed, "I do think people ought to make some little effort and try and be on time for rehearsals, don't you?" When he blandly answered, "But don't you think that might cramp their individualities?" she fretted, "Now I'm sure you don't mean that—a real, earnest young man like you—my gracious, I thought *you* were one of the young actors who realized that an actor's career is just one long devotion to duty."

Mabel's dressing table, in the theater, was as domestic as Grover's Corners. She did not carry a steel make-up box, but a litter of salves and pencils and powders and brushes in a pansy-embroidered linen bag—once white, now stained with every shade of faded carmine—which she spread out on the shelf, with a little ivory Egyptian cat-god, her mascot, and a photograph of her nephew, who was "doing very well" as accountant in the South Tallahassee Power and Lighting Corporation.

She had, to some degree, a husband, but she had no children. She spoke well and often of children, to whom she invariably referred as the "dear little ones" or as the "chickabiddies." But personally she had no children. She had cats.

She had, she explained to everyone, seven cats, reluctantly left to the unfeeling care of her husband in the flat in New York. The husband meant well but, it seems, he never could remember that Frou-Frou had to have liver ground, not mashed, and Kittenkatz (aged nine) required three drops of cod-liver oil in her liquor, which had to be two-thirds milk and one-third cream.

"That woman's got cat blood," said Zed, as he heard Mabel explain to Charlotte that "kittens are just as knowing as children—the way they look up at you with their sweet little eyes—like forget-me-nots—and they're so much more sympathetic. You can get just as fond of them as of children."

Said Zed, "Yeah, but there's not much fun planning future careers for cats, Mabel."

Doc Keezer, tolerant as sunshine, had always been amused by Mabel where the others were itched. And not even in Tertius Tully did Doc find so much of the ardent recollection of unimportant gossip that keeps the true trouper happy.

When he yawned at Mabel, "Say, which of the Trout sisters was it that played Agnes on tour with Ambrose Gillyflower in *The Brave Die but Once,* in 1906?" she did not flee. She rubbed her nose, and looked eager, and sighed, "Now, isn't that funny—I guess I'm losing my memory —oh well, we all grow old—I often say, 'It don't matter what you forget if you can still learn your parts'—but isn't it funny—oh yes—now I remember—it was Tacoma Trout —Cheyenne Trout was in burlyque that season and Albany Trout was singing the Duchess of Dantzig?"

In a café, between midnight and train time, Doc Keezer noticed a kitten, a small highwayman kitten, white with a black mask over one eye, sitting on the bar among the port and sherry bottles, washing its nose. Having had three quick gin-and-vermouths, Doc was certain that it winked at him with its masked eye. He thought sentimentally of Mabel's loneliness, bought the kitten for fifty cents, went, with the highly encouraging Tony Murphy, to awaken an infuriated veterinary surgeon, bought a cat basket, and on the train presented the treasure to Mabel Staghorn.

He had been slightly mocking, but Doc was touched when Mabel lifted the kitten out of the basket, curled it on her bosom, looked up at him (she seemed so old and tired, in a cotton nightgown, with gum of make-up still crusted on her weary eyelids) and began to cry.

"No one's ever been so sweet to me, Doc," she wept. "I didn't know I had any real, warm friends in this company. Now I know. And that makes me even happier than this dear kitty. . . . We'll call it Pippy." Very cheerfully: "It 'll make Mrs Boyle and her Pekingese sore as crabs. Oh, I could just kiss you for this, Doc!"

Mrs Aurelia Boyle, the permanent Juliet of the Anglo-American-Australian-South African stage, was reserved and County English; she was well bred and bad-tempered; she often informed Andy—one of the few people to whom she ever spoke, off stage—that she demanded nothing of life, and indeed she did demand nothing much beyond top billing, a salary equal to half that of all the other nineteen actors put together, the box-office statement for every performance, delivered—without fail—in her dressing room before the third act, the bridal suite in hotels (at half rates), a drawing room on trains, a combination of never being bothered by reporters or photographers and of daily seeing extensive and reverent biographies of herself in the press, a daily supply of whisky, and viceregal precedence for her snarly-faced Pekingese, Pluto.

Andy walked it, Hugh Challis fed it lamb chops, Charlotte, slightly shuddering, petted it, and (though she declined) Bethel was once invited to shelter it for the night in her upper berth, when poor Aurelia could obtain nothing but a compartment. Aloof though Mrs Boyle might be, her mutt was full of a sinister friendliness. Happy bridge players of the company, planning to overbid in hearts, would feel a queer, ghostly presence about their lower legs and look down to see Pluto grinning at them and thinking about nipping their calves. Sleepers on daytime jumps would dream of seven-headed serpents and start awake to find Pluto dribbling on their bosoms.

Not a popular dog.

But to Mrs Boyle, who often bemoaned her childlessness, in some forgetfulness of a son by her first marriage, a son who now lived in Maidstone Hill and had two children and played badminton, the hound Pluto was her child and her soul.

When she saw the cat Pippy, in her miserable basket, being carried on the train by Mabel Staghorn, she screamed. She really screamed. She wailed at Andy, "As if I hadn't suffered enough having that Staghorn woman for Nurse! And now she has that mangy animal. I won't endure it! You may laugh, my good man, but I tell you Pluto is sensitive as Shelley. He'll be terrified by that alley tiger."

For once Andy stood up to the prima donna and said, soundly, "Oh, don't be silly." But it was worse than Aurelia had expected.

Pluto was fascinated by Pippy at once, and then enamored of her. He showed all the antics of a small boy in love. He stalked round and round the bored Pippy, while the company embarrassed him by giggling. He feebly smiled at her and invitingly paddled with his paws. He escaped from Mrs Boyle's drawing room on trains at night and sat lovingly before the berth in which reclined Miss Staghorn and Pippy, and from time to time he awakened everybody with a thin celestial howl, and when they popped out of berths and cursed him, he looked at them with an evil, aged, oriental guile and howled again.

And he almost broke the granite heart of Mrs Boyle by desertion.

Meantime, Pippy brought those aging innocents, Mabel Staghorn and Doc Keezer, together.

Being responsible for the cat, Doc went on, in duty to it, buying liver and catnip and cleaning its basket. He found something homelike in caring for a rather helpless woman and her feline child. Hour on hour the three of them, Doc, Mabel and Pippy, sat together in the plush seat of a day coach, relaxed in such warm and velvety communion as "Well, I can remember when Walter Huston first decided to play in *Desire Under the Elms*. He says to me, 'Doc,' he says —of course him and me were old friends . . ."

It occurred to Bethel, a little wretched that she had never seen it, that Doc had overwhelmingly wanted someone who wanted him. He was exhilarated by having a friend who depended on him for small cold walks in unknown streets between matinée and evening, for getting a taxi, for finding the drugstore with the best ten-cent coffee.

His fondness for Bethel had cooled into an amiable "How's tricks, child?"

Doc Keezer had come home, and she was the more homeless in it. A little frightened, she reached tentative hands out to Zed and Andy.

Zed invited her to attend the *Pygmalion* movie, and then forgot the engagement.

Andy was too busy quarreling with Mahala to notice anybody else.

She was truly alone.

She had never in any moment loved Doc or Fletcher Hewitt. But had she ever loved Andy? Or had it been just gratitude and dazzle? Had she ever been on the verge of falling in love with Zed? Or had it just been stimulus and curiosity and the compliment he paid in bullying her?

She had supposed that, whatever complications and dizziness there might be once you were plunged into love, there was first a divine certainty about knowing that you were in love. She felt lost now, and insignificant. She felt like an understudy.

And understudies suffer not so much from cruelty as from invisibility.

It has been recorded that Bethel was naturally of the lonely type—of the loneliness that is the pain and penalty of being individualistic. In the gregariousness of rehearsals and the first credulity of the tour, she had seemed cured. But now she settled down, apparently for the rest of her life, to Steak Medium Rare with Tertius Tully, Hugh Challis, Jones Awkwright (Wyndham Nooks's successor, a poolplaying man) and occasionally Doc Keezer.

They never talked of anything but the stage.

Challis referred to "the drama." Doc Keezer said "the theater." To Tertius Tully, it was always "show business." To all of them, it was all that was important and pleasant in life.

And so it was with Bethel Merriday as, lonely or no, she became a trouper.

29

THE TELEPHONE jeering beside her bed. Her whole body
trying to shut it out. Sliding instantly, when the bell ceased,
into a gulf of sleep. The bell again, ringing for hours and
hours, while for hours and hours she tried not to hear it.
The sick weakness with which she fumbled for the telephone
instrument. The voice, cool, wakeful, in the little black-
rubber magic cylinder, "Six-thirty." Her body collapsing
again into sleep, but her mind making her swing her legs
over the edge of the bed, so that she could not yield. . . .
To miss the train, the performance? Horror!

She had got to bed at twelve-thirty; she had had six hours
sleep; her body was wailing for eight hours—ten—the
clock round.

Feebly she picked up the telephone again. Room service.
"This is 1679. I want a pot of coffee and some buttered toast,
right away. I've got to catch a train." "Yah, right away,"
said the Mid-European who, in all mannerly hotels, mis-
answers the room-service telephone.

Through a fog she tottered into the bathroom, still

wobbly at the stomach, and slapped her cheeks, her eyes, the back of her neck, with cold water. No time for a cold bath —and no energy, either, nor any warmth to spare, this December morning.

She meditatively scratched her knees, and looked down at her toes, reflected that Iris tinted her toenails, thought it would be rather fun to do the same, also thought that it would be intensely wicked, wriggled her toes—then yelled, "Wake up, *you!*"

She stalked back to the telephone.

Now six months ago Bethel would have felt herself a fiend to talk loudly to shut-ins down in the service department, and an ingrate and a heathen to have doubted their zealous desire to serve, but she was "not going to have any more of this business of having to catch a train with the room waiter coming in just as she had to run for the elevator." She yelled, "This is 1679. Where's that order of coffee and toast? I've been waiting half an hour."

" 'S on the way up," said Room Service, as mendacious as herself.

Dressed, she tried to stuff the mixture of stockings, handkerchiefs, clippings of reviews, hairbrush, into a suitcase. They were all growing in bulk, or else her bags were shrinking in the winter cold.

The coffee had come. She tipped the waiter—resenting the tip—and drank the coffee—resenting God. She called a bellboy, thought that he looked at her admiringly, foggily forgot it, and staggered after him to the desk, downstairs. The old, old business of the girl cashier's mechanical, dehumanizing, slot-machine demand "Whacha room number?", of waiting for her bill, looking it over (just to seem wise, not because she could ever add it), making sure that she had left her room key, wavering through the pillared lobby and down crimson-carpeted steps to the sidewalk, to a taxi, counting her bags to make sure she had them all. . . . She would probably, in her continued state of drowsiness, have counted two or even one as three, and been wearily content.

Driving through the city in a dream. Half conscious that about her were new buildings, new people. Take that cheery policeman talking to the man opening up a cigar store, both of them laughing, their words coming out in white steam; he was probably important to himself, and worth knowing, but she must forget him and keep going.

One-night stands!

Stiffly climbing out of the taxi at the huge wide sidewalk in front of the railroad station's Corinthian pillars. The rest of the company coming up in taxis behind her, but the loving greetings pretty shy now and doubtful and hungry-sounding, even Andy's affectionate "Hello, kitten; still alive?"

A safari of silent actors following silent redcaps, luggage-laden, through the vast sonority of the waiting room, down a gold-and-marble corridor, down stairs to a mysterious dark underpass, like a corridor from the Bastille, with arches along it labeled Track One, Track Two, Track Three, which gave on cinder-smeared stairways. Then up again and into the open air, on a long cement runway between sunken tracks, and, despite a determination never to feel human again, fresher and gayer and full of hope . . . hope of glory and more coffee. And the train pushing in, with white smoke against a flashing winter morning sky.

One-night stands!

At five in the afternoon, after her nap on a strange bed in a strange room in a strange city, she awoke when the telephone again called her. She stretched happily. She yawned with unrefined noisiness. In her negligee she moved across the dark room and raised the blind. Down there was an unknown main street, the shuttle of an unknown corner, and headlights and taillights and neon signs dancing a dance of flame through falling snow. She half remembered thus looking at a city inferno in New York, when she had been hungry and depressed. Now it was all hope and waiting eagerness, for in three hours she would be made up and before an audience. She lifted the window; the wet air was exciting.

A new city, and tomorrow another new city—on forever through the mighty land.

One-night stands! To Jeff Hoy and Mabel Staghorn, purgatory. One-night stands! To Bethel, "the very name was like a bell——"

Even if at six-thirty A.M. it was like a telephone bell!

Since it was the only permanent furniture in her wandering home, Bethel became absurdly familiar with her own baggage and every most trivial detail of her small possessions. The theater trunk, with her costumes, and the other suit, to which she changed for the street at every other town. And maybe that wasn't a proud thing to see: a trunk with her initials and the licensed word "THEATER" painted on it. Her make-up box, severe and professional, of olive-green light steel. Her dressing-room slippers, mules of blue wool, and her dressing gown for making up, near-silk, its pattern of mignonette soon indecipherable among red stains of powder.

In this negligee she was accustomed to run up and down dressing-room corridors. All of them were used to popping into one another's rooms half dressed, and they had all the innocence of children. All the Mrs Worthingtons who want to put their daughters on the stage are advised that nowhere is the virtue of maidenhood less likely to be assaulted than in the theater. The Zeds, themselves no celibates, are curiously fastidious, and the Lyle Johnsons—who in the classic shades of country clubs and campuses are such successes—become mere bores to wise and traveled young ladies.

This trunk, with these working clothes, met her daily, deposited in her dressing room. She herself took care of her three pieces of hotel baggage.

The Big Suitcase, canvas-covered, rickety from much closing by standing on it: an inheritance from Sladesbury; ugly enough but, once opened, a delight to Bethel with its fresh blouses and slips and her two proud afternoon frocks.

The Middle-sized Bag, with stockings, handkerchiefs and doggy copies of Shakespeare.

And the new, quite expensive Overnight Bag, with pajamas, dressing gown, slippers, toilet things.

Night after night, on one-night jumps, this last was about the only piece that ever got opened. To the trouper, packing and unpacking are luxuries, like golf or families.

Each tiniest possession became familiar and important against the changing backgrounds. When her canary-yellow-handled toothbrush, whose color cheered her when she wearily brushed her teeth, wore out, she felt as lost and guilty at throwing it away as though it were an old companion.

But nothing of her own could be more familiar than the sets of the play, to whose comfortable greeting she kept returning in the strangest places—once in a hall that was practically part of a stockyard, chummily near the pigpens.

Watching Gene Doric, the master carpenter, mount and shift these sets, watching him curse and pray over the resident stage crews whom the local manager dug out of the Civil War Home, Bethel loved Gene and admired his endurance (supported entirely on coffee and chewing gum) He called her Beth and looked at her as though she were his younger daughter, and advised her one by one against the machinations of all the males, from Challis to Ernie the Program Boy.

On long daylight jumps, some six or eight of the company would always enter the car with books under their arms and with loud protests of "It makes me sore; I never get any time to read." And with that they would begin eight hours of play at bridge or poker, on folding tables when they were favored with Pullman cars, on suitcases on their knees when they had only day coaches.

Only Zed, Bethel, Douglas, Charlotte, Purvis, Andy, ever really settled down to reading anything but tabloid newspapers or picture magazines.

They who did not play cards talked (of the stage!) or slept, fantastically curled in car seats. From time to time these earnest sleepers were awakened by the cries of the bridge players and the triumphant slap of cards, and turned and grunted and went back to sleep.

Thus too they variously used their leisure in the hotels, between shows. When they spent only one day in a town and left by train at night, only Andy and Mrs Boyle took hotel rooms. The others roosted in Andy's place, and a whole series of young women were to be heard, though not to be seen, innocently taking hot baths in his bathroom.

But Bethel's true home was not in trains or hotels but in the theaters themselves.

She liked to be in her dressing room early. It had the security and the peace of a convent cell, and all its detachment from the outer world. It was pleasant not to have to hurry; to paddle about the room in her blue wool slippers, to sit before her mirror, one bare foot swinging, carefully putting a red base on her cheeks, and small touches of white along the side of her nose—which otherwise would seem a bit too small—patting it with a cool wet wad of cotton, smoothing it, smoothing it; to sit and recall her lines as Epilogue; to run over the Juliet part (some night, Mrs Boyle *might* be ill!) until the dressing room changed, in Bethel's imagination, from horse stall to palace.

She felt modestly and gratefully superior to all the dull people at dinner outside—such serfs as bankers and plumbers, schoolteachers and clerks.

Outside, the voices of the arriving actors were cheery. Hilda was ironing Mrs Boyle's costumes and singing "Kom' mit mir, du kleine Prinzessin." Zed was whistling the Brahms Fourth, down the dressing-room alley. Mabel Staghorn was chirping, "Come Pippy, Pippy, Pippy."

They were her family. She loved them all, for their gaiety, their courage, their endurance, their devotion.

The odor called "the smell of grease paint" grew thicker,

more enchanting. It was composed of face salves and powders, eyebrow pencils, cold cream, cigarette smoke, silk, old dresses, wigs, decayed flowers. Outside, the stage manager called "Half-hour," "Fifteen minutes," "Overture," then "Places, please," like an Old World watchman with his "Two o'clock and all's well"—a lingering, tender sound that made her nod in security. Only the last, "Places, please," startled her and brought, for a moment, the familiar frightened sinking in the stomach.

Then she was calmly, evenly as a cogwheel in a watch, moving to the entrance. She was passing Doc Keezer, sitting on a backless chair, nothing of him moving save his lips in smiling. He could sit like that all through a performance, when he was not on stage; waiting—for nothing. He whispered only "Good luck!"

Eldred, the stage manager, was waiting for her; he smiled; with outstretched forefinger he gave her the signal; she slipped through the draw curtain and stood between it and the drop curtain; the drop rose, with its familiar low roar, like wind far away; she was conscious of the golden glare of a spotlight engulfing her eyes, and mysterious dimnesses beneath it where the high lords of the audience were veiled from her, and she was safely plunged, no more in panic, into the dear familiar music:

> "Two households, both alike in dignity,
> In fair Verona, where we lay our scene,
> From ancient grudge break to new mutiny . . ."

Then her first stint was done; she was sitting near Doc Keezer, silent as he, till Romeo should come by—Romeo, Andy, so handsomely swaggering in tweed jacket and gray bags and careless cherry-colored tie; and she went back to her dressing room, another evening begun safely.

Once her dressing room was on a balcony above the stage. As she stood by the rail, looking down on the set, Hugh Challis stopped beside her and reflected:

"Like a big sailing ship at sea, isn't it, down there. A ship at night, good weather and clear stars. The cyclorama's like a huge sail, so steady, going up into the darkness—you can't see the top of it. And the set, with the light just dimly shining through it, is the lighted cabin. The stage planks are the deck. And we shall come safely to port—no fear!"

She could see it, though the nearest she had ever come to ships was in the movies. Yes, the stage manager, sitting down there behind the right tormentor, holding the script, their map, and quietly following the lines as they ran smoothly on, was the first officer or the pilot; the electrician, at his switchboard, was an engineer. This must be a sailing ship with auxiliary engines! The dialogue, coming distantly from on stage, was a steady, low sound, confident as a ship's soft throbbing . . . and, like a ship, it all went on night on night on night . . . the steady ship bearing her to glory . . . the voyage to Verona.

That was the final quality of real actors, she saw; not so much fantastic imagination, or neat imitation, or golden voices, but the patience to go on, night on night, and never quite let down. They never tired of the same play. They could always laugh anew at the Nurse's jeering, at Capulet's tantrums, and when they themselves slipped, when they "fluffed," they came off stage grinning and with never-faded excitement whispered, "Did you hear me say 'exiled' instead of 'banished'? Golly!"

Like all artists—all painters, all musicians, all poets, even some of those plodding recorders, the novelists—actors are glorious children, with a child's unwearied delight in the same story over again, and the child's ability to make dragons grow in a suburban garden, but with an adult magic of crystallizing the daydreams into enduring life.

Agreeably she waited each night for Doc Keezer's inevitable curfew after the curtain call: "Well, another day, another dollar." Agreeably she lost herself in the inevitable midnight post-mortems which are the actor's chief reward.

Wherever they were, in cafeteria or Chinese restaurant, hotel room or train, they went detail by detail over that night's performance. "Say, did you see the way Boyle pinched the masquerade scene off Andy by standing back humming when he first looks at her?" "Was I sore at Harry Purvis! He was kidding all through my duel with him!" "What was wrong with Hugh tonight? He was late on all his cues, and he almost blew in Thirty-five, where he bawls Juliet out for weeping."

It was the beloved repetition of lovers, of doctors; it was the sweet, long, important talk of theologians in the monastery; and like these other initiates, the actors resented laymen who intruded on them at table with unlawful talk of the outside world—laymen, nonprofessionals, whose heathen awfulness could be realized only when they said "practising" for "rehearsing," or in deepest depravity asked, "Does she *take off* her part well?"

When the nightly details had been fully gone into, they could always recall the time when Lyle was arrested by a traffic policeman just before a performance, the time when Romeo's trousers were stolen and he went on in gymnasium slacks, and Mabel Staghorn's spraining of her ankle by stumbling over a stage screw. She, equally the New Thoughter and the old trouper, played with her ankle bandaged, and was heard to warble, when the ankle was dressed, "Oh no, dear, it doesn't hurt the teeniest, weeniest bit, if you have faith in the Inner Resources—ouch, damn it!"

Yes, thought Bethel, perhaps their shop talk was thinner than the profundities of philosophers, but it was gayer, and more dear to the frail human soul.

For all their Pullmans and electric heaters in dressing rooms, they did not altogether lack the pioneering that the old-time saints of trouping had known, when Hamlet rode atop the stagecoach, through a snowstorm, in stovepipe hat and dogskin coat.

They had snowstorms that delayed the curtain. They went through the flu epidemic; Mrs Boyle was almost carried on the stage by her maid, and Andy played Romeo with a fever higher than that of love.

All these emergencies Bethel found enchanting. But she noticed that Andy was using them for what the business management of a show calls "the alibis"—the excuses to prove that a show is not really a failure. The alibis for the Romeo company were numerous. They had failed to have better houses not because people didn't vastly like their play but because of:

The cold, which kept people home.

The thaw, which kept people home.

The flu epidemic.

The rival high-school basketball game in Waterloo.

The rival National Guard exhibition in Sioux Falls.

George Cohan's tour in *I'd Rather Be Right,* in which the dean of American actors was, said Tertius Tully, taking away all the show money there was in the country.

The fact that there hadn't been enough shows in this city lately, so that people were out of the habit of theater-going.

The fact that there had been too many shows.

The fact that Andy was too chummy with reporters, so that they gave him no reverence.

The fact that Mrs Boyle was too unfriendly with reporters.

The fact that Mahala had worn red shoes at a Baptist church supper.

The fact that Shakespeare was Shakespeare.

The more the alibis, the more certain was Bethel that Andy was continuing to lose money. But lose or not, she went sweeping through her new America.

Waterloo and Des Moines and Cedar Rapids and

Davenport and Burlington and Omaha and Lincoln and Kansas City! Sedalia and Columbia, Jefferson City and Springfield; Little Rock, in the state of Arkansas that had seemed to her, from Connecticut, as far away as Alaska; Memphis and the naïve surprise that there were more filling stations in the South than moonshiners, more advertising men than colonels; the spacious and pleasant city of St Louis, royal city by the royal river; then into smaller and smaller towns in Kansas.

From Omaha to Lincoln the company went in two buses. Mabel Staghorn indicated that this was to save money, and she began to worry about their future, but the bright young people loved it, and as the huge green buses swayed through a land of small sturdy cottages, lost in white vastness, they sang Noel Coward's ballad, "Don't Put Your Daughter on the Stage, Mrs Worthington."

The party started just after the performance on Christmas Eve, in Cedar Rapids, and since Christmas was on a Sunday, continued on the train and all the next day, in their hotel in Davenport. On the train two days earlier, Andy had announced to the company that he would be their host for Christmas, but he said, cheerily, casually—only Bethel read anxiety underneath—"Let's all be merry, but let's be economical, at least till the show goes over. No presents from anybody to anybody, if you can help it. And we'll stick to beer."

Mahala flared up: "Is that your idea of Christmas in Newport, R.I.? Even in the chorus we'd get champagne. Romeo the spendthrift!"

"The fool. That ends her!" quaked Bethel, and Charlotte and Purvis exchanged glances. But Andy sounded bland:

"All right, if you feel that way, my dear. If it can be done. Did you ever try to buy champagne in Cedar Rapids?"

He did. The train left for Davenport with Tudor Blackwall waving a bottle of champagne and crying, "Company, attention! Corporals Swenson, Murphy and Keezer will distribute old Mother Pullman's best paper champagne glasses! Fill 'em up, gents and girls. You too, Comrade Purvis—tonight, at least. Now I'll give you a toast! To Andy Deacon, the best boss and the best friend an actor ever had! Skoal!"

They drank—none more cheerfully than Zed and Murphy and Jeff Hoy, the rebels against Andy's style of producing.

From his drawing room, Andy carried out a little silver tree. Despite his own order, he had hung on it a tiny present for every member of the cast and the stage crew: a gold pencil, engraved "An old accustom'd feast, Xmas '38." When the tree stood in the aisle, on a porter's footstool, shaking and glittering in the train's motion, when, holding high their paper cups dripping champagne, the whole company chorused, "Silent night, holy night," then Bethel dropped inside her berth and wept, her eyes against her arms.

It was her first Christmas away from Sladesbury and the big tree in the sitting room.

She loved her new family, though, and she forgot crying, sang sentimental songs with all of them—till Tertius Tully, usually the rock of discretion but now a little loose with champagne, whispered to her, "I hope Andy can pay for all this, but we've been dropping a wad of money every night this last week. Exeunt bearing corpses."

The loving-kindness of their Yuletide companionship had worn a little thin and gray when they assembled for Christmas dinner (donated by Mr Andrew Deacon, the producer) in a private suite in the hotel in Davenport.

They had none of them slept enough; they were homesick and tired of pumping merriment; and Tony Murphy had started breakfast with brandy in black coffee.

Bethel had been conscious of a waxing criticism of Andy and a pessimism about the tour. The malcontents felt, variously, that Andy was a shallow, unauthoritative actor, that the presentation of the play was too contemporary, that it wasn't contemporary at all, that Andy was paying Mrs Boyle too much money—a thousand a week against ten per cent of the gross, that he wasn't paying the particular person then speaking (even if that person happened to be Mrs Boyle) anything like enough, that he was losing so much money that he couldn't carry on, that Tertius and he were falsifying the box-office statements and Andy hideously expropriating them all and making money in carloads.

But now, at this edgy Christmas dinner, Bethel was able clearly to pick out the rebels.

Before the long Christmas afternoon was over, before the Scotch and port had stopped circling, as everybody moved from place to place about the huge table in the suite the malcontents were tending to sit together and, thus emboldened, to be openly doubtful of the weary charms of Andy. The sharpest conspirators were, she saw, Zed, Antonio Murphy, Geoffrey Hoy and Lyle Johnson, that Balthasar with the bark on.

Tony and Lyle could be discounted. They were the sea lawyers of the company; the inevitable complainers; the kind of mutineers who earnestly believed that this theatrical producer Andrew Deacon, born in 1910, had deliberately designed the smothering dressing rooms of a theater built in 1895.

But Jeff Hoy—Benvolio—was a man of competence, of technic and reason. He was the grim comedian. He never gave another actor a wrong cue, a kind word or a dollar. Acting was his business, and he paid his spiritual debts and collected his artistic bills with tight accuracy. He had never liked any other member of any theatrical company in his seventeen years (ever since he was twenty) on the stage, and had never been interested enough in any of them to dislike them. He was as courteous as an executioner, and in his handsome eyes there was no human feeling, no human weakness, no human love. He was married to a stately woman who was the daughter of a lieutenant governor of Ontario and who despised all Americans, all Canadians, all Englishmen and all actors. Jeff Hoy agreed with her in everything.

Not so resolutely mutinous as Jeff, but a little doubtful of Andy and very doubtful of the tour's long continuance were Douglas Fry, Iris, Harry Purvis and Charlotte, Victor Swenson . . . and Mahala Vale.

Loyal to Andy in everything, never believing in him so much and so adoringly as when they disbelieved, were only Hugh Challis, Mabel and Doc, Tudor Blackwall, Nathan Eldred, Vera Cross, Tom Wherry . . . and all the stage-hands . . . and Tertius Tully . . . and Bethel Merriday.

It shook Bethel enough, at this Christmas feast, to find that the competent Mr Jeff Hoy was allied with the plotters, but what crushed her was the sudden evidence that the cloistered Mrs Lumley Boyle could have any opinion whatever on any matter whatever aside from her salary and playing center stage, and that this new opinion of hers was that the tour was going to blow up, and she didn't care much if the explosion came soon.

Mrs Boyle had, at first, declined to come to the dinner. But perhaps sitting alone with Hilda Donnersberg and with thoughts of Devon mulled wine, in a moldy hotel suite on Christmas Day, was too much for her. She appeared just after the turkey came on—and she was about one-quarter drunk.

"Sit by me," said Andy. But Mrs Boyle looked swiftly over the assembly—far more men than women—and, as fluttery as a girl on Saturday afternoon at a summer resort, she swished over to young Lyle Johnson and youngish Jeff Hoy, gurgling to Andy, "Oh, darling, let me take this wonderful opportunity of knowing some of the boys I haven't played so much with."

Lyle and Jeff set a chair for her between them.

Bethel, not far down the table, thought she heard Hoy growl at Mrs Boyle, "Why didn't you say to him, 'Wherefore the hell art *thou* Romeo?'" She certainly heard Mrs Boyle giggle, then yelp at a waiter, "Whisky-soda, and do be generous for once, Herr Ober."

It was a rather makeshift dining place. The large table was made up of half a dozen tables of not quite the same height, so that the topography was mountainous and you went uphill from pumpkin pie to mince pie to plum pudding to candied orange peel. The tables so crowded the suite that you had to squeeze between the wall and the chairs, which varied from a saddle-back chair to a piano bench. On the walls, green below and pink above, were pictures of the various state governors who had graced the suite.

Mrs Boyle, never more than one-half drunk and certainly never less, was lavish. She told Hoy that he would give new life to the London stage, if he would ever condescend to go there. She told Tony Murphy that his humor was in the "classic tradition." She told Purvis and Charlotte—now lovingly sitting in one chair—that Andy had not had "the imagination to comprehend the aristocratic significance of *Romeo and Juliet.*" They bubbled back at her, and Hoy told the "raw one, but I'm sure you can stand it," about the preacher and the woman missionary, and Lyle whooped, and kissed Mrs Boyle—which, on any day save December 25th, was as improbable as his kissing Queen Wilhelmina—and she kissed him back.

Mrs Boyle's relationship to the continuation of the run of the play was different from that of any other member of the company. She had a "run-of-the-play contract," whereby she could neither quit nor be discharged except by common agreement between her and Andy, under penalty of the thunders of Equity. She might dislike everything about the show—and in Aurelia Boyle there were truly great powers of disliking—but she could not, the lone, lorn, exiled Pluto could not, return to New York without Andy's willingness. It was a horrid case of the capitalistic oppression of the intellectual proletariat.

While Mrs Boyle was surrounded by merriment at one end of the table, at the other Andy and his palace guard grew momently more grave and silent.

Mrs Boyle began effervescently to take them all, the young and provincial, into the sacred places of English stage life. Laughing, friendly, making fun of herself, she told them how Sir Johnson Forbes-Robertson had taught her that no one had learned how to walk across a stage so long as any observer could recall the way in which she had walked; how she had been reintroduced to Mrs Patrick Campbell seven times—five of them, Mrs Campbell had pretended not to remember her name, the sixth, she had pretended that Mrs Boyle was named Blievazatski, and on the seventh had sighed, "But you can't be Ellen Terry."

By now, the temptress had everyone but Andy, Bethel, Hugh Challis and Mahala.

She sighed along the table, and in the voice of the Lorelei called, "Dear Miss Vale, do come down here. I want to tell you how very charming I think you have made Lady Capulet."

Mahala went. She might have returned to the folds of righteousness, but suddenly Zed Wintergeist, who had been drinking, discovered Mahala as a new adventure. He put his arm about her with infuriating casualness. He took enough interest in her to be rude to her. He said that it was a shame that Mahala, obviously the most beautiful and flexible of all actresses next to Mrs Boyle, was yet so lazy that she didn't settle down to work and show up all the young leading women of her own vintage.

Mahala simpered.

At the Boyle end of the table the chairs were now two deep and the conversation tenfold. At the other, Andy and Bethel and Challis and Tertius sat solemn among empty chairs. Andy tried to look satisfied with his party, and he interrupted a long Challis story to mutter, "I suppose I ought to make some kind of a little speech."

Bethel wanted to beg, "Oh, don't." Before she could get started on it, Andy was up and, while the heathen end of the table looked embarrassed or derisive, he struggled, "Before we have a chance to break up, I want to tell you

that this has been the greatest Christmas of my life, and
I'm sure that all of us will say that, next to the chance of
spending the day at our own hearthsides, we have found
this the best bunch of friends and co-workers that has ever
been known, so, with Tiny Tim—or was it Alexander
Woollcott?—let us say, 'God bless us everyone.' "

Bethel was never quite certain whether Mrs Boyle interrupted him or just capped him, but their embarrassment
glided away on her voice, soft as across wide waters, singing
"D' ye ken John Peel?" It was a hunting song and then a
lullaby and then the inexplicable magic of her homesickness
for Devonshire mornings.

When Bethel turned from the singer, she found that
Andy was gone. She sprang up, blundered away without
tactfulness. She knew where Andy's room was—who could
have missed his laughter that Christmas morning?

Perhaps to make up for the feast, Andy had taken the
cheapest room in the hotel. She tapped at his door and,
unanswered, peeped in. The room was primitive: a brass
single bed, a bureau, one chair, an unshaded electric bulb.
Most of Andy's luggage was piled outside in the hall, and
his imperial black-and-gold dressing gown lay bunched on
the gritty matting on the floor. She saw all this only in pity;
for Andy lay on the bed, face down on the pillow.

She sat on the bedside; stroked his hair. He looked up
angrily. He looked fifty years old, and gray. Then he smiled.
He took her hand, tucked it under his cheek, and again
buried his face. For minutes they talked thus, without words,
comfortingly.

He sat up abruptly, his arm lightly about her. He said,
"Shall I give up the tour?"

"Oh no—no!"

"Most of the gang are discouraged. They blame me for
everything. That's all right—that's my job as producer, I
guess. After all, if we went over big, it 'd be me who'd get
the profit. They think the show is a flop."

"I don't!"

"Well, I'll stick as long as just one person believes in me —especially if that one person is you, because—— Oh well, I remember the case of firing Mr Nooks! That is, I'll stick it as long as I have one cent left, though——"

There was an astonishing change. He broke instantly, and his round face was bewildered.

"Why do they all buck me so? I can stand audiences not being so crazy about me, but when my own fellow troupers let me down—— I'm going to chuck it!"

"Fight 'em!" She heard herself as strident and demanding as a battling old woman. "You've been too good to 'em. They all take advantage of you. You're too apologetic to 'em. If *you* keep saying you're an amateur, what do you expect *them* to say?"

"I can't stand ill will around me."

"Oh, are you a child? Have you got to be coddled? Have you always got to stay in Newport, with the dear old loving nurse, and in Yale, with the dear old loving senior society members? You're out in the world now, Andy, and people aren't so awfully sweet. I'm ashamed of you, my dear!"

She was astonished. To have talked thus to her Sun God!

He spoke, and he sounded confident again:

"Yes. You're right. Thanks! I just needed a shot in the arm. I'll go on. But Beth, tell me—I haven't anybody except you and Tertius that I can really talk to, on the level. Did you feel this afternoon that there's a kind of organized conspiracy now to crab the show?"

"Yes."

"With Zed and Tony and Jeff the chief assassins?"

"Yes. You might try firing the whole lot of 'em."

"Even Zed?"

"Sure."

"I thought you were pretty strong for him."

"I am. I think he's a fine actor. And honest. But he's so young." (Venerable, wan, world-weary Bethel!) "He's a spoiled brat. If he doesn't get his own way exactly, he has a tantrum and lies on his back and kicks."

Andy fretted, "Yes. I wouldn't mind his being pretty rough on me personally, if it didn't affect his acting, but of course his work—the work of most of 'em—is going off. They're just saying lines."

"I doubt if Zed realizes that. Why don't you have a knockdown talk with him, Andy?"

"He wouldn't listen to me. Why don't you?"

This time she was not astonished that he turned to her, and it was with all gravity that she consoled him, "I'll see if I can't. But Andy, do you realize the real trouble we've got ahead? Mrs Boyle! She'll join the conspiracy."

"Never. She's a conscientious artist."

"Is she? She's also a woman, and she wants every advantage for Pluto. If she thinks the tour won't succeed, she'll want to get back to New York before it's too late to get another job this season, and we can look for some pretty fine tour-ending and play-busting tricks on Aurelia's part."

"You really think so?"

And stoutly, very maturely, she said, "I really do."

Among all the celebrated crises of burgeoning youth, first dancing, first powerful oration in school, first money earned, first love that comes from another human being and not from books, one triumph has gone unsung: the first time that an adult takes your advice seriously. With a sageness at which neither of them laughed, she theorized:

"Zed and Douglas just have vague feelings that they don't like the method of production. Tony Murphy doesn't ever like anything. But Boyle, and maybe Jeff Hoy, want to get home without having it on record that they've been fired. Oh, you will fight them, Andy?"

He was turning his head to the pillow again. "Yes. Because you're such a true woman. But—— I am so tired."

That Christmas night, in a strange town, she walked the streets half the evening.

If this tour closed, would she ever have another engagement—ever have the luck of finding another royal and job-bearing Andy? Would she be just a girl back home in Sladesbury, boasting to bored friends of having "once been on the stage myself," and hoping that a Charley Hatch—almost any Charley Hatch—would marry her?

30

DURING THE HOLIDAY WEEK, between Davenport and
Kansas City, Bethel was not certain whether Mrs Boyle
had consciously joined the conspiracy of failure. But she
was certain enough that Mrs Boyle was drinking too much.
She arrived at the theater sober and soreheaded; by the beginning of the last act, she was superb; but she left the
theater benign and domestic-looking and quite drunk.

Night on night (Andy was frank enough with Bethel
now) they were losing money, and neither of them knew
quite what to do about it. If the malcontents were not acting
so well, it showed only in the slowness and lackluster of the
play.

Bethel's one blow was in Doc Keezer, Mabel, Purvis and
Charlotte. Very mysterious, feeling herself a fixer and a
diplomat, practically a female Basil Zaharoff, she got these
four into the Purvises' room at Omaha, after their morning
arrival. She felt confident. When she had been waiting her
turn for a taxicab that morning, on arrival, the December
day had been so fresh and brave and sunlit; from the

plaza before the Union Station she had looked down on the tracks and on locomotives casting up a coil of bright smoke into bright air.

She fussily got her four statesmen seated on the bed, gave them cigarettes, and said enthusiastically, "Look: this is a public meeting. I want us all to do something big—get together and see if we can't save the Romeo tour. I know we all love Andy——"

Harry Purvis yawned, "Not enough to work miracles for him, and only a miracle will save this tour. I give it four more weeks."

"You honestly think so?" wailed Bethel.

"Well, maybe three," said Charlotte happily.

"*Or* two," smiled Doc Keezer.

"But don't any of you *care?*" demanded Bethel.

"Why?" wondered Doc. "It's just another flop. I've been in dozens of 'em. Andy's a good guy, but why all the fuss? We'll hustle back to New York and get busy looking for another job——"

"And that's that," said Mabel Staghorn, comfortably.

"You don't see something special about this production —making *Romeo and Juliet* real and important?" said Bethel.

"It's just another show," said Doc.

"Just another show," said Mabel.

"I'd like to hear Toscanini in New York," said Purvis.

"My baby shall," purred Charlotte.

And then did Bethel disgrace herself, and blow up with a wail of "Oh, I hate you, all of you! I hate you!"

What they said then, lengthily and affectionately, can be summed up as There there, you're a dear child, never mind, we'll all have dinner together when we blessedly get back to New York.

She bounced off to her own room, flaming, but she didn't even unpack, or wash her face. She telephoned down for the number of Mr Zed Wintergeist's room. She would go there, right now, and keep her promise to Andy, and eloquently win Zed over to righteousness.

But she stopped in front of the blank grained pine of his door.

No. She couldn't do it. She was being a busybody, intrusively busy about good works, and she hated women who were like that. And you didn't go lightly into Zed's room. Mahala and Iris and she popped innocently enough and frequently into Andy's apartment, and no one thought anything of seeing him wandering down every corridor in pajamas. But the intense Zed was not like that. No.

She turned away, and in her room she cried a little.

That afternoon Andy summoned her. "Well, kit, you were right. I've just had a talk with Mrs Boyle. She'd like to break her run-of-the-play contract. I wouldn't do it. She didn't say much, but she was pretty bleak. So I saw Hoy and Murphy—I'm leaving Zed to you, you know."

"Uh-yes," said Bethel, uncomfortably.

"And they both—they didn't exactly give me a two weeks' notice, but they both admitted that they think the tour's going to blow up and they don't much care, and I'm a parlor player. Swine!

> "God's bread! it makes me mad.
> Day, night, hour, tide, time, work, play
> Alone, in company, still my care hath been
> To ——

to keep their jobs going, to keep the play going, and they won't even gamble with me for a few weeks."

"We'll beat them yet!" cried Bethel.

"Ye-es," said Andy.

She marched now relentlessly to Zed's room. He was in. She found him lying on his bed, like a jackknife, his legs up against the wall, reading *Coriolanus* aloud, gently waving one foot in time to the beat of the lines. He went on a moment after he had shouted "C'm in" and she had entered. Then he looked up at her, amused.

It was just a little odd, standing back of him, seeing his face thus, upside down. Faces upside down are disconcerting and not altogether endearing. She let him have it. It was Coriolanus who spoke, as much as she:

"I just dropped in to tell you that you are a coward and a traitor, and that you are willing to ruin an honest theatrical experiment to butter your own vanity."

He whirled around all in one piece, like a top, and came to, sitting on the edge of the bed, glaring at her. "I'm a *what?*"

"You're an amateur actor!"

"Whatever you can call me, that's the one thing I won't stand!"

"You can't even endure discipline. You're the typical ham. You're willing to ruin the whole play if you don't get what you think you want."

"My good Merriday, when you come out of this dramatic scene you're throwing, I imagine I'll find you're referring to the fact that I think our presentation of *Romeo and Juliet* has been atrociously misdirected and mismanaged from the beginning, and that I'm quite willing to see it terminated, even to the considerable disadvantage of my own pocket-book, and if you call *that* being an amateur, why—why—you're crazy!"

She didn't remember ever being asked to sit down, but she was sitting on a straight chair, looking at him sitting on the side of a reproduction mahogany colonial bed. The room was small, tight, but neat as a candy box, and the wall was a temperate gray. She felt that for years now she had been talking to people who sat on the edges of brass beds, maple beds, mahogany beds, iron beds, Pullman berths. Had the whole world turned to sitting on the edges of beds and being querulous? Had chairs gone out? Did anyone anywhere still lie under the shade of trees and seem human?

"So you think it's all misdirected?" she was saying. "And just how would *you* direct it?"

"I'd make it really modern. What do the clothes matter,

if Andy keeps the whole feeling phony and bookish—the whole reading of the lines? Youngsters today love just as passionately as any blasted Elizabethans, but they have humor, and a realization that everything in the world has double and triple meanings, and that if you tell a gal her face is a lotus flower, you'd better be wary about your metaphor or it may fly up and trip you, for God knows what the lotus flower may mean to Freud! I'd have Romeo throw away a line like 'Yon grey is not the morning's eye, 'tis but the pale reflex of Cynthia's brow'—say it lightly, and not croon it like the prayerbook, the way Andy does. He reads like an elocutionist. Orson Welles and Co. made *Julius Caesar* sound like human beings really being sore and scared. And Maurice Evans's *Hamlet*—remember what a glorious female fool Mady Christians made of the Queen? No, of course you don't remember it! The only real play you've ever seen in your life was some tryout in Hartford. You're a pure little college girl from a fine old farmhouse o'erlooking the Connecticut River, and you think that a Saint Francis in tweed pants like Andy Deacon, that holds the record for chinning himself in the Y.M.C.A., is the hope of a newer and nobler drama with a moral lesson——"

"Zed! You've done a better job than you have any idea. You started making fun of Andy. You've ended by ruining him."

"He's ruined himself, by not having any dramatic sense."

"He's done *something,* while you just sit back and grouch."

"You sound like the wife of a popular publicity-grabbing clergyman, defending him."

"Whatever you think of Andy, he's put every cent and every ounce of energy he has into this tour, and now that you've made him ridiculous, you've enabled Mrs Boyle, that queen of the cats——"

"She sure is!"

"—to show her proper contempt for all of us—poor American amateurs—and kill her contract by ruining the whole show. She won't have to do much. You and that great comedian Tony Murphy have sneered at all of us so effectively that everybody's self-conscious and afraid to cut loose and do some vivid acting, and the show's flat as ditch-water, thanks to you——"

"Thanks to *me?!*"

"—and so now your fellow conspirator, Mrs Boyle, has only to step in and do a few sloppy performances and we're finished. Yes, you didn't like Andy. So you betrayed him for the great Mrs Aurelia Lumley Boyle!"

"Now by God I won't stand your—— Even if you are a girl——"

"Yes, I'll go back to the pure old homestead by the Connecticut. You bet I will! I came on this tour terribly fond of Andy, for his sweetness, as I still am, but feeling that it was an opportunity to work with a really creative actor like you, and you prove to be another smart amateur that hasn't the temperament to be a serious actor, that's just playing at it before he goes off to his proper hideaway in Hollywood."

"I'm going to choke you—I really am going to choke you to death, Merriday. Nobody can insult me like that and live."

"To think that I once admired you more than anybody on earth!"

"You certainly never showed any signs of it! I could have gone for you big. I think maybe you have some of the real fire, under your layers of women's college and butterscotch sundae."

They were not sitting now; he had sprung up, lifted her to her feet; and his soul was no longer lying on its back and waving its spiritual feet. He was frantically earnest and young:

"I liked you, but you were such a baby, and I didn't want to make a fool of myself—funny, isn't it: much safer to be naïve and longing with a wise woman of forty than with an airy brat of twenty! But you really did believe in me?"

"Yes."

"And you really think I let you down?"

"Yes. You did let me down, Zed."

He was, after all, only a year older than she, this embryo dictator, and she realized, as he put his arm about her with an embrace too trembling to be anything but sincere, that he was near to bawling like a baby.

"Oh, I never thought I could do that, pet. Tell me, oh, tell me honestly, darling, no kidding, do you really mean that the Boyle is trying to bust the tour, and I was her stooge?"

"Yes."

"That old witch! When I come to think of it, I hate her more than anybody else I know, because she *can* act, and doesn't care. She can simply lure your heart out, when she gives that slow, scared half-turn and says, 'Trust me, gentleman, I'll prove more true than those that have more cunning to be strange'—she's twice as young as you are, then! Yet she'd give it up for a country-house comedy. She's a traitor. Oh, we'll squash her! Come. Let's go see Andy. He and you and I will put this tour over, Beth! Come on!"

"Now I love you, Zed!"

He stopped, on the way to the door. He said sharply, "How literally do you mean that?"

"W-why," was her answer.

"You knew I began to fall for you, after I got over being a fool about Iris?"

"I don't think you really fell."

"Why do you hold back so with me?"

"You haven't one tiniest little bit of kindness for women. You order them around like waiters."

"Of course I do. Every epicure orders waiters around and bawls 'em out—just because he cares for his food. It's only the thick-ear that'd just as soon have pork chop as grouse that calls the waiter 'George' and asks about his health instead of about his sauces. . . . Are you going to fall in love with me?"

"No."

"Not even to save this tour?"

"Don't be so conceited again! How do you know you can save it?"

"I'll show you. I'll do it. And then I may discourse with thee sweet numbers, pet, of love. Come on!"

They hastened, hand in hand, to Andy's room. Between his own door and Andy's, three floors above, the nimble Zed had evolved a plan.

Andy's room was, again, the cheapest in the house; cheaper than Zed's, with an aspen instead of an iron bed. When they knocked, he gave them "Come in," but when they entered he was telephoning . . . long-distance telephoning.

The worst vice of Mr Andrew Deacon was telephoning, preferably to as distant a spot at as expensive a rate as was possible. When in doubt, he reached for a receiver. He was one of a whole new race of executives who take out their escapism not in liquor or South Seas or war, but by instantly transporting themselves across the continent. They may economize on salaries and socks, they may be stay-at-homes, but they will rise up at three A.M. and leap at a telephone instrument and call up some poor unfortunate girl downily asleep in her own decent bed in a city a thousand miles away.

They will have no time to write letters, no, not so much as a postcard with a picture of the Empire State Building, but they will with complaisance spend three hours tracking some distant quarry from home to office to restaurant to theater to places where he decidedly ought not to be.

And of these telephoniacs, Andy was a chronic case. He telephoned greetings to actors on their opening nights, thereby forcing them to go out to the box office and almost miss their first entrances; he telephoned filial greetings to his mother when she was at crises in bridge games; he telephoned to sick friends in the hospital, just at the times in their lives when they most wanted to be left alone. But today he had more apparent reason for telephoning.

As Bethel unavoidably listened to the end of the call he was making, she guessed that he was trying to get more backing for the show from some friend in the East . . . and that he had been making this effort often and recently.

". . . oh yes, it's picking up. I get reports of a swell advance sale all through Kansas. . . . Why of course, I expect to run at a loss for some time yet, till the country gets sold on a novelty. . . . No, I can't guarantee a thing. I won't fool you about that. But all I can say is, I'm putting in all I got. . . . Well, think it over and I'll phone you again tomorrow."

He looked up from the telephone as brightly as though he had just heard that the Daughters of Israel had taken a block of two hundred seats.

Zed struck quickly. He stalked to Andy holding out his hand.

"Listen, boss; Bethel has been jumping my neck, and I guess she's right. I'm opposed to you on some of your theories of production. I've never concealed that. But I never realized that my criticism had played into the hands of a gang like Tony and Jeff, that are natural sourballs, and I certainly never realized it could give aid and comfort to mankind's natural enemy, Aurelia Boyle."

(As Zed continues with his surrender to the beaming Andy, who pats his sleeve in gratitude, it should be noted that Bethel is so remarkable a linguist that she perfectly understands, though she cannot fluently speak it, the astonishing new language of Zed, Andy and Lyle, whose vocabulary contains such words of unknown etymology as phony, stooge, blow, flop, wow, bust and okay.)

"So here's my idea, Andy," Zed was finishing. "You've worked the radio and interviews and hens' luncheons pretty hard, and some of the colleges, but we haven't touched the high schools and normal schools, and there's where the cash customers for Shakespeare ought to be. If you want, and if Bethel will back me up and Tertius will get me the dates, I'll make some spirited addresses in high-school auditoriums.

God knows I'll hate it, but I swear, I'll coo you as gently as I can, and maybe it 'll help."

"Oh, that's swell, Zed. I certainly appreciate it. I think it's a swell idea. It's too late for this and next week, but I'll wire—no, I better telephone—and get you dates for our seventh and eighth and ninth weeks—Missouri and Kansas and Colorado. I can't tell you how this touches me, Zed."

They made a family portrait—Andy with his arms about his two children, Zed and Bethel.

31

Kansas city, which is in Missouri and not in Kansas, and which was the terminus of the Santa Fe Trail and the arena of Yankee Abolitionists and Pro-slavery riders, is one of the remarkable cities of the United States. But to Bethel Merriday, on the gloomy first to the fourth of January 1939, Kansas City was the Golgotha where the *Romeo and Juliet* company first met unconcealable disaster.

It was not only meager, unconvinced audiences; it was Mrs Boyle.

On New Year's Day, on Sunday in Kansas City, Mrs Boyle was drinking by midmorning. Naturally, there was no one large feast, if Andy did not give it, but there were a dozen small ones, with Scotch and White Rock in tooth-mugs and paper cups in bedrooms. Andy himself impressively dressed up in morning coat and striped trousers and attended church with Mahala, who liked that sort of thing once a year. Bethel sat and did a good deal of small weeping, in between letters home. In Lyle Johnson's room, next to hers with both hall doors open, she could hear Lyle and Mrs

Boyle and Jeff Hoy and Harry Purvis and Tony Murphy and, surprisingly, the new Apothecary, Jones Awkwright, telling stories and singing "The Old Man Came Rolling Home." She heard Zed join them, and distinctly heard him hold forth:

"No, I *won't* have a drink. I'm on the water wagon. . . . Eh? As of right now! Harry—Jeff—I want to run through the Death of Tybalt scene. We're doing it too mechanically. . . . You won't, eh? Then to hell with you. You're getting so you play like a stock company, all of you, including me. . . . What? Oh no, Mrs Boyle, I couldn't possibly mean *you*—how could I!"

That's what Bethel heard.

He came into her room and sat down—by some amazing lapse of direction not on the edge of the bed, but just on the floor, in the corner, his knees up to his chin, looking twelve years old and sulky. They stared at each other for some time. He grumbled, "They've got the right idea. I think I'll go out and get cockeyed. No, I haven't even got the spirit to do that. You're certainly a hell of a girl to think about falling in love with. You're so pink and white and black, so respectable, so milk-sick, so fussy, so generally Yankee, I *mean* it."

He bounced out. She could see his rough, quick-changing face, his strong hands, after he had left the room. Oh, why couldn't he have taken her to the movies, at least, this lonely New Year's Day?

She did go to the movies, with Purvis and Charlotte, that evening, and she told herself that she was homesick for the Fletcher Hewitt who would have had surprises and kindness for her on her holiday in exile.

But her mind's eye could see only Zed.

Late that afternoon and all that evening, Mrs Boyle was not to be seen or heard, but there were rumors that she had gone to a very wet party in the Country Club district, and been convoyed home at four A.M.

Bethel was, as Mrs Boyle's understudy, supposed to look in on her dressing room at seven-thirty, and when she did so on Monday evening, the first of their three performances in Kansas City, she found the star blank and doubtful, with a bottle of Scotch on her dressing table.

Ever since Zed had called her a "tattler" and "teacher's pet," Bethel had hated going to Andy with reports. She had to, now.

Andy cursed—much better than he was wont to. He penetrated the star's dressing room with an awkward excuse about props, and reported to Bethel, standing aquiver in the dressing-room alley, that "the old girl is certainly a little soused, but she's so well trained, I think she'll get through."

She did. The only remarkable thing about Mrs Boyle's performance that evening was its ponderous sobriety. She made Juliet as dull as the minutes of a house committee. And after the show, when Lyle Johnson ventured in to invite her for a drink, she was to be heard demanding, in tones ministerial but fuzzy, "Who may you be? I am a leading lady. I never shaw you before. I am not cushomed to associate with minor members of my company."

At one in the morning, as Bethel lay on her bed, reading, Andy telephoned:

"Beth? Come quick. No, not bad news *exactly*—maybe not."

She found him exalted with disaster.

"The Boyle is not only drunk but promises to go on all night. She's down in the Old Canteen Room. When I saw her last, she was dancing the tango, except that she was rendering it as the St Vitus Dance."

"With who?"

"Lyle Johnson. . . . He says she called him up at midnight and bawled him out for not keeping some boozing date she seemed to think they had made. I tried to get her to go to bed. She told me—oh well, why remember that? I can't get her arrested. I certainly would if I could. She'll never be able to play Juliet tomorrow night. You'll have to, Beth darling. And it's your great chance!"

The understudy who, by tradition, should have hurraed at her slow-coming "great chance" was appalled.

"Oh, I don't know. I don't know if I can. The part is so long. I'm scared to death!"

"You've got to. And you will. And well."

"Oh, I will try, if I have to."

"Of course you will. I'm going to cue you all night long. I've taken a suite down the hall for it. . . . Hm!" He laughed at himself. "I guess I was glad of an excuse to get out of this hard-times room. Come on. We'll order up some coffee and begin."

Mahala's voice, just then, at the door:

"Andy, are you still awake? Come on down and buy me some grub?"

And, when he opened the door, Mahala's presence, lovely in coy blue organdie with white cuffs and collar.

But Bethel was suddenly thinking that when she had first seen Mahala, descending from the train at Grampion Center, only six months ago, she had seemed a great lady, a fabulous actress, while now she was just another girl in the touring company . . . prettier than most, but not beautiful like Charlotte, not radiant like Mrs Boyle.

Mahala glided in, looked astounded at Bethel's presence, said—oh, you know, just what Mahala Vale or Mabel Staghorn would have said: "I hope I'm not interrupting." Significantly, you know.

"Very pleasantly," purred Andy. "Keep this strictly under your hat, but the Boyle is boiled and Beth may have to play Juliet tomorrow night. And I've got an idea. Prob'ly be a good thing if she got cued all night. You start in with it, and I'll get a couple hours sleep, and then I'll take over and give the third degree to the poor darling the rest of the night."

"Oh, you and the 'poor darling' seem to be quite happy without me. I wouldn't intrude, not for words, I mean, not for worlds. I hope you have a happy night!"

Afterward, Andy said only, "I agree with you! I don't know how I got the Mahala habit. They're putting it in cigarettes now, you know. . . . Come on, to work, dear."

Shaking, sick, while he kept hurling her cues at her and making her go on steadily, without a recess, through the huge long speeches, Bethel went over the Juliet part till dawn—at first sitting in a large chair, cool and amused, trying to look like a veteran actress, like Mahala; at the last, leaning her cheek against Andy's sturdy shoulder and whimpering while, more savage than Zed, Andy kept whipping her on.

She slept till noon and awoke too tired to wonder whether she was really going to the gallows that night.

She was. Andy reported that Mrs Boyle was in her room, abed and yelling for cognac.

Before Bethel was out of bed, Andy and Hugh Challis and Mabel and Charlotte and Harry Purvis and Iris—the last a delicate green of incredulous envy—were all jammed into the room, offering to help. "Get out of here, all of you, and I'll order the child some coffee and start a little slave-driving again," said Andy, affectionately.

For the first time in a week, he seemed his old, gay, adventurous self.

The others had scarce gone, and Bethel was just sitting up, a modest gray blanket thick about her shoulders, when Zed galloped in.

"This is great! Now you'll have your chance, Beth," he exulted. "Tonight a new Star is born! You'll wow them. Maybe you won't be as smooth as Mrs Boyle——"

"She won't!" said Andy, sourly.

The two young men had instantly changed roles; Andy was hard now, and demanding; Zed was all one sun of certainty.

"How do you know she won't? It's true that Mrs Boyle has talent and a technic that clicks like a——"

"Like a safety razor," from Andy.

"Oh, shut up, boss. But what Beth has, I think, that the

Boyle can never buy, is a feeling for all the human emotions
in the world. I don't know how she does it. I wouldn't call
her sentimental, and yet she has a feeling for everything
from a baby bawling for its rattle——"

"Babies don't have rattles any more."

"—to an old farmer who's going to have the mortgage
foreclosed. She has a real grandeur of emotions——"

"You haven't seemed to think I had any kind of emotions
worth paying attention to, these last few weeks, Zed,"
snapped Bethel.

"Huh? Me? Why drag that in? . . . Andy, don't cue
her any more. Mahala says you did all night—and oh, say,
is our Mahala sore that Beth is our new star. *Let her alone
now.*"

Andy turned on Zed with, "I thought you believed in
driving 'em! I seem to remember some powerful remarks
about no rehearsal being worth anything unless it lasted
all night and the actors dropped in the wings sobbing."

"I think I have said something of that sort, but I'll bet
the poor kid's already done her sobbing. Let's take her to
the theater, and just run through her crosses, and fix up her
costumes, and then I'll take her for a drive, and at four-
thirty there's a recital by the Schnoelberg Chamber Quartet
—a lovely lot of Brahms—and that 'll rest her."

Bethel looked brightly and beady eyed from one to the
other of the young men (sitting on the edge of her bed!)
fighting over her welfare. They had both pretty well managed to forget it till now.

Andy complained, "No, that 'll just tire her out. *Let her
alone now!*"

It was, rather surprisingly, Zed who was discerning
enough to suggest, "Of course we might ask Beth what she'd
like to do? Little drive, pet? Some nice, rich, chocolaty
Brahms?"

"Yes! That's what I'd like."

And Andy was generous, as only Andy could be. He broke
out smiling. "Good! I just wanted—— Now we're really

getting some action on our tour. Beth! Maybe you can go on playing Juliet. I can drop Mrs Boyle if I want to, now, on threat of charges filed with Equity, and if I could just save on her salary, I think we could afford to keep going. Bless you both, and happy afternoon. See you at the theater in an hour about costumes, Beth? I . . . I . . . sort of wish I were going with you two!" He sounded wistful but he looked content.

"And if you'll get out of here now, Zed——" said Bethel.

"Eh? What? Oh, that's so. I suppose you do want to put on some clothes."

As she dressed she thought how odd it was that Andy, reared to a family which probably took an annual subscription to the Worcester symphony concert series and gave its young a choice between Piano, French, and Small Boat Sailing, would not have thought of preparing for a crisis by going to a concert, while to Zed, brought up on a Montana ranch, music was as daily and as necessary as bread.

There was a hectic hour at the theater while Mrs Golly, the wardrobe mistress, made safety-pin alterations in Mrs Boyle's costumes. The star was not much taller, but vastly more expansive at the waist, and Mrs Golly kept admonishing Bethel, "Listen, dearie, I guess this will hold, but in your emotional scenes don't emote too much or the Citizens of Verona are going to see your maidenly dresses turning into Mother Hubbards right before their eyes. My! I'll never forget one time when I was playing bits with David Warfield, and . . ."

Zed took her to a slow and expensive and beautiful lunch at the Muehlebach. The talk was good. It dealt entirely with the theater.

In a taxi they drove out to the cliffs above the plain of the Missouri River, looking on a valley whose wide snowfields not long ago had known the Caw Indians and bearded men with rifles. Shivering there, while in his seat the driver of the taxi shivered also and looked annoyed, Zed was moved to remember his own West: the first show he had ever seen, which was Old Dr Kippipoose's Navaho Elixir International and Oriental Al Fresco Entertainments, with the Old Indian Doctor, who had a charming singsong Swedish accent, making a violent ventriloquist melodrama with three puppets. And so, at sixteen, Zed had run away from home and a widowed father of no particular sobriety and had joined another Indian Doctor and himself become a ventriloquist.

"No! You're *not!*" thrilled Bethel. "You can't do ventriloquism!"

Seemingly it was the taxi driver who answered her: "Certainly he can. And in this state Zed gallops night by night through Bethel's brains, and then she dreams of love."

"Oh, you're wonderful! Anybody can be a perfect Mercutio, but to do ventriloquism——"

And she hugged him impulsively, and, arms about each other, in great good spirits, the two children of the stage went back to the taxi, and on to the melancholy sweetness of Johannes Brahms.

He held her hand through the concert—not too tightly, just comfortingly.

Zed was the excellent concert companion. He neither chattered, nor yet frowned if she moved in her seat. And whenever she fell down from the heights of the music into worrying, and was seized with the fear and nausea of First Night Sickness, he seemed to know it and pressed her hand, and she felt part of his angry strength. And when, at the close, he said, "Darn swell concert—that cellist is one grand fiddler," she understood that he had expressed it all with poetry and elegance.

Dinner was tea and toast, and it lasted four or five years.

She had, for this week, a dressing room of her own. No one dared suggest that she take that of the star—who was now reported to be smiling in her sleep—but for her changes she did have Mrs Boyle's maid, Hilda. She would gladly have lost Hilda and Hilda's stare. Now Bethel knew what a basilisk looked like. Trembling, she tried to make her eyes particularly large and yielding. She didn't feel yielding at all. She felt sick.

When she was in her first costume, Juliet's tight youthful house dress, Andy came in, looking weary.

"Darling, did you have a good afternoon with Zed?"

"Oh yes. He was sweet. I think he kept me from committing suicide. Andy! He can do ventriloquism!"

"He wasn't rude? Didn't bawl you out?"

"Of course not! He knew what I've got ahead of me."

"Yes. I'll hand it to Zed, he has a real devotion to the stage. We all love you, and we're all rooting for your success. And you're going to put it over tonight, and you'll be our permanent Juliet, maybe, and with good old Zed and me and you working together, this whole tour is going to take on a new life and go over with a slam."

"I'm sure of it!"

Before the curtain, Andy announced that Mrs Boyle was suddenly "indisposed with the flu, and though we have every hope and expectation that tomorrow evening she will again be with us, tonight I have a pleasant surprise for you, and the part of Juliet will be played by one of the most brilliant and lovely of the young modern actresses, Miss Bethel Merriday." He said nothing about the audience getting their money back, and only five people did go out to get it, which was just as well, considering that the audience was merely a fan-shaped darkening of the middle of the theater.

Nathan Eldred took Bethel's place and spoke the prologue, wearing—after hasty consultation about it with Andy —the morning coat and striped trousers which he had in reserve as understudy for Capulet. Later, nobody could quite remember just why he had worn this banker's uniform for a prologue.

He did fairly well, though he had never rehearsed the speech. He left out the line "From ancient grudge break to new mutiny," but apparently no one noticed. Certainly there was no sound of new mutiny breaking, out there in the awesome dark majesty of the audience.

Through the prologue, Bethel stood in the wings and listened and suffered. She was too frightened to go back to her dressing room and relax.

She did not come on till fourteen minutes after the rise of the curtain. During those fourteen centuries she tried to listen to Andy, Zed, Challis, Charlotte and several thousand others telling her that she was an admirable Juliet. She heard nothing but her own misery and, having quietly determined that she couldn't remember one line of the play, she saw that the catastrophe was complete and there was no use in worrying about it, and she sat stooped and steeped in misery, till Eldred's signal, and her cue, Mahala's voice cheerily calling, "Where's this girl? What, Juliet!"

She ran on, her voice saying "How now! Who calls?" as gaily and sweetly and naturally as though she had been doing this for a thousand nights.

She even had presence enough to be able to look at Mahala, in Lady Capulet's velvet house dress, and to react to the Nurse's fond smile. She had dived. She was swimming. She was playing. She was Juliet!

She had her first agony in the first long colloquy between her and Romeo.

She started off confidently enough and winningly enough on her first tremendous speech:

> "Thou know'st the mask of night is on my face,
> Else would a maiden blush bepaint my cheek."

Yes, she had said that much, or that much had mechanically got itself said, when she stopped with an incredible jolt. She hadn't an idea how the speech went on. Utter blank. She could see the long lines there before her, like a black wall, but she could not climb them.

She had, by stage usage, "blown"; she had "blown higher than a kite."

And the blessed Andy was "throwing her the line"—giving her her own words, with variations; speaking as cheerfully as though all was well:

> "Thou meanst for that which thou has spoke tonight?"

Glory! She almost had it again!
He was going on:

> "Fain would'st thou dwell on form, fain, fain deny
> What thou hast spoke?"

She had it! She snatched the speech from him, and capped his interpolation triumphantly with:

> "Aye! Farewell compliment!
> Dost thou love me? I know thou wilt say 'Aye'!"

And then she was singing on, flawless, to the end of the speech.

Only afterwards did she think that Eldred, holding the script in the wings, must have prompted her and she, in her agitation, not have heard him.

She marched on well enough until the Nurse gave her Romeo's summons to the friar's cell for marriage. Then suddenly she had left in her no blood, no voice. She was not Juliet revealing love and fear; she was a Miss Bethel Merriday reciting lines. When she addressed the Nurse, "O Lord, why look'st thou sad?" it sounded as though she were speaking to a stranger named Mr Lord. At the end of the scene, when she made exit, to fly to Laurence's cell with a joyous "Hie to high fortune!" there was not a ripple from the audience—and here the valiant Juliet of Mrs Boyle had invariably floated out on applause.

Before the intermission—they were playing *Romeo* in two acts—she had only one more scene, and then, six minutes before the act-end, she fled to her dressing room and while

Hilda Donnersberg, gaunt and high, looked down at her with Mid-European scorn, she wept on her arm on the dressing table.

She was finished forever as an actress.

"In Austria, where there is a really *great* theater, a real German theater, we would never allow a young girl like you to play Juliet, but always a woman with some sense and art, like Frau Boyle."

"But Juliet's only fourteen in the play."

"Oh no. That's yoost a mistake in the English translation of Shakesbur," said Hilda.

"And I ought to be at the hotel with poor Mrs Boyle. She is sick of the stomach," said Hilda.

In all that fifteen-minute intermission, the only persons who came into her dressing room were Andy and Zed and Tertius Tully.

Tertius said, "Good girl! We're all rooting for you. Well, got to hustle out and count the cash."

Andy said, "Good girl! We all think you're swell. Well, I got to hustle in and change."

Zed, who was Mercutio, and was therefore now dead except for the resurrection of the curtain call, said, "Good girl. You've got through the worst of it. Good luck!"

She never remembered anything of the second act. She tried to practise the stage art of listening, but she heard nothing the other actors said to her. She was busy running over what her answering speech would be.

While, preparing to drink the sleeping potion, she soliloquized:

> "I have a faint cold fear thrills through my veins,
> That almost freezes up the heat of life,"

her inner thoughts were somewhat less lyric:

"Got to remember, lay down the dagger with the cue

'Lie thou there.' Yes, this speech ends the scene; thank heaven I don't have to give anybody a cue. . . . That woman coughing in the front row again. Why doesn't she take a lozenge? . . . Oh, dear, why did I jump Mahala's cue? . . . Did I leave the cover off my powder? I'm almost sure I did; I can see it lying there with the cover off. . . . She coughs all the time. . . . To have a chance like this and not be able to *do* it! I can just hear how Katharine Cornell would be playing this; her voice so warm and sure; I just squawk and move like a stick. . . . Hey! Careful! Don't hurry that line so much! . . . If I ever play this again— fat chance!—I'd like to try giving most of this speech with my back to the audience—dressing table or something, and they see me in the mirror? . . . Now there's another cougher, center."

The speech was going on:

> "There's a fearful point,
> Shall I not then be stifled in the vault?"

and her small girl's thoughts racing with it:

"If I only had the training. I swear, maybe I could do it. . . . Oh, I do think I'm getting some of the horror into it now. . . . Curious, I can say the lines, and really feel them —oh, but *really*—and still have other thoughts. . . . Project—project—look up at the balcony—oh dear, that spot simply blinds me.

> "Where bloody Tybalt, yet but green in earth,
> Lies fest'ring in his shroud.

"I am *so* tired; I feel dizzy; I hope I'm not going to faint. That would be dreadful. Shall I fall on the bed now? No, I guess I can get through. I've *got* to. . . . That woman coughing . . ."

She existed to the end of the play.

All through the final scene her voice seemed to her more quavery and more colorless with every word, and at last, incredulously, she had the relief of stabbing herself and lying motionless and silent.

When they took the curtain calls, when Andy pushed her on for the star's call by herself, there was no spontaneous general applause but only a scattering of hard mature hands, as of grown men who had daughters like her and who were sorry for her.

Angrily, head up and proud, she made her way to her dressing room.

Her only remark to herself was, "Well, I flopped!"

Six or seven of the company did come in to see her. None of them said anything but a noncommittal "Fine, you got through it all right" that was worse than damning. Only Tudor Blackwall, who had a gift for it, was able to gush: "You were a perfect duck! I think it's wonderful that you could have got clear through when you've only been having understudy rehearsals, and not really playing in the set. I thought you were so young and sweet—the *real* Juliet!"

Not till after she was dressed for the street, in a Sladesburian mustard-colored suit now growing shabby, did her real masters come in—Zed and Andy.

They looked as if each resented the other's intrusion, and then in chorus they made just the same vapid, hearty sound of *"Well!"*

Andy opened up:

"You did really fine. I think it's remarkable, your being able to get through at all, with so little time for rehearsal. You didn't let us down one bit. Just—uh—swell. I haven't one word of criticism. You've carried us through the most dangerous spot of the tour. I'm sure Mrs Boyle will be able to carry on tomorrow night. I've got a doctor working on her—I've just been talking to him on the phone. And you did—uh—swell!"

He kissed her forehead—with all the passion of a box-office treasurer. And, she noted, he said nothing more about her going on playing Juliet, about dropping Mrs Boyle.

Well, why should he! Dear Andy! If he hadn't been the kindest person living, he would be flaying her for ruining the Great Chance.

Zed was talking:

"No, you weren't so 'swell.' You were pretty wooden. In fact, terrible. It's curious: talking to you, I feel as if you were at least as mature as Mrs Boyle. You have fundamental wisdom. You know how things should be acted. Yet you have no application of your knowledge yet. It's training that you need, of course. I'd like to stick you in stock and make you play fifty roles in fifty weeks. Just now and then tonight, you really were that naïve, lovely Italian kid, in love with real flesh and blood, and *then* you had something that no old war horse like Boyle could ever get. Boyle and her damn dog! But mostly you sounded like the radio. Too bad."

Bethel was reflecting, "Andy says I was good, and didn't like me. Zed says I was terrible, and liked me a lot."

Andy boomed, "Look, darling, I've got to hustle upstairs to the office and check some bills with Tertius. Got to be paid tomorrow. But can you wait half an hour—not more'n an hour, anyway? I'd like to buy you some food. Of course I'd be delighted to have you come, too, Zed."

"Hang it, I can't. I promised Doug Fry, two days ago, to go out to the house of a Kansas City University prof and look over some plans with them for a *Coriolanus* production. Well, good luck, pet. See you tomorrow, Andy."

She sighed, "Oh, I don't think I'll wait, Andy. I want to get right to bed."

On the first night of her playing Juliet, Bethel Merriday walked to the hotel by herself, a small figure alone at night in the empty business streets of a strange city.

32

I'M MORE SENSITIVE than you give me credit for. I've
noticed how you cock an eye at me every time you catch
me long-distance telephoning. Well now, I can't do much
more phoning even if I want to. I'm too busted," said Andy
to Beth, and in the presence of his palace guard: Mahala,
Zed, Hugh Challis, Doc Keezer and Tertius Tully.

"But at the same time, I've just really started my campaign to get more backing. I'm going after every poor unfortunate that I know or that my dear mother knows. Beth,
you can type, can't you?"

"Yes."

"Want to be my stenographer—unpaid—along with your
acting?"

"Yes, sure."

"I can't afford even hotel stenographers any more—and
I don't want them to know too much about our difficulties,
and maybe let them out to the press. So we'll start in."

Mahala had an icy explosion.

"My dear Andy, if you want to play around with Miss Merriday all the time——"

"With *who?*"

"Miss Merriday!—and if you can't endure being separated from her, why don't you say so? Why all this pretense about her being a secretary? I'm sure I don't care."

Andy let her have it. "Maggie, your sudden anesthesia to my charms couldn't have anything to do with the fact that now I'm just another poor young man, could it?"

"Oh, you are vile! I knew you were phony—Andrew Deacon, the great. Yale amateur!—but I didn't think you could so misjudge one who's been your best and truest friend!"

Mahala swept out of the room, at her most sweeping.

All this was at midafternoon, in Sedalia, Missouri, on Thursday, January 5, 1939.

Mrs Boyle had re-arisen from her abyss of Scotch and cognac on Wednesday, the third and last day in Kansas City, and had played Juliet more wistfully, more movingly than ever before. Watching the two parts of her, the sick and trembling woman and the serene actress, move deftly on together, Bethel the Understudy again savored her own failure.

But Andy expected the spree to be repeated. And he had thus called, in Sedalia, the meeting of his inner ring.

He went on, after Mahala had done her aristocratic outsweeping:

"The next thing is: I've got to ask for a fifty per cent cut in all salaries over eighty dollars. I know that's like the verdict of guilty and you just wait for sentence to be pronounced and the tour ended, but I honestly believe that if the cast will vote and take this cut, we can pull through. If they won't take it, I'm finished. I'll have to put up our closing notice on next Monday. So, Doc, as Equity deputy, I want you to call a meeting of the cast after the show this evening."

Doc hemmed, "All right, Andy. But you know this cut will break your run-of-the-play contract with Mrs Boyle, if she wants to take advantage of it, and she can give you her two weeks' notice."

"I know, and I don't care."

It is not festive for the cast of a touring company to meet and vote on the choice between taking cut salaries and seeing the closing notice put up on the call board. That notice, put up on Monday, will, unless it be taken down by Thursday night, end the tour the following Saturday night.

Andy, though he was actor and Equity member, was, as producer, not permitted to attend. And Mahala murmured that Bethel ought not to be—she was only a miserable junior member of Equity and, as Andy's new and slightly irregular secretary, was completely suspect.

Bethel glared at her and attended the meeting, in the littered storage room beneath the stage where the musicians played pinochle. They perched on a workbench, on broken chairs, on paint buckets. A few minutes ago, they had been the gentry of Verona, noble in their woes, above such sordidness as jobs and meal tickets; now they were an anxious group of workers, with street clothes not quite so fresh as when they had left New York six weeks ago.

Doc Keezer made a speech voluminous and abstruse:

"Well, boys and girls, I guess you all know why we've got together. Andy is asking for a fifty per cent cut above eighty. He's a straight guy, and he wouldn't ask for it if he could help it. Personally, I think that with the cut, the show has a chance. All in favor sig'fy raisn' ri' hand."

Oh no, none of that for Mrs Boyle, with the Scotch still in her, and a pretty good grievance.

She said that she was a very fine actress, and that she had come on this tour for a miserable thousand dollars a week merely to bring culture and . . .

She would not vote against the cut; but if it came, she would give notice; and after two weeks more of such inexpressible tortures as having to sleep in hotels and travel on trains, she would return to decency.

Doc looked at her as he would look at a handsome specimen of the three-toed sloth, and remarked, "A'favor sig'fy rice'and."

The cut was accepted, and they all looked relieved.

That night, from midnight till two in the morning, when their train would leave, Bethel and Andy sat in a cold "parlor" on the hotel mezzanine getting out letters to be sent off by air mail; letters to friends of Andy's family— Boston cotton brokers, Harvard overseers, Worcester bankers; to classmates of his own and to their parents— New York stockbrokers, Yale trustees, Pittsburgh bankers. The letters all said the same thing: he honestly believed that the troubles were over; he wanted them to invest not less than one hundred and not more than a thousand dollars in the show; he could give them no guarantees whatever.

He dictated to her, on the machine. Her typing was rusty, but as she began to regain speed, it had the exhilaration of swimming. He worked unnervously, gently, but he was disconcertingly swift. Once he smoothed her hair. Mostly he seemed not to know that she was anything but part of her typewriter. But never, not even in acting, had she had more joy than out of this working, as a partner, mature, respected, with a man she liked.

As they drove to the train, she inquired, "But what are we going to do for a Juliet, with Mrs Boyle gone?"

"I'm going to give it to Mahala, if that elegant young woman shows proper appreciation."

"And who's going to take Mahala's place as Lady Capulet?"

"You are."

"Me?"

"You!"

"After—oh, Andy, after my flop night before last?"

"As a matter of fact, I've talked this over with Zed, and

it was he who suggested you. I'm fond enough of you so I don't like the queer fascination that young desperado apparently has for you, but I guess I'm too dumb to lie, and truth is, Zed thinks much more of your performance Tuesday night than I did. It's his theory that you stumbled so just because you did have a big conception of the part— weren't content to play it prettily, but wanted to put more into it than the training you've had would carry. Anyway, you're to play Lady Capulet, and we'll work out your make-up, with the help of Mabel, and Zed and I both think you'll make a small-size Lady Capulet, very cute. Kitten, I think you may have quite an interesting life for the next two weeks. You'll have to learn and rehearse the new part in that time, *and* play your present parts as usual (we'll put Vera Cross on the prologue, when you switch), *and* be my secretary two or three hours a day, *and* travel, *and* merely give up all sleep and eating. Can you stand it?"

"I'll love it," she said drowsily.

She was too drowsy even to enjoy fully the comedy on the Pullman, when Andy told Mahala that she could have the part of Juliet if she behaved herself, and she told Andy that she might consent to play the part of Juliet if he behaved *himself,* but instantly gave herself away with an excited, *"Say! How many sides is the Juliet part?"*

Sedalia and Columbia and Jefferson City and Springfield, Missouri. Little Rock, Arkansas. Memphis, Tennessee. But Bethel saw nothing but theater, hotel rooms, her Lady Capulet part and her typewriter.

One night in each of these cities, and then in St Louis for a three-night and matinée run: the Thursday, Friday and Saturday of the seventh week of the tour.

The learning by Bethel and Mahala of their new parts was hectic. They were to assume them not in two weeks but in ten days, in Topeka, Kansas, on the Monday night after the St Louis run, in order to keep the week's advertising consistent.

The moment of that nightmare that she best remembered was playing Prologue and Page and Epilogue with a flu temperature of 99½°, and then being cued, for two hours, by Andy, whose own temperature was 100¼°, and who was succeeded, in a hot little reception room upstairs in their old hotel in Little Rock, by Zed, who disdainfully declined to have anything so popular as the flu. All three of them were in rather disgraceful sweaters and overcoats over pajamas, and the cuing threatened to end forever when Andy was so foolish as to speculate to Zed:

"Do you know there's one way, perfectly legitimate, that we could put this show over? I'm a better comedian than a romantic, and Doc and Mabel are pretty good. Why not punch the comedy lines a lot harder, even if we do sacrifice some of the poetry?"

Zed yelled:

"Every once in a while I realize that I was a traitor in going against my better judgment and throwing in with you and helping you put this show over—me actually starting in next Monday trying to coax Kansas school kids to please come see the monkeys—instead of letting it die painlessly. 'Merely sacrifice the poetry'!"

"But I thought you didn't care so much for that."

"Andy, I don't suppose you ever can understand even the simplest principles of the modern drama. I want to emphasize the poetry a lot *more* than you do, but the real poetry, with biology and individuality in it, and *use* the fine, juicy words, not be used by them, not drool them out, long and lingering, like a poetic congressman quoting Tennyson!"

"I see," said Andy, placid. "Well, keep up the cuing as long as you can stand it."

With Andy gone, Zed was still unpleasant. Bethel didn't like him very much. But he didn't seem to care what she thought, for in face of an Icy Stare—Bethel was sure that not Mrs Boyle herself could have done you a better Icy Stare —he went on raging:

"I don't know why I take the trouble to cue you. Mahala

was right: you're still Teacher's Pet, and what's worse, you sat there and listened to that half-back proposing to hoke Shakespeare, and never raised an eyebrow."

"Of course I did, you baby. I don't always show what I think."

"Don't you, pet? Do you ever think? Come on now—see if you can make Her Ladyship sound like anything besides Sladesbury, if that's its name. Oh, why do we go on with all this farce? Just to enable me to address Sunday school maidens in Alhambra, Kansas? Come on—come on. Start with:

"Ho, daughter, are you up?"

St Louis, in the three days there, was kind to them, and they were kind to St Louis. It was Mrs Boyle's last days with the company, and she was enough of a trouper, despite a weakness for vicarages and cold toast which years of Old Fashioned cocktails and America had only partly corrected, to play at her burning top; and Andy desperate enough to throw himself into Romeo with none of the proprieties of the gentleman amateur. And the critics were benevolent. Writing in the *Star-Mail,* Ben Talerick said:

To confess a boredom with the average production of Shakespeare is as dangerous as to admit a dislike for dogs, and this column declines to state his general position. But he will say that in Mr Deacon's grand, boyish manner of playing Romeo, and Mrs Boyle's literally thrilling revelation of youthful beauty in Juliet, he found the most cheering show of this whole current season. By all means go and see it, and learn how the theater can be experimental without being freakish.

And they did go and see it, in considerable numbers . . . not quite enough, Andy sighed to Bethel at her stenographic labors, to pay the back debts of the company and still have an adequate reserve for starting off across Kansas next week. But the company was cheered up enough so that Andy received only one two weeks' notice—from Jeff Hoy.

Zed had, presumably, been struggling in prayer with Mr Hoy, for he was almost human as he gave notice. He even went so far as to hope that the tour would go on even when, he being gone, there would be nobody left in the company.

And as producer, Andy gave only one two weeks' notice— to Iris.

"You can't do that!" Bethel wailed, when Andy told her his intention. "The poor kid! She's just the proud kind that thinks she never could be fired, and 'll be all the more broken by it."

"She's the only one that's dispensable, and you know I've got to save every penny, or go under. It's a choice between her and Vera Cross, and Vera doesn't mind touring, while with Iris it's just too painful for a humanitarian to have to watch her."

This time Andy did not ask Bethel to do his slaughtering. When she saw Iris on Saturday evening, saw the soreness of tears in the corners of her eyes, Bethel herself wanted to cry, and swore a great vow that she could never again hate any woman . . . not even Mahala . . . much. And she saw Iris draw Doug Fry into the prop room, argue with him, plead with him.

All of Iris's spun-glass superiority was gone then; she was merely a frightened, anemic girl. Douglas was casually listening to her, indifferently patting her shoulder in comfort. Bethel guessed that Iris was begging him to give his notice, so that they might depart together.

But when the company started off for Kansas, Sunday morning, Douglas still had not quit, and all day long, across the snow-blind plain, he sat cheerfully reading Adolphe Appia on scenery, beside a silent Iris, suddenly ten years older and hungry.

As all women do think, now and then, Bethel thought, "I hate all men!"

Andy was almost cured of extravagance. He gave no parties in St Louis except that, in exaltation at the good reviews, he did invite all the cast in for drinks after the show on Friday evening.

He had no suite of his own now to house them; for the party, he borrowed one, with a noble kitchenette with electric stove and icebox.

In gaiety, it was a children's party; they played The Game, and Harry Purvis imitated Sir Cedric Hardwicke and Wallace Ford. But it was not childish in the gallantry with which the company put aside the fact that, two weeks from tomorrow evening, they would either be safe for months, or be working people without jobs in midwinter.

Andy was gayest of all.

Bethel and he were the bartenders. They were in the kitchenette, mixing Cuba Libres, and he had just tweaked her ear, with no particular frenzy, when they were aware of Mahala in the doorway.

She stared at them, long, silently, enjoying her own nobility. Her line, thrown at them as she turned away, was, "So! I thought so! You two are sweethearts!"

But Andy laughed, after Mahala's exit.

"Poor kitten! That settles you. I think her idea is a pretty good one, at that. But anyway, I guess you're stuck with me now. My mother has disowned me, and Joan Hinterwald has broken our engagement about seven times now—she alternates letters, telegrams and telephone calls—and the company, they're casting dice for which gets first stab at Old Man Caesar. So you're about all I've got, my darling!"

He sat, looking charmingly absurd on a small folding stepladder in the kitchenette, to talk:

"This isn't apropos of anything, but I have a picture that comes to me whenever I feel lonely and put-upon. Prob'ly I got it out of some movie accompanied by tin-pan-alley music. It's of flying across the continent, very eager to get back to my girl and to my home, which is on an island, I think, or maybe it's a peninsula. It's not an extravagant place, but there's a big living room lined with redwood, and from the porch you see the Pacific beyond the pines. And my girl's standing out there when I come home, after hustling from the aeroplane. . . . Oh, well, come on; let's take in the drinks."

On Saturday, after the evening performance, Mrs Lumley Boyle said farewell, or in a distinguished manner declined to say farewell, before catching the midnight train for New York.

When they had arrived to make up, she had rather lingered in the dressing-room alley, with little cries of "Well, I'll have breakfast in New York Monday morning!" Nobody said anything more than "That's so." Even Lyle Johnson and Tony Murphy looked bored. "Well, good luck," they droned.

She caught their indifference. She slammed her dressing-room door. And after the show, as Bethel waited for Andy, she saw a procession: Mrs Boyle, looking old and tired, a little shabby in a three-year-old suit, carrying her jewel case and the dog Pluto; Hilda Donnersberg carrying a suitcase and the make-up box. They marched to the stage door. The doorman looked up benevolently, with a look that spelled two dollars, and maybe five. Mrs Boyle halted, shrugged, dropped a fifty-cent piece into his hand and marched out, unspeaking.

But after her galloped Mabel Staghorn, carrying her kitten, Pippy, in its cage.

She came back weeping.

"What *is* it, Mabe?" said Doc.

Mabel wailed, "I thought poor Pluto would be so lonely without his little friend, so I offered Pippy to Mrs Boyle and—the son of a gun, she *took* her!"

That was the star's farewell.

Their long Sunday daytime ride in a day coach across Missouri, from St Louis to Topeka, Kansas, was a gray ride, and a depressed ride. Even the bridge players were quiet.

When Bethel looked out of the train window, the farmhouses, which had come to seem sturdy to her, seemed to crouch amid the snow-waste.

All day Andy alternated cuing her with dictating letters. She was tired. This didn't seem like great acting, like the creation of fabulous queens. Zed stopped by them derisively. "The Deacon Theatrical Enterprises doing a big business?"

Andy muttered, afterward, "Sometimes I could almost dislike that brash young man."

"Why only sometimes?"

"I agree."

"Cheer up, Andy. Tomorrow night you'll have a wondrous new Juliet and a pretty good new Lady Capulet."

"Yes. Actually, the show will be better knit, a better unit, without that blasted star. And so it's a pity——"

"What? What?"

"I've got to put up the closing notice tomorrow night."

"Got to?"

"Yes. We made money in St Louis, but not enough. And I've received only eleven hundred dollars from all our begging letters. But don't worry. And don't tell anybody else. Let them be happy till tomorrow night."

"We'll be closing next Saturday night? It will all be over?"

"No. Not necessarily. With this new streamlined set-up, we've got the best chance in the world to put it over. I feel thoroughly optimistic." He didn't sound so. "I'm sure as anything that I'll be able to take down the closing notice next Thursday evening and that we'll be able to go on for months yet—weeks, anyway."

She heard none of that; she knew only that tomorrow night, the very night when she would first play a major role of her very own on the professional stage, the closing notice would be put up.

That wasn't at all good enough.

Yes, it had to be! she scolded herself. She would have one

week's chance, at least. And she mustn't load any more woes on Andy's now unsteady shoulders.

She patted his hand, she chirped, "I'm sure everything will go fine. I'm going back and get you some coffee."

"Good," said Andy.

33

THIS TIME, in Topeka, she had been too busy all day to let her imagination work up the sick suspense that had broken her down as Juliet, back in Kansas City. She had just time to make up and take her place; she went on and played Lady Capulet with only a shaky qualm or two, a quiver or two as lines came slowly to her. But they came.

She was a clove-sweet, slim little old lady, unexpectedly comic, a husband-ridden aristocrat who was afraid of the babbling old nurse who dominated the house, and awed, just a bit, by the splendor of her daughter.

Mahala was too weighty and too stately for Juliet, but she was not offensive. There was dignity in her role, and some skill. Never had the company been more heartily applauded than at the curtain calls, and Andy shouted, "The miracle's happened! The closing notice will come down on Thursday, and the tour will go over!"

To Mahala, this probably meant no more than the fact that she was now nightly queen of Dressing Room 1—the star's dressing room. It is doubtful if it ever occurred to her that any other star would ever have the impudence to come along and occupy it later. If she had been so profoundly imaginative as to think about it at all, she would have seen those few cubic feet of air known sacredly forever after, through all history, as "Miss Mahala Vale's Dressing Room." She really was wrong, though. Four days later, a celebrated lady strip-teaser who had never heard of Mahala was treating the room as exclusively hers.

Monday morning, slightly sweating in the zero cold as they drove up to the great high-school building, stage-frightened as he had never been on the stage, Zed addressed a high school at assembly hour.

Bethel sat in the very back of the auditorium and adored him, and watched the teachers, in the row of seats beside her, being astonished by him. That strong face, not ironed out by spiritual massage like most Americans today, that face of a strong workman, became the glowing face of a poet, the profound face of a scholar, as he told them, with simple confession, that to him the theater was both scrupulous priesthood and eager adventure.

And after the performance, Monday night, before they went to the Pullman which they had engaged for the whole week, it was Zed who gave them a party. A rather simple party: beer and tomato-and-bacon sandwiches, at Mike's Le Bon Louvre Lunchroom, but friendly.

Tony Murphy, the Trotsky of the party, arose with a toast:

"Andy, if we get many audiences as good as tonight, the tour will go on. And if it does, I want to get in under the line, and not have you think I'm turning decent just because I'm sure of the cakes. I'm afraid I've done a little crabbing. I swear I didn't mean to. I guess it's just a bad habit I've got. And now that the Boyle—of whom I may say that I fell for her like a ton of brick—has gone, and we're all a rough-neck bunch of American troupers—including you, Hugh, who have practically lived down London and have gotten converted to liking ice water—I think we'll do something. But of course the big idea of this toast is that all of us now get up and tell Mahala and Bethel they did a perfectly magnificent job tonight, and they got a lot of swell poetry and a grand quick tempo into their performances, and we're proud of them as hell. Skoal!"

And so they were all very happy, even if Bethel did hear Mahala croak to Jeff Hoy, as they settled down on the train, "Andy cheerful? He ought to be! He's saving a thousand bucks a week on the Boyle's salary, and if maybe I'm not as good as she is, I haven't played it for a quarter of a century!"

The tour had begun to drain Bethel's secure youthfulness, and, for almost the first time in her life, she could not sleep. She lay in her rocking berth, listening to the car wheels till the strain rose to an intolerable wakefulness. She tried to read herself to sleep, but she read herself awake. She turned off the bed-head light in this tiny, low-ceiled rolling home of hers, raised the curtain and watched the specks of light streak by.

Who were they out there, awake in isolated farmhouses so late, cold wind in cottonwood groves and the cold timbers crackling? . . . She saw herself as the young farmwife, with her first baby coming, lying in a spool bed—what memory was that?—with the doctor watching. But he was not the doctor of the chromos, whiskered and weighty; he was young and fiery, as rough and scolding as Zed.

But the young husband who stood back in the shadows had the solicitous kindness of Andy Deacon.

And Bethel was asleep, while the lone lights hurried by.

She had been alive and competent as Lady Capulet; no amateurishness and no languishing. She had merited the good hand at the curtain call. But she never would know that the "spontaneous applause" on her first exit had been about as spontaneous as a department-store Santa Claus.

Doc Keezer, as he had done a hundred times on half a

hundred tours, had been kneeling way down left, just behind the tormentor, and at her exit had given one mighty smack of his hands. That had started the clapping of the innocent audience for the innocent Bethel, and everybody had been very happy about it, including Doc.

The Andy who vowed to Bethel that he had become so economical that he was washing his own socks in his hotel bathroom had had the Topeka morning-paper review telegraphed ahead, and it greeted them at their hotel in Wichita:

One of the most significant theatrical events with which Topeka has been favored in years, equal to seeing Our Helen in *Victoria Regina,* was the performance last evening of the "Romeo and Juliet in Modern Dress" company, starring Andrew Deacon and Mahala Vale. Their performance, brought up to date, made the famous old love story seem as real as the boy and girl next door. We understand that Miss Vale, who turned out a first-rate performance full of beauty and wearing clothes that made the hearts of all feminine auditors go pit-a-pat, and Miss Bethel Merriday, who turned Mrs Capulet from the ordinary stuffed shirt of hackneyed theatrical tradition into a darling, fussy old lady, are new to their roles. We wish them every success, and predict for them a great future. Who can be pessimistic about the Theater of Tomorrow when he sees lovely young ladies like these give such skill and devotion?

"Swell! This tour's just begun!" said Andy.

"Maybe it was my being scared and not my skill at playing fussiness," said Bethel.

"What a lousy review! My first chance at Juliet, and all that reporter could find to talk about was my *clothes*—and they just some rags we picked up in St Louis," said Mahala.

Andy had another rich cousin in Wichita—Andy had other rich cousins almost everywhere, but the Wichita example was a particularly luscious widow, with a Renaissance house containing the interior of a beech-paneled room from a dismantled château in Touraine. She invited the cast, entire, for an after-theater rout.

Zed descended on Bethel. "Going to the party?"

"Oh, I don't know; I haven't anything to wear."

Zed took a fifty-cent piece out of his left-hand lower vest pocket and put it in the right.

"Eh?"

"I just bet myself on what you'd say. You know, pet, you're just the opposite of Iris. You need bringing out. You need to be pushed into grabbing your own kingdom. You'll probably become a competent actress, and then a theatrical miser, like Doc or Mabel; you'll save everything, including your ability, and so land up in a two-room cottage and spend your declining years reading your Iowa clippings. You could be beautiful, in a timid sort of way, but you let yourself look like the housemaid. Come on, I'm going to take you out now, before I make my high-school speech, and make you buy a swell party dress. There's a good department store here."

"No, no, no!" wailed Bethel. "I've paid all my debts, and now I want something to make me secure while I find my next job."

"I'll buy you one."

"You will not!"

"Why not?"

"I don't like you well enough."

" 'A whining mammet, in her fortune's tender, to answer' —'I'll not let you be my friend, and blow me to a single decent dress.' Okay. Hell with you!"

Zed slammed on his disreputable hat and walked out of the hotel lobby, and she could not tell whether his pickle-ish aspect was from real dislike or a sour approbation of her remarkable virtue.

So she went in her habitual blue taffeta to the noise and milling and rum punch at the Rich Cousin's Château, but Zed's jeering had given her what actors call a "mental hazard"—the blind spot in the mind whereby, for some

reason obscure and absurd, you never can remember one
certain word in a speech. Andy seemed desirous of bringing
her out, of making his cousin understand that here was his
pride and his darling, but Bethel flinched and turned silent,
and the unquenchable Mahala—that longer-legged Iris—
stepped in.

Apparently, with the success at Topeka and a good house
tonight in Wichita and with this view of a new and richer
cousin, Mahala again saw Andy as a most estimable young
artist. She danced with him and wriggled at him. . . . And
the amiable Andy fell, and Bethel stood back in an indecisive
rage at Andy's indecisiveness.

Before the party there had been the inevitable trunk-
packing in her dressing room that had always been her worst
chore, except for dragging your own bags across the waiting
room and heaving them up to a train platform, in towns
where there were too few redcaps and the train halted only
three minutes. Now that she was Lady Capulet, she had
twice as much to pack, and this back-breaking stooping, this
fussy patting of frocks on hangers, this trying to force shut
a trunk that was too full, was enough to soil the glory of
acting.

She went so far as to yelp at Doc, in the next dressing
room, "Oh, for one week when we could leave everything
hung up in the dressing room!" Appalled at her own sharp
voice, she went to Doc's door and implored him, "I'm sorry.
I didn't think I'd ever be the kind of actress that kicks all the
time."

He laughed at her.

"My dear, if you never kicked, I'd know that you were
just another amateur that only takes one tour, and finds
everything just lovely—even railway-station beans and no
water in the dressing room—and raves so much about it that
it makes the rest of us low, beefing, vulgar troupers sick,
and then goes home and never tours again. Darned if I know
which is the real mark of the professional—not to kick at

the right things or always to kick at the wrong ones. You're a trouper now!"

It considerably increased Bethel's dislike of packing that Mahala now had her own maid.

This was a pretty young colored girl whom they had acquired in St Louis. Mahala, herself long a nightly kicker about the horrors of packing, could now sit in ecstasy, before the after-theater party, and watch her dresser do the work. And into every conversation she could, and did, lug a reference to "her dresser."

And as she packed tonight, remembering Zed's admonition to be gaudier, Bethel noticed how all her small sacred possessions were becoming shabby. Her Lady Capulet gowns, too, made over from Mahala's, were shabby. She realized that all the costumes of the company now shamelessly showed red stains at the neck from grease paint, and two or three of the men were becoming slack about make-up. Tony Murphy, who at the beginning had always been in his dressing room three quarters of an hour before curtain rise, now rushed in, smelling of beer, just at the fifteen-minute call, and sometimes he went on still wearing his street shoes.

All this frightened her about the fate of the tour even more than Andy's whisper that, for all the size and enthusiasm of the audiences in Topeka and Wichita, they hadn't quite met expenses.

Topeka and Wichita were metropolises, with 66,000 and 115,000 population. But Dalesburg, Kansas, in which they awoke on Wednesday morning, was not so mammoth. It had 27,000 population, and the theater was a motion-picture house, with too large an auditorium, an almost total lack of acoustics, and an audience trained to believe that seventy-five cents should be the top for all theater seats. Even Zed's passionate exposition, at the high school in the afternoon, of the superior emotional orgies of the living stage did not move Dalesburg.

Four hundred and twenty people huddled protectively together in the center of an auditorium meant for thirteen hundred. They felt naked to the cold prairie winds, and were afraid to laugh or to give that sighing shiver which tells the actors that a love scene is "going over."

It is a fable that the "fourth wall" of the stage is empty. There, massed, are the most influential part of the cast: the audience. On their acting, their timing, their professional training, depends the contributory vividness of the rest of the cast. And audiences differ, from night to night, at least as much as individual actors. An untrained audience is as uncomfortable a collaborator as an untrained surgeon or an untrained lover.

Tonight's audience, at Dalesburg, was the clammiest the company had ever encountered, and it was not entirely the fault of Mr Andrew Deacon & Associates if they played *Romeo and Juliet* like the last week of a lawsuit. It wasn't merely that they dropped lines; they didn't know whether they dropped them or not.

Tonight, after the show, instead of his usual benedictory "Another day, another dollar," Doc Keezer grunted, "Well, got the chores done again, and the cattle are all safe for the night. Ain't this a hell of a way to earn a living!"

With exasperating innocence Andy went on supposing that it was a good notion to escort Bethel and Mahala to the train together. Tonight, at Dalesburg, the three of them came out of the theater into a world blind with snow, a half-gale that felt uneasy and threatening, like the gasping pause before a thunderstorm.

Dalesburg was almost taxiless. The citizens felt as suspicious about a stranger who wasn't driving his own private car as their cattle-herding grandfathers had about a stranger with no visible horse.

The three tired and unromantic workers, idle singers of an idle day in a town where idleness was discreditable, wavered through snow and blast, holding together, skidding across ice-scurfed street crossings. They saw the lights of the bleak station as heaven, and crawled silently into their berths on the Pullman.

The journey from Dalesburg to their next stand, Alhambra, was supposed to take two hours and a quarter—their Pullman to be picked up by the three-A.M. Westbound, to arrive at a quarter past five and lie in the yards till seven. But when Bethel shivered awake at eight in the morning and pulled up her window shade, she saw, through an unnatural gray night, that they were somewhere out in the country, in a confusion of cruelly charging snow. She dressed hastily. . . . On tour, washing and powdering become rapid and none too delicate. . . . Andy, invariably the first of the caravan to awaken and be disgustingly cheerful, was typing at a portable machine in his drawing room.

"Yump. Full blizzard. We may be stuck here all day, and late for the show tonight," he chanted. "Sit down, darling. I've got some coffee coming."

And all day long everybody drank coffee from the diner on the stranded train, and played cards, and tried to do charades, and talked about exactly three things: the blizzard, 1 per cent; Hitler and Stalin, $1\frac{1}{2}$ per cent; and the theater, $97\frac{1}{2}$ per cent. They were gay, they sang, but all of them except such veteran troupers as Doc and Challis and Mabel felt apprehensively that they would starve here, or here, in nameless frozen farm lands, they would freeze to death. Every time they looked out of the windows the smother of snow seemed, beyond all mathematics, to be twice as thick. And though the train heating system, hitched to the great Western locomotive, did its best, outside it was five above zero, and the Pullman grew steadily colder, so that you beheld Juliet wearing her pink bathrobe over her furs, and Lord Capulet with a blanket around his shoulders.

The dining-car supplies were, by two in the afternoon, reduced to coffee and griddle cakes.

The train moved now and then, perhaps a mile; and everybody jumped up and laughed and said that in Alhambra they would have a "lovely great, big, juicy steak, in a warm dining room." They now saw Alhambra as a combination of Simpson's Chop House and a beach in Samoa.

By five in the afternoon the storm had thinned to a nasty gray fog. The train moved on, slowly, and at eight in the evening they arrived in Alhambra.

The actors could have dined and been made up and have started the show by eight-thirty, but the scenery had to be trucked to the theater, through the tail of the blizzard. Everybody hoped that there would be no show, but Andy hurried to the theater and back and announced that a few hardy lovers of the Bard were already seated, and he hoped to have the curtain up by nine-thirty. They all sat down to dinner in the Alhambra House, which still has vinegar cruets, and there was no question any longer about the steak being lovely, great, big or juicy. There wasn't any steak.

Now Alhambra was not so mammoth as Dalesburg. It had nine thousand population, and the theater wasn't a theater— it was the auditorium of the high school.

At eight-thirty, Andy commanded them, "Take your time and eat. I'm going to the shop and try to keep the customers amused. Zed, I want you to come with me. You can talk better than I can. You wouldn't do some ventriloquist tricks for them, would you?"

"I would not!" yelped the outraged Zed, but he went along.

At nine-fifteen, word came to them from Zed that they hoped to have the curtain up at ten, that sixty-seven patrons were waiting, and that his ventriloquism had gone over big.

Not even Tony Murphy or Jeff Hoy suggested that it was foolish to give the play at all. Whatever lamentable crimes they might conceal, they were troupers.

As they ran along the streets, the town, with its warm lights shut away from them behind frost-glittering windows, seemed dug-in and unfriendly to vagabonds.

The dressing rooms were classrooms, and Bethel was so taken back to Point Royal College and *A Doll's House* that she giggled as she sat in a row with Mahala, Mabel,

Charlotte, Iris and Vera, their small mirrors on school desks and their rouge and mascara staining the virgin maple slabs dedicated to Evangeline and the square of X.

And that night, before sixty-seven patrons, they played well.

For the sixty-seven, feeling as heroic as the actors themselves, were a good audience who were willing to enjoy themselves, and the whole show had the gay insanity of a Christmas party in snowbound mountains.

But tonight was Thursday, and tonight the closing notice did not come down.

The call board was hung in the school corridor, and the closing notice was still on it. Bethel thought of *A Tale of Two Cities* and the aristocrats awaiting the morning's list of the condemned. The company sneaked to it, one by one, and stood in a shaky group, re-re-reading it.

"It *would* come during a blizzard," sighed Tudor Blackwall.

"Say, Andy couldn't just possibly have forgotten to take it down?" hoped Harry Purvis.

But Andy came by, glanced at the notice, regretfully patted Hugh Challis's shoulder and passed on.

Between acts Andy called Bethel into his star dressing room—which was the office of the high-school principal. Not speaking, he held her to him. He was shaking; he seemed to be weeping without tears.

"The tour's really over, then?" she said.

"Yes. Finish on Saturday. I wish I could say something in excuse, Beth."

"I wish I could say something in comfort!"

"Your being here comforts me. You're the only one, baby, that I want to see. . . . I think that the latest bulletin, as of five minutes ago, is that Mahala again considers me a poor young man."

It was inconceivable that she should be so intimate with this king whom she had seen red-gold on his red-gold throne six months ago; but it was doubly and tragically inconceivable that she shouldn't very much care, and that the touch of his hand should be only the amiable contact of a passing friend.

He explained to her the deadly financial aspect of the closing—and after that not even all her fancy could give her hope.

They needed about six thousand dollars a week barely to pay expenses, and on one-night stands, with only six performances a week, that meant a gross of a thousand dollars a performance. In Topeka they had grossed $856.50; in Wichita, $922.70; in Dalesburg, $368.75; but tonight, with the blizzard, they hadn't done quite so well—they had just $99.65 in the box office.

"And so," said Andy, quite cheerful now that he had pencil in hand, "that means an average loss of about four hundred dollars a day, spread over the past four days—and all I have in the world is enough to finish up this week and take us back to New York. I'll be paying these debts for the next ten years. Well, it's been worth it. The Forty-niners never had so much fun as a theatrical tour—with Hugh and Zed and Mabel and *you!*"

After the play the younger members of the company left the two available taxicabs, which were Ford sedans, to the seniors and ran to the station, Zed and Lyle dragging Bethel through the cold hell of wind that bit her nose, through the great sculptured snowdrifts that were golden with purple shadows under the street lights. And then, since their Pullman would not have heat till it was connected with a locomotive, they waited for the train in a small station waiting room stinking with cheap tobacco, overheated from a sheet-iron box stove whose sides turned cherry. Douglas Fry brought out a Temple *Hamlet,* and they passed it from hand to hand, reading aloud. Zed made the astonished station agent, in his coop, seem to be saying, "This is the brightest night I've had since Edwin Booth was here when he was out with *Tobacco Road*."

Doc Keezer forgot the sanctified, the basic rule of all trouping, which is, "I love you, dearie, but carry your own suitcase," and dragged across the street to a decayed boardinghouse and brought back a gallon of coffee. The train came in, and they panted to lift their bags aboard before it should contemptuously pull off without them, and, half undressed, they fell into a dense sleep, and awoke to tranquil sunshine on the snow in the vastly greater town of New Prague . . . population 16,000!

They still had to get through to the fatal Saturday night.

In New Prague, Friday night, they were so successful, their take was so large, that Andy lost only about two hundred and fifty dollars that beautiful starry evening.

And so they came to Pike City and to the end.

Pike City had seven thousand population; it was much the smallest town in which they had played, and the most barren. The New York booking office, which controlled their fate with all of Providence's indifference to results, had sent them there because in Pike City was the Santa Fe Trail Opera House, the grand old theater in which four thousand people, cowmen and gamblers and ladies of a certain fashion, had once listened to Melba and Patti. Pike City had been larger then and more famous than Dodge City, and its saloons more crimson. There was still a reckless, friendly, pioneer blood in the people, but the Romeo Company had no chance to encounter this. All they saw was one long street, open at either end to the hungry ferocity of the winter plains, unprotected and most unprotective of the tender arts, and on either side of it, streets that after a scattering of small wooden houses wandered off discouraged and were lost on the prairie.

"This," said Andy, at the frame hotel where he would send his final telegrams, make his final gay long-distance calls, "is really the jumping-off place."

Before an audience next in smallness to the blizzard-blown huddle at Alhambra, they gave, as their last performance, the best they had ever done. They played like a May breeze; there was a lightness to Mahala's pedestrian Juliet; Andy was so manly and incurably young that Bethel, glowing from the wings, fell in love with him all over again; Zed was a newly polished blade; and Bethel, Lady Capulet, had an inner light.

She had youthfully imagined that at the end they would all sing "Auld Lang Syne," or else that all the feuds of Tony and Zed and Jeff against Andy would break out in unconcealed brawling, now that school was over. But everybody packed mechanically, as on an ordinary night. Doc Keezer could be heard calmly arguing that Raymond Massey had played Shakespeare, and the Tony who had always planned to have a three-day drunk when the run was over was gurgling bottled orangeade in his dressing room.

Mr Andrew Deacon was responsible for transporting all of them back to New York. As far as Chicago they would occupy the Pullman which, since St Louis, had been their home. It would be hitched on an eastbound train that left Pike City just after midnight, so there was no time for parties, for regrets, and they hastened direct from theater to train.

Bethel saw that Andy was innocent of baggage. "Where is your stuff?" she wondered. Then he admitted it:

"I'm not going with you to New York. I'll follow in a few days, but I have to stay here in Pike City and, uh, finish up some bills and things. I'll come soon, and then we'll talk about our next theatrical venture, kitten."

This story he told to half a dozen. They all accepted it; they were busy admiring the bunch of roses for each of the women that he had conjured out of Pike City. Mahala said that they must dine together next week. But Bethel noted that Andy got out of the Pullman, still on a siding, needlessly early, and as he stood on the cinder-lined ground looking up at it, there was a youthful desperation about him. . . . It would not be impossible that, left alone here, in a spasm of loneliness and depression and humiliation, he might——

She busied herself with quietly moving her bags one by one to the farther vestibule platform of the Pullman; then, in the darkness, lifting them down to the ground and carrying them to the station platform. She rejoined the bustling, home-going exiles in the Pullman; she talked of the beauties of New York, but as the Pullman was attached to the train, she slipped out to the vestibule again.

She looked back, perhaps for the last time, at her beloved family: kind Doc and Mabel, already playing pinochle, handsome old Hugh Challis and——

She could not endure looking long at him, but her whole vision was flooded with the sight of Zed Wintergeist as he wedged himself in a seat between piles of books. His shoulders were relaxing, strong shoulders on which she would never rest her forehead. If she was to go, if for loyalty she was to give up Zed, it must be quickly.

She scuttled down from the vestibule to the platform, on the dark side of the train, just before the porter closed the vestibule doors.

When the train moved away, with Andy running beside it and waving . . . and crying . . . she was watching from the station waiting room.

Andy tramped away, up Main Street. She left her bags with the friendly night operator at the station and followed him.

He entered Pete's Lunch—one of the scores of Pete's Lunches they had known since New York. He sat at the end of a long marble-topped table and ordered a hamburger and coffee. . . . Two nights ago she had been taken back to the memory of dressing for *A Doll's House;* now, in the spiral of life, she was taken back seven years farther, to Caryl McDermid and Elsie Krall at a beanery table in Sladesbury.

She sat two chairs away from him; she ordered coffee in

a half-whisper. Andy did not see her for two minutes. Then he raised his head, stared at her, dropped his eyes, looked at her again—yes, a "double take," right out of farce technic —and said, as inevitably he must say, "What are *you* doing here? Did the train stop?"

"No. I did. I was worried about you."

"I couldn't stand seeing any of them again, except you, and I didn't see how I could detach you from the others. I'm glad you did the detaching."

"What are you going to do, Andy?"

"Before I finish this hamburger sandwich, I'm going to decide whether I'll take my estimable place in Uncle Alex Pilchard's bank, or start writing to the theater managers— the real managers!—for a job. And I suppose that decision will govern the rest of my life."

"But aren't you broke? You shouldn't have bought us roses. And listen, Andy, if you are broke—please let me!— I've saved up a little——"

"Darling! I can wire home for enough to get back to New York—though as my faithful secretary you know that's all I can get, now!"

"But you'll come back to the stage."

"You bet I will!"

With one of the complete changes she had often seen in Andy, he was suddenly confident.

"And I won't just go on acting, either. I'll be producing again, in a couple of years. Maybe as early as this year, I'll have a summer theater again—and not with Roscoe Valentine—I don't like the way he gyps the students. I know where I can get one for almost nothing. And I have plans: A big Shaw festival in summer, like the musical festival at Stockbridge! A New York stock company! I can do it now. I've learned my lesson on this tour. Better casting and stricter discipline. Oh, a thousand things I want to do . . ."

He raved on, while Bethel was glad to hear the youth in his assured voice. He ended abruptly with:

"And that's why I want you to marry me, kitten!"

"Eh?"

"Sort of funny, isn't it!—proposing to you at Pete's Lunch, in Pike City, Kansas, with the counterman trying to hear what we're saying! But it wasn't till I thought you'd gone off on the train and I was left flat that I realized how for months I've depended on your affection and loyalty and good sense—and your eyes—always such a gay light in them. Oh, my Beth, I do long to:

> "seize
> On the white wonder of dear—Bethel's—hand
> And steal immortal blessing from her lips."

He was holding her hand so tenderly, his smile was so expectant, that only by compulsion could she make herself speak:

"Andy, you don't love me the least bit—really love—just all out—nothing held back."

"Why of course I do!"

"No."

"But anyway, Beth, you love *me* a little?"

"I don't think so. You're my dearest friend, but you don't make me into any kind of a glorious fool!"

At that moment Zed Wintergeist walked into the lunchroom and came up to them, observing without any punctuation:

"It's a damn good thing that train stops at a junction two miles out I managed to get a fellow to drive me here he stung me five dollars to drive me here the dirty hound Bethel come here and stop this nonsense you know we love each other and stop this nonsense hello Andy."

Andy spoke. Bethel didn't hear too much of it because her face was against Zed's coat, which seemed to have grown enormous and enveloping. But the end of Andy's oration, presented with reason and a good deal of manly indignation, was:

". . . I've stood a lot of impertinence from you, Zed, but

when it comes to your trying to rush my girl off her feet by your backwoods tactics, I'm—I'm not going to stand it!"

Zed answered cheerfully, "Sorry, old man, I really am, but this seems to have been settled for us."

"Will you kindly sit down and give me a chance to talk?"

"Okay. I'm hungry."

Zed casually dropped her into a chair, yanked out a chair for himself, ordered Western sandwiches all around, and commanded Andy, "Shoot!"

But it was at Bethel that Andy scolded:

"I can understand your being fascinated by Zed. But he'll make you horribly unhappy. He'll be cruel. And he'll never be true to you."

Zed cried, with none of his mockery, "That's a lie! I *will* be true to her. I've grown up that much, these last few weeks. Beth, please believe that!"

Andy was going on—to Bethel:

"Never. And he'll ignore you. He'll scoff at your dearest beliefs. He represents the return of barbarism to the theater, the revolt against civilization: lights and sound tracks and trick stages instead of beauty and dignity. He belongs with a Wild West Show. He's one of the young men who get credit for genius by wearing flannel shirts and never getting their hair cut. You can't see *him* in a gracious New England farmhouse!"

Quite cheerfully this time, Zed interrupted again: "I don't know about that. The guy's a good actor. Maybe he could learn to feed clover to a polo pony—is that what you feed polo ponies?"

Zed had stopped gobbling his sandwich long enough to hold Bethel's hand. The back of her hand felt cold against the marble top of the table.

From Andy:

"I won't say anything about your rudeness, Zed. Or your letch for power over everybody around you. Or your contempt for the gentler drama, like Barrie. You *are* a good actor. You have power and a love of life, and that's what we chiefly need in the theater. But I think it's time to speak of myself a little! Before you charged in, I was telling Beth of some of my future plans. I'm not sure that, without her help, I can tackle them. I need her more than ever, now that I'm completely broke——"

Zed snarled, "What does a scion like you mean by 'completely broke'? Only got a hundred thousand dollars left?"

Andy counted the bills in his fold, the change in his pockets.

"It means that I have, in the whole world, exactly seventeen dollars and forty-three cents—plus a promise from my mother that I shall not get one cent more from her, beyond carfare to New York, until she dies. Maybe I really do need a little coddling."

Zed stood up abruptly; he spoke earnestly; he looked worn.

"Yes. You do need her, Andy. And when you need her so much, she won't desert you. This is the one thing that could lick me. And so: good-by and bless you both."

He had started for the door. Bethel flew after him, tugged at his sleeve. "Don't! Zed! I won't give you up again! I won't!"

Zed turned with a smile like heaven.

"Not even for what you think is your duty? You love me enough to give up your baby, your Andy?"

"Oh, Zed, I don't know how much I love you, but I love you!"

That was late at night on Saturday, January the twenty-first, in Pike City, Kansas.

They were married in Pike City on Monday the twenty-third, and Andy, the best man, wasn't too insultingly cheerful about it, and Zed lent him the money for his fare back to New York.

On Thursday, February sixteenth, Bethel awoke in their "one-room apartment" in the Hotel Mountbatten, on West

Forty-eighth Street, and smiled at the sleeping Zed, who was sternly clutching his pillow, with nothing much of him to be seen but his thick hair.

In dressing gown and mules, she cooked their breakfast of fried eggs and toast and coffee. Their kitchen was a percolator, a two-burner electric stove, and a pint-sized electric icebox in the bathroom, and their dining room did not for the moment exist, since it was a folding card table stowed under the bed.

She was singing, minutely, happily.

She went over to kiss his ear and cry, "Breakfast! Wake up, stupid, or we'll be late for rehearsal."

She gave her lord and master the morning paper.

"Looks like war in Europe before 1939 is over," he yawned. "If America gets into it, I'll be just right for cannon fodder—strong young gent with no dependents but a smart wife who can support herself by high-class refined work on the stage."

"Will you go in?" fretted Bethel.

"That's like asking somebody if he'll go into an earthquake if it comes along, or just ignore it. My only propaganda is against these apologetic actors who say that their work seems insignificant compared with the big events abroad. Now's just the time when every artist has got to take even his tiniest job more seriously than ever, so that civilization may have a chance to go on. Come on, pet. Let's get going."

They trotted, arm in arm, two blocks over to the Acanthus Theater; entered it proudly not by the stage door but at the front.

In that dark Mammoth Cave, Bethel sighed like one happily at home. Only the stage was lighted. On it, Nathan Eldred the stage manager and Jerome Jordan O'Toole the director were moving chairs about, to outline an imaginary set that would represent a New York penthouse.

It was the first rehearsal of *Alas in Arcady,* a comedy about a world-weary New Yorker who was smug about his cosmopolitan vices until he went for vacation to a New England village and, among the young jitterbugs, discovered that he was nothing but an old-fashioned Puritan.

Zed was to play a country beau, and Bethel his girl, whom the alarmed urbanite tried to reform.

"We may not have another chance to play together till we organize our own company—as we *will!*—so let's enjoy it, my rabbit," said Zed.

O'Toole shook hands. "Glad to see you children. Here's your parts. I'll give you an hour to look 'em over, and then we'll start right in walking the play."

A man with silver hair but a face round and youngish marched out on the stage.

"Do you know Caryl McDermid?" said O'Toole. "This is Mr and Mrs Zed Wintergeist—Beth Merriday."

"I've never had the pleasure of seeing them before," said McDermid, "but I've heard a great deal about you, Zed. I hear you're our future Sacha Guitry. It'll be a pleasure to play with you."

"Beth is to be your daughter, Caryl—on the stage, I mean," said O'Toole.

"Off stage too, I hope, when we get into the terrors of touring," said McDermid. "Have you done any touring, Miss Merriday?"

"Oh, sure—she's a veteran trouper—she's a real actress," said Jerome Jordan O'Toole.

"You bet she is!" said Zed.

So Bethel had come home, and it was good.